W9-BUG-413

BCrasemann

UNITED STATES DEPARTMENT OF COMMERCE • John T. Connor, *Secretary*

NATIONAL BUREAU OF STANDARDS • A. V. Astin, *Director*

Atomic Transition Probabilities

Volume I   Hydrogen Through Neon

A Critical Data Compilation

W. L. Wiese, M. W. Smith, and B. M. Glennon

Institute for Basic Standards
National Bureau of Standards
Washington, D.C.

NSRDS–NBS 4-

National Standard Reference Data Series

National Bureau of Standards 4

(Category 3 — Atomic and Molecular Properties)

Issued May 20, 1966

For sale by the Superintendent of Documents, U.S. Government Printing Office
Washington, D.C., 20402 - Price $2.50

Library of Congress Catalog Card Number: 65–60078

National Standard Reference Data System

The National Standard Reference Data System is a government-wide effort to give to the technical community of the United States optimum access to the quantitative data of physical science, critically evaluated and compiled for convenience. This program was established in 1963 by the President's Office of Science and Technology, acting upon the recommendation of the Federal Council for Science and Technology. The National Bureau of Standards has been assigned responsibility for administering the effort. The general objective of the System is to coordinate and integrate existing data evaluation and compilation activities into a systematic, comprehensive program, supplementing and expanding technical coverage when necessary, establishing and maintaining standards for the output of the participating groups, and providing mechanisms for the dissemination of the output as required.

The NSRDS is conducted as a decentralized operation of nation-wide scope with central coordination by NBS. It comprises a complex of data centers and other activities, carried on in government agencies, academic institutions, and nongovernmental laboratories. The independent operational status of existing crictical data projects is maintained and encouraged. Data centers that are components of the NSRDS produce compilations of critically evaluated data, critical reviews of the state of quantitative knowledge in specialized areas, and computations of useful functions derived from standard reference data.

For operational purposes, NSRDS compilation activities are organized into seven categories as listed below. The data publications of the NSRDS, which may consist of monographs, looseleaf sheets, computer tapes, or any other useful product, will be classified as belonging to one or another of these categories. An additional "General" category of NSRDS publications will include reports on detailed classification schemes, lists of compilations considered to be Standard Reference Data, status reports, and similar material. Thus, NSRDS publications will appear in the following eight categories:

Category	Title
1	General
2	Nuclear Properties
3	Atomic and Molecular Properties
4	Solid State Properties
5	Thermodynamic and Transport Properties
6	Chemical Kinetics
7	Colloid and Surface Properties
8	Mechanical Properties of Materials

Within the National Bureau of Standards publication program a new series has been established, called the National Standard Reference Data Series. The present report, which is in Category 3 of the above list, is Volume I of Number 4 of the new series and is designated NSRDS–NBS 4 Vol. I.

A. V. ASTIN, *Director.*

Contents

General Introduction

List of Tables

*I = spectrum of neutral atom, II = spectrum of singly ionized atom, etc.

ATOMIC TRANSITION PROBABILITIES*

(A critical data compilation)

Volume I

Elements Hydrogen through Neon

W. L. Wiese, M. W. Smith, and B. M. Glennon

Atomic transition probabilities for about 4,000 spectral lines of the first ten elements, based on all available literature sources, are critically compiled. The data are presented in separate tables for each element and stage of ionization. For each ion the transitions are arranged according to multiplets, supermultiplets, transition arrays, and increasing quantum numbers. Allowed and forbidden transitions are listed separately. For each line the transition probability for spontaneous emission, the absorption oscillator strength, and the line strength are given along with the spectroscopic designation, the wavelength, the statistical weights, and the energy levels of the upper and lower states. In addition, the estimated accuracy and the source are indicated. In short introductions, which precede the tables for each ion, the main justifications for the choice of the adopted data and for the accuracy rating are discussed. A general introduction contains a critical review of the major data sources.

A. INTRODUCTORY REMARKS

After a long period of limited activity in atomic spectroscopy, the last half dozen years have brought rapid growth to this field. This has been sparked largely by urgent needs from areas in which basic atomic data are employed, namely plasma physics, astrophysics, and space research. As part of these developments, the pace and scope of determining atomic transition probabilities has greatly increased, so that the amount of accumulated material appears now to be sufficiently large to make a critical data compilation worthwhile and desirable. To realize this idea, a data center on atomic transition probabilities was established at the National Bureau of Standards in 1960. As a first step of the program, a search for the widely scattered literature references was undertaken. This phase of the work was essentially completed in 1962 with the publication of a "Bibliography on Atomic Transition Probabilities" (NBS Monograph 50) [1]. After that, only the monitoring of the current literature had to be kept up, and the emphasis of the work therefore could be shifted to the critical evaluation of the literature and the tabulation of the numerical data. Since the lightest ten elements have been of dominant interest, and on the other hand, the largest amount of data are available for them, it was decided to concentrate on these and publish their "best" values as the first part of a general compilation. pilation.

When the present tabulation was started, it was hoped that sufficient reliable material was available for a fairly comprehensive list, which would contain data for at least all the strong prominent transitions. This hope materialized only partially. A number of gaps and large discrepancies were found, and the theoretical and experimental efforts of several members of the Plasma Spectroscopy Section at NBS were needed to remedy the most critical situations. Furthermore, the Coulomb approximation of Bates and Damgaard [2] was extensively applied to obtain additional data. Although this unforeseen extra work delayed the publication of this compilation somewhat, we feel that we are now able to present a more useful and substantial collection of data.

B. SCOPE OF THE TABLES

In the present compilation the "best" available transition probabilities [1] of allowed (i.e., electric dipole) and forbidden (i.e., electric quadrupole and magnetic dipole) lines of the first ten elements, including their ions, are tabulated. The hydrogen-like ions are excluded; their transition probabilities may be obtained by scaling the hydrogen values according to the formulas given in table I. Furthermore, f-values or absorption coefficients for continua, i.e., bound-free transitions are not listed. As source material all the literature given in Ref. [1] plus later articles obtained from continuous scanning of the current literature are available.

It is our opinion that a tabulation of the present kind must contain fairly reliable values for at least all the stronger, characteristic lines of the various ions in order to be of general usefulness. We have tried to adhere to this goal from the start. More specifically, we have felt that for most atoms and ions at least the "prominent" half of the multiplets listed in the "Revised Multiplet Table" [3], and the "Ultraviolet Multiplet Table" [4] should be included in the tabulation, and uncertainties should be smaller than 50 percent. A number of gaps in the data and inferior values were noticed at the start, and—as already mentioned—it has been largely due to the efforts of some

---

*This research is a part of project DEFENDER, sponsored by the Advanced Research Projects Agency, Department of Defense, through the Office of Naval Research.

[1] Hereafter, we shall use the equivalent terms "transition probability, oscillator strength or f-value, and line strength" on an interchangeable basis. The numerical relationships between these quantities are given in table III.

members of the Plasma Spectroscopy Section at NBS and the availability of the Coulomb approximation [2] that the most glaring defects could be eliminated. Although we still must compromise in some cases by including inferior material (marked in the accuracy column as "E") we feel that waiting for these improvements would unduly delay the publication of the table.

Aside from this objective of including at least all the stronger lines, we have listed all additional available material with uncertainties smaller than 50 percent. We have deviated from this scheme only in a few instances: In these cases we have excluded data for very highly excited transitions, because these transitions have never been observed (no experimental wavelengths are available) and are of little practical interest. However, we have listed this additional material by spectrum in table II.

Most final tabulations were undertaken during 1964. Thus the literature through 1963 and in some cases even later work could be included. However, a few 1963 articles, which have been found in abstracting journals, came to our attention too late. These are listed, together with other recent material, in the list of additions at the end of the tables.

C. REVIEW OF THE DATA SOURCES

The present status of our knowledge of atomic transition probabilities must be considered as being far from ideal. The available material leaves much to be desired in quality as well as quantity [5]. This becomes especially evident if comparison is made with the other most important quantity of a spectral line, its wavelength. The only transition probabilities known with an accuracy comparable to that for wavelengths are available for hydrogen and hydrogen-like ions and a few lines of helium. For all other elements more or less reliable values have been obtained from various experimental and theoretical approaches. While experimental work has provided, with very high accuracy, practically all the data for the wavelengths of lines, it could not accomplish nearly the same in the case of transition probabilities. The measurement techniques are quite complicated and laborious, and it has proved to be very difficult to obtain accuracies of 10 percent or better. On the other hand, advanced theoretical approximations have been quite successful for the light, relatively simple atomic systems, and large amounts of data have been obtained from their applications. But the theoretical methods have the shortcoming that they do not permit estimates of the size of the errors as do the experiments.

In view of this reliability problem it is very important to discuss in detail how the accuracy ratings for the tabulated values have been obtained. For this purpose, a brief discussion is given in the individual introductions for each ion. Furthermore, to provide a better background and understanding for these short explanations, we include the following discussion of those major experimental and theoretical methods from which the bulk of the material for the lightest ten elements has been obtained.

1. Experimental Sources

a. Measurements in Emission

Experimentally, the largest number of f-values has been obtained from measurements of the intensities of spectral lines which are emitted from plasmas under known conditions. With this method the first and second spectra

of carbon, nitrogen, and oxygen, the third spectrum of oxygen, and the first spectrum of neon have been studied. The plasma sources are various types of stabilized arcs, and, to a lesser extent, shock-tubes. In brief, the method [6] is as follows: The transition probability for spontaneous emission from upper state k to lower state i, A_{ki}, is related to the total intensity I_{ki} of a line of frequency ν_{ik} by

$$I_{ki} = \frac{1}{4\pi} A_{ki} h \nu_{ik} N_k \tag{1}$$

where h is Planck's constant and N_k the population of state k. A_{ki} may therefore be obtained from the measurement of I_{ki} and the determination of N_k.

The experimental conditions are chosen so that the plasma is approximately in a state of local thermodynamic equilibrium (LTE), because N_k is then a function of temperature and total density of the species only, and may be determined from the application of equilibrium and conservation equations and measurements of the temperature and electron density. The measurements have always been done spectroscopically from the determinations of the intensities of lines and continua of known transition probabilities and absorption coefficients, or by measuring line profiles and utilizing the results of line broadening theory in plasmas.

Checks for the existence of LTE have been made repeatedly. It appears to be always closely approximated, except in the high-temperature magnetically driven shock-tubes where only partial LTE exists [7]. Also, the investigated lines have generally been checked for self-absorption. A demixing effect in arcs [8, 9] has introduced uncertainties into the results of some earlier arc experiments with gas mixtures, in which the mixture ratio was employed for the analysis. Since primarily the densities are affected, larger uncertainties in the absolute f-value scale are likely, but the relative f-values should be still quite accurate. However, this effect has been circumvented in most of the recent arc experiments used for this data compilation. Significant errors in emission experiments may arise from difficulties in determining the continuous background, from neglecting intensity contributions of the distant line wings [10], from uncertainties in the calibration of standard light sources, and from uncertainties in the high-density corrections in plasmas [11]. Applications of wall-stabilized arcs [12, 13] have given the most accurate results of all emission measurements.

The best absolute f-values obtained from emission experiments are estimated to be accurate within 15 percent, but for the bulk of the tabulated data errors between 20 to 50 percent must be expected. It should finally be noted that absorption measurements (only one is encountered in the case of Ne I) are quite analogous to the above mentioned emission experiments.

b. Lifetime Determinations

The direct measurement of lifetimes of excited atomic states has important applications for helium and neon. The method [6, 14] employed here consists essentially of exciting atoms by radiation or electron impact in short bursts and of observing the subsequent depopulation of excited levels by studying the time decay of the emitted radiation (delayed coincidence technique). The population N_k of an excited state k decays according to

$$N_k = N_{o,k} \exp(-\gamma_k t) \tag{2}$$

where $N_{o,k}$ is the population at time $t=0$ and γ_k the decay constant. Thus, an exponential decay in the radiation is observed. The mean lifetime $\tau_k = \gamma_k^{-1}$ of the atomic state is related to the transition probability A_{ki} for spontaneous emission by

$$\tau_k^{-1} = \sum_i A_{ki} + Q \qquad (3)$$

neglecting absorption and induced emission. Q denotes a term for collisional population and depopulation rates. In order to obtain $\sum_i A_{ki}$, one has to choose experimental conditions such that the collisional term Q (as well as the less critical absorption and induced emission) becomes negligible. This condition is achieved at very low densities.

It is seen that from lifetime measurements generally the *sum* of all probabilities for transitions to lower levels i is obtained, and individual transition probabilities may be obtained explicitly only in the following two cases: (a) The sum reduces to a single term, i.e., only transitions to the ground state are possible. This is, for example, the case for resonance lines. (b) The sum is dominated by one strong term (this is likely if it contains a transition of comparatively high frequency $\nu_{ik}(A_{ki}$ is proportional to ν_{ik}^3), or if all transitions but one are "forbidden", i.e., have very small transition probabilities). Furthermore, one may use lifetime experiments to normalize available relative transition probabilities to an absolute scale, if all relative probabilities contributing to the sum are known.

The lifetime method is, therefore, limited to only a few lines per spectrum, namely those originating from the lowest excited levels. But the results should be very accurate, with uncertainties less than 10 percent, since the method is simple and the instrumentation is by now well developed [14]. The major uncertainties arise from radiative cascading from higher levels, which repopulates the initial level, and from depopulation by collisions.

c. Measurement of *f*-values from the Anomalous Dispersion at the Edges of Spectral Lines

This method has found applications for lines of neutral lithium and neon. It is based on the following relation: In the neighborhood of a spectral line the index of refraction n varies according to

$$n - 1 = \frac{e^2 N_i f_{ik}}{4\pi m_e c^2} \frac{\lambda_0^3}{\lambda - \lambda_0} \left(1 - \frac{N_k g_i}{N_i g_k}\right). \qquad (4)$$

Here g denotes the statistical weight; λ the wavelength; N_i the population of the lower state i; and e, m_e, c are the usual natural constants. The experimental conditions are chosen such that the excited states are populated according to the Boltzmann formula, so that generally $N_k << N_i$, and the term $N_k g_i / N_i g_k$ may be neglected. For the determination of $N_i f_{ik}$ the index of refraction n at the wavelength distance $\lambda - \lambda_0$ from the center of the line, λ_0, has to be measured. This can be done most precisely with the "hook" method developed by Rozhdestvenskii [15] and recently reviewed by Penkin [16]. In this method the gas to be studied fills a tube, which is part (one arm) of a Jamin or Mach-Zehnder interferometer. The tube must be at an elevated temperature to achieve sufficient population of the excited levels. Light from the continuum source penetrates the tube as well as an evacuated comparison tube of the same length, and the resulting interference fringes are sent into a spectrograph. On either side of an absorption line the interference fringes are characteristically bent due to the rapid change in the index of refraction. By introducing a thick glass plate into the compensating arm of the interferometer, a tilting of the fringes and the formation of the hooks is accomplished. The measurement of the wavelength distance between the extrema then permits a precise determination of the index of refraction. In the three experiments encountered for this compilation, the absolute number densities for the lower states N_i could not be determined, so that only relative *f*-values for lines originating from the same lower levels were measured. Uncertainties in the relative values should not exceed 10 to 20 percent. In the original papers, absolute *f*-values were then obtained from applications of the Thomas-Kuhn-Reiche *f*-sum rule, but for this compilation we have normalized the relative values to different scales, which are based on other, more accurate material.

2. Theoretical Sources

a. The Coulomb Approximation

Under the assumption of Russell-Saunders (or *LS*-) coupling, which is generally very well fulfilled for the first ten elements, the line strength S may be expressed as the product of three factors [2]

$$S = \mathfrak{S}(\mathfrak{M})\mathfrak{S}(\mathfrak{L})\sigma^2. \qquad (5)$$

(The relations of S with A and f are given in table III.) The first two factors in eq (5) represent the strength of the multiplet ($\mathfrak{S}(\mathfrak{M})$) and the fractional strength of the spectral line within the multiplet ($\mathfrak{S}(\mathfrak{L})$). The numerical values for these may be obtained from tables by Goldberg [17], and White and Eliason [18], which have also been reproduced by Allen [19].

The difficult problem is the evaluation of the transition integral σ. Bates and Damgaard [2] showed that for most transitions the main contribution to the integral comes from a region in which the deviation of the potential of an atom or ion from its asymptotic Coulomb form is so small that it may be replaced by the latter. Since for the Coulomb potential the transition integral may be expressed analytically, it is possible to calculate σ^2 as a function of the observed term value and the azimuthal quantum number. Bates and Damgaard have thus compiled tables with numerical values of σ^2 for $s-p$, $p-d$, and $d-f$ transitions.[2]

The Coulomb approximation is restricted to transitions between levels having the same parent term. It gives the best results if the degree of cancellation in the transition integral is small, i.e., if σ^2 is not too close to zero, and if the upper and lower levels of the excited electron are in a shell which contains no other electrons. This is true for the moderately and highly excited levels. But even if the lower level is in a shell which contains other electrons, the results often agree fairly well with those obtained by other methods.

On the whole, the Coulomb approximation has given impressive results and has proved to be of great value. In most cases where comparisons are available—there are several hundred of them for the first ten elements—the results agree within 20–40 percent with those from advanced theoretical and experimental methods. We have therefore made extensive use of this approximation [3] to supplement

---

[2] The customary spectroscopic notations are used throughout.

[3] We have been fortunate in obtaining a computer program for the calculation of Bates-Damgaard values from H. R. Griem to whom we would like to express our special thanks.

the available material. However, we have restricted ourselves to the medium-strong or stronger lines (as judged from the intensity data supplied in the multiplet tables) for which experimental wavelength and energy level data are available and for which the lower state is significantly above the ground state. If the need for f-values of other higher excited lines should arise, we strongly recommend the application of the Coulomb approximation.

On the basis of many comparisons, the uncertainties of the Bates-Damgaard values have been estimated as follows: For transitions between excited states in the spectra of neutral helium, lithium, beryllium, boron, and their isoelectronic sequences they do not exceed 25 percent and in favorable situations may be as low as 10 percent. For the more complex atoms among the first ten elements, namely carbon, nitrogen, oxygen, fluorine, and their equivalent ions, we have estimated the uncertainties to be within 50 percent for the moderately excited transitions including $3s - 3p$ and within 25 percent for the medium and highly excited lines, i.e., transitions of the types $3p - 3d$, $3d - 4f$, etc. A few of the tabulated values may be much more uncertain than the stated error limit because of cancellation in the transition integral which we did not check in each case.

It is worth noting that in many instances the results of the Coulomb approximation appear to be as good as those from other, more elaborate theoretical treatments, such as the self-consistent field approximation with exchange. This is primarily indicated from comparisons with the most advanced theoretical and experimental methods.

b. Calculations Based on the Self-Consistent Field (SCF) Approximation

This method has found, in varying degrees of refinement, widespread use for the calculation of f-values. It provides a set of wave functions for the atomic electrons which produce an approximately self-consistent electric field. The transition probabilities are then determined by integration over the radial parts of these wave functions. A short outline of the procedure, developed by Hartree, and extensively described by him [20], is given below:

It is assumed that the charge density distribution of the atomic system is spherically symmetric, i.e., the potentials of the electrons depend only on their radial positions. Correlations between the electrons are at first neglected; all are supposed to move independently in the central field, experiencing only the averaged charge distribution of the other electrons and the nucleus. With these simplifications the motions of the individual electrons can be calculated by assuming trial wave functions for the others, and from the resulting wave functions the charge density distribution is computed and compared with the initial one obtained with the trial functions. If self-consistency is not achieved, the new, computed wave functions are used as trial functions, and the procedure is repeated until initial and final charge distributions are identical, i.e., the field is self-consistent.

This basic procedure was improved by Fock [21], who included exchange effects between the electrons, by Trefftz et al. [22], and Biermann and Lübeck [23] who in the special cases of He I and C II took into account other correlations between the electrons. More recently, large-scale computations were made possible after the introduction of elaborate computer programs by Roothaan and co-workers [24].

An assessment of the errors resulting from the various approximations in the calculations has not been feasible. But a number of comparisons with experimental results and with more accurate variational calculations, as well as consistency checks made by applying the dipole length and dipole velocity representations of the matrix element have shown that for simple atomic systems accurate transition probabilities with uncertainties smaller than 10 percent may be obtained when a refined procedure including exchange effects is applied. This is particularly true for He I and Li I and their isoelectronic sequences, for which the extensive calculations by Weiss [25], and Trefftz et al. [22] are available. The large-scale computations by Kelly [26] for lines of nitrogen and oxygen contain the exchange effects only in an approximate way (the exchange term is replaced by an averaged potential) and errors of about 20 percent must be expected for most of the moderately excited transitions as judged from many comparisons. In a few cases, the positive and negative contributions to the transition integral are almost equal to each other (the ratios are listed by Kelly); i.e., cancellations are encountered and a much lower accuracy must be expected. In these cases we have given preference to available experimental results.

For the breakdown of the transition integrals into multiplet and line values we have used the LS-coupling strengths [19] unless special results have been available, as for example for O II. We have generally avoided using SCF calculations if they were done without considering exchange effects, but have had to make an exception for some important lines of B I because no other comparable material is available.

Large uncertainties in the SCF calculations as well as other theoretical treatments are expected for transitions where configuration interaction becomes important. For the first ten elements these transitions are of the type $1s^2 2s^m 2p^n \rightarrow 1s^2 2s^{m-1} 2p^{n+1}$. Only a few attempts have yet been made to take configuration interaction into account. Very recently, Weiss [27] has undertaken limited calculations for some C I and Be I lines and Yutsis, Bolotin and co-workers have for some time employed a "many-configuration approximation," [28] as they call it. The Russian group has greatly simplified its approach by including only one interacting term for the lower state, which is always the ground state ("double configuration approximation") and none for the upper state. In addition to this simplification, relatively crude wave functions have been employed, namely analytical one-electron wave functions or SCF functions without exchange. Unfortunately, practically all these transitions are in the far ultraviolet; only two experimental investigations by Boldt [29] and Labuhn [30], both done with a wall-stabilized arc, are available for a detailed comparison. From the experimental results one must judge that the success of the many-configuration method in its present form is only fair. Errors of factors of two or more must be expected. This seems to be also the case for Weiss' somewhat more elaborate treatment of configuration interaction (up to three interacting terms for the lower state). Thus, the transition probabilities for the $1s^2 2s^m 2p^n \rightarrow 1s^2 2s^{m-1} 2p^{n+1}$ transitions are among the least well known for the lightest ten elements, and further improvements for these lines are urgently needed.

c. Quantum Mechanical Calculations of Forbidden Transitions

We have considered as forbidden lines all magnetic dipole and electric quadrupole lines. The extensive calculations by Garstang [31, 32, 33] and Naqvi [34], and—to a lesser extent—the papers by Seaton and Osterbrock [35], Yamanouchi and Horie [36], and Ufford and Gilmour [37], have been principal sources. All these calculations have as a common starting point the general expressions for the line strengths of forbidden lines in the p^2, p^3, and p^4 configurations, which were given algebraically and tabulated by Shortley et al. [38], and later extended by Naqvi to the few transitions of the sp, p, and p^5 configurations.

The principal differences between the various calculations are the approaches chosen to determine the most important parameters:

(a) The "spin-orbit," and "spin-spin and spin-other-orbit" integrals, usually designated by ζ and η, have been determined either empirically or by using available wave functions. Garstang has compared the empirical and theoretical values for some ions—the latter obtained from SCF functions with exchange—and has found differences of up to 20 percent for ζ and up to 30 percent for η. When a choice is available, we have given preference to the empirical values.

(b) The term intervals. Here one has the choice between using exclusively experimental energy values or combining some of these with the results of the Slater theory [39] for inter-multiplet separations, that is, by employing the Slater parameters F_2. Differences between the two approaches arise mainly due to the effects of configuration interaction. These are neglected in all calculations and may cause deviations up to a factor of two. A study by Garstang [40] in 1956 led to the result that the exclusive use of observational material partially includes, at least in simple cases, the effects of configuration interaction, when the latter is otherwise not taken into account. Thus the work based on experimental term intervals has been adopted whenever available.

Naqvi used in his calculations essentially the second of the above-mentioned approaches. He compared empirically determined Slater parameters F_2 for the various term intervals with theoretically derived values, and selected the one experimental parameter which was in best agreement with theory. Then he employed this particular F_2 and the Slater theory for the determination of all other term intervals. In view of the above mentioned study by Garstang we have used from Naqvi's work only the transition probabilities based entirely on this initial parameter, i.e., based exclusively on observational material. Consequently, his data for the p^3 configuration have not been applied, with the exception of the ion F III, since in this case his work was the only available source. On the other hand, Naqvi's calculations for the simpler sp-configuration are all based on the empirical value for the one term interval there and should, therefore, take the effects of configuration interaction partially into account.

(c) Transformation coefficients. The atoms and ions under consideration are most closely represented by the intermediate coupling scheme, but for the calculations of transition probabilities the actual wave functions are more conveniently expressed in terms of LS-coupling wave functions. The transformation coefficients were first derived by Shortley et al. [38] and were later refined by several others, in particular by Naqvi [34]. Thus, Naqvi's results have been adopted whenever the choice of the transformation coefficients became important and when he accounted for the effects of configuration interaction in the above-mentioned manner. It is especially worth noting that by including the effects of spin-spin and spin-other-orbit interactions on the transformation coefficients of the p^4 configuration some results are improved by about 10 percent.

(d) The integral s_q for electric quadrupole transitions. This depends principally on the quality of the employed wave functions. We have preferred calculations with SCF wave functions over those with hydrogenic functions or screening constants and, among SCF calculations, we have preferred those with exchange effects included over those without exchange. The improvement with SCF wave functions is estimated to be of the order of 20 percent. In general, the electric quadrupole transitions are not as accurate as the magnetic dipole values for transitions of the same general type because of the additional uncertainty in the determination of s_q. This uncertainty should generally be in the neighborhood of 20 percent.

A good assessment of the uncertainties in the calculated values for forbidden lines is possible due to the fortunate circumstance that some forbidden lines of O I have been determined experimentally. These lines appear strongly in the aurora, which has been utilized as a "light source". The transition probabilities could be accurately determined via a measurement of the lifetimes of the upper atomic states. Extensive auroral observations by Omholt [41] gave for the $^1D-^1S$ transition a transition probability of 1.43 sec^{-1}, while the best calculated value is 1.25 sec^{-1}. For another case, namely the lifetime of the ^1D state, the averaged experimental result is approximately 160 sec, while the theory gives 135 sec.

The theoretical transition probabilities involved in this comparison depend sensitively on the choice of some parameters, particularly s_q and ζ. The good agreement with the observations indicates that uncertainties no greater than 25 to 50 percent have to be generally expected.

For a number of magnetic dipole transitions, the uncertainties should be even smaller, since the results are almost independent of the choice of the parameters. In the p^2 and p^4 configurations these are the transitions $^3P_2-^3P_1$ and $^3P_1-^3P_0$, which have, near LS-coupling, the strengths of 2 and 2.5 respectively. In the p^3 configuration one encounters the transitions $^2P^{\circ}_{3/2}-^2P^{\circ}_{1/2}$ with a strength of 1.33 and the transition $^2D^{\circ}_{5/2}-^2D^{\circ}_{3/2}$ with a strength of 2.4, again near LS-coupling. For all these lines the effects of configuration interaction and deviations from LS-coupling do not enter sensitively into the results. Thus, these transition probabilities should be considered accurate to within 10 percent, while all other magnetic dipole lines are uncertain within about 25 percent.

Analogously, the transition probabilities for a number of electric quadrupole lines depend essentially only on the quadrupole integral s_q. These are the transitions $^1S_0-^1D_2$, $^3P_2-^3P_1$, and $^3P_2-^3P_0$ for the p^2 and p^4 configurations and $^2D^{\circ}_{5/2}-^2P^{\circ}_{3/2}$, $^2D^{\circ}_{3/2}-^2P^{\circ}_{3/2}$, $^2D^{\circ}_{5/2}-^2P^{\circ}_{1/2}$, and $^2D^{\circ}_{3/2}-^2P^{\circ}_{1/2}$ for the p^3 configuration. Within a given spectrum these should be the best available quadrupole lines and they have been estimated to be accurate within 25 percent, while the rest of the quadrupole transitions should be accurate within 50 percent. On the whole, electric quadrupole lines have been rated to be of lower accuracy than magnetic dipole lines, since the uncertainties in the quadrupole integral must be added to the other uncertainties already present for the magnetic dipole lines.

Further details on the calculations of forbidden line strengths may be found in the recent review article by Garstang [42].

D. METHOD OF EVALUATION

We shall now discuss the general steps in the evaluation of the data: The literature, as taken from the files of our data center, has first been screened for outdated and superseded material. The remaining articles have then been individually studied and the results collected in comparison tables. Additional values have been computed by employing the Coulomb approximation by Bates and Damgaard [2] whenever this has been considered necessary and useful. When large discrepancies or odd values have appeared in the comparison tables, we have searched for likely sources of numerical errors, and have also communicated in many instances with the respective authors.

The evaluation and final selection of the sets of best values depends so much on the particular material available for each ion that the main justifications for the selections has to be delegated to the individual introductions. Only a few general rules on the selection may be given now:

Thus, self-consistent field calculations with exchange effects have been regarded as superseding those not including these effects[4]; the Coulomb approximation is generally not employed when the transition is very far from being hydrogen-like, e.g., when the lower state is the ground state or when it contains two or more electrons of the same principal quantum number; experiments employing photoelectric techniques are preferred over similar experiments utilizing photographic detection; measurements with wall-stabilized arc sources are considered superseding analogous measurements with fluid- or gas-stabilized arc sources because of the stability problems of the latter. For forbidden lines, the calculations based on empirical term intervals are preferred to those based on the Slater theory for inter-multiplet separations, since a theoretical study [40] shows that the effects of configuration interaction, which are often important, are at least partially taken into account by the first approach.

When several methods of comparable quality are available, the results are averaged to obtain the best value. If one method appears clearly better than the others, only those results are employed.

The final step in the evaluation is the estimate of the uncertainties. At the present status of our knowledge, we find it impossible to assign specific numerical error limits to each transition. Instead we have introduced a classification scheme with several classes of accuracy, and assigned each transition probability to a certain class. We have used the following arbitrary notation:

AA	for uncertainties within	1%
A	do	3%
B	do	10%
C	do	25%
D	do	50%
E	for uncertainties larger than	50%

The word uncertainty is being used in the meaning "extent of possible error" or "possible deviation from the true value". We are aware that this is far from being a precise definition of error, but, considering the multitude of approaches to the error discussions in the various papers (or the lack of them), it seems impossible to find a better common denominator. Uncertainties of class "AA", i.e., values that are essentially exact, are found only in hydrogen and a few transitions of helium. Going to the other extreme, we have included class "E" data, i.e., very uncertain values, only in those special cases, when for the most important and most characteristic lines of a spectrum no better data are available, so that otherwise these lines would

have to be omitted. Occasionally, we have made a further differentiation in the classification scheme by assigning plus or minus signs to some transitions. This serves to indicate that these lines are significantly better or worse than the average values, but do no quite belong into the next higher or lower class. They should be therefore the first or last choice among similar lines.

Since the theoretical treatments essentially do not permit error estimates per se, these have to be obtained from comparisons with experimental and other theoretical determinations or from general consistency checks, such as applications of f-sum rules, etc. A few rather audacious extrapolations have had to be undertaken, when no reliable comparison material was available. On the other hand, the errors given by the experimentalists are sometimes only indications of their precision, and no allowance is made for systematic errors. Therefore, we have generally been more conservative with our error estimates, and hope that we have arrived at a realistic and consistent error presentation.

E. ARRANGEMENT AND EXPLANATION OF COLUMNS

We have adopted the present arrangement of the tables after consulting with a number of physicists working in three fields from which—it is anticipated—most of the users of this compilation will come, i.e., spectroscopy, astrophysics, and plasma physics.

We feel that of the multitude of units in which transition probabilities are expressed, the adopted combination of the transition probability for spontaneous emission A_{ki} (in sec^{-1}), the absorption oscillator strength f_{ik} (dimensionless), the log gf (a further discussion of the statistical weight g is given in Appendix B) and the line strength S (in atomic units) gives a very adequate representation. The other units are either not commonly used or, in case of gf and gA, may be obtained by simply multiplying two columns of the table. The units that are only occasionally used are:

1. The transition probability of absorption B_{ik} ($i=$lower, $k=$upper state) which is related to A_{ki} by

$$B_{ik} = 6.01 \ \lambda^3 \ \frac{g_l}{g_i} \ A_{ki} \qquad (6)$$

(λ is the wavelength in Angstrom units, and g_i, g_k are the statistical weights, further discussed in Appendix B)

2. The transition probability of induced emission B_{ki}, which is related to A_{ki} by

$$B_{ki} = 6.01 \ \lambda^3 \ A_{ki}. \qquad (7)$$

3. The emission oscillator strength f_{ki}, which is related to the absorption oscillator strength f_{ik} by

$$f_{ki} = -\frac{g_i}{g_k} f_{ik}. \qquad (8)$$

In addition, some authors have introduced still other quantities, but these have not found general acceptance and will not be considered further.

The conversion factors between the tabulated quantities A_{ki}, f_{ik}, and S are listed in table III, as reproduced from reference [1]. (For the case of hydrogen, we have employed the reduced mass and other appropriate constants in the conversion factors.)

---

[4] Fortunately, most of the selected self-consistent field calculations include exchange effects in varying degrees of refinement.

The general arrangement of the tables according to increasing atomic number and stage of ionization needs no further comments. The material for the individual ions is further subdivided into sections for allowed (electric dipole) and forbidden transitions. As forbidden transitions we have considered all magnetic dipole and electric quadrupole lines. Intercombination lines, although they are forbidden in the case of pure LS-coupling, are listed under allowed transitions, since they are electric dipole transitions.

The tabulations for each ion start out with listings of the ground state configuration and the ionization potential, both taken from ref. [43]. In all cases, where we have tabulated more than 20 allowed lines per ion, we have then assembled a "finding list," i.e., we have arranged the lines in order of increasing wavelength and indicated their position in the main tables—which are arranged according to spectroscopic notation—by listing their running numbers. The latter are given in front of the spectroscopic notation in the tables. These finding lists should, for many applications, permit one to find out quickly which lines are covered in the present tabulation.

Each table is then preceded by a short introduction containing in brief the major reasons which have led to the selection of the presented data and their classification in terms of accuracy. This is followed by a reference list of the selected articles.

It remains to discuss the columns of the main tables: The first part of the tables contains data connected with the identification of lines, i.e., spectroscopic notation, wavelength, and energy levels. All these data have been taken from the compilations by Mrs. Moore-Sitterly, i.e., the "Revised Multiplet Table" [3], the "Ultraviolet Multiplet Tables" [4], and "Atomic Energy Levels," Vol. I, and addenda in Vols. II and III, recent reports of the Triple Commission for Spectroscopy [44], and from newer material generously furnished by her. All designations, as usual, are written in terms of the absorption process, i.e., the lower (initial) state first. For the classification of the lines we have employed the standard spectroscopic notation for LS-coupling, with the exception of Ne I, where we have used the jl-coupling notation, all in accordance with the above mentioned "Atomic Energy Levels" tables. In listing the transition arrays, we have presented only the electrons in the unfilled shells. Furthermore, to distinguish between the different supermultiplets, we have inserted the parent terms in the notation. If they are given only once, as is generally the case, then no change occurs from lower to upper state.

For all spectra with pronounced multiplet structure, i.e., for Be I through Ne I and their isoelectronic sequences, we have arranged the lines according to a configurational order: They are grouped to multiplets, supermultiplets, transition arrays, and increasing quantum numbers. Within the transition arrays, the multiplets are in order of increasing lower energy levels. Individual lines within the multiplets are listed whenever the total wavelength spread amounts to more than 0.01 percent. This arrangement is convenient for the application of f-sum rules[5] and to the similar one used in the "Revised Multiplet Table" [3] and "Ultraviolet Multiplet Tables" [4]. At first we attempted to copy and extend these older arrangements, but this would have meant that many new multiplets had to be inserted. Therefore, we abandoned this plan. We have, however, made reference to

the two multiplet lists by including the multiplet numbers in the present tabulation. The numbers are given in parentheses under the multiplet designation. The letters "uv" are added if the numbers are from the "Ultraviolet Multiplet Tables."

For the He I isoelectronic sequence we have changed the arrangement slightly by listing the singlets and triplets separately.

For hydrogen we have made several changes in the arrangement to adapt the tables to the very divergent applications in theory and experiment: The tables are split into four separate parts: In table A we list the "average" transition probabilities, etc., for the transitions between lower state of principal quantum number n_i and upper state n_k.

These are defined by the following relations:

$$A^*_{n_k,\,n_i} = \sum_{l_k,\,l_i} \frac{2l_k+1}{n_k^2} A_{(nl)_k,\,(nl)_i} \tag{9}$$

$$f^*_{n_i,\,n_k} = \sum_{l_k,\,l_i} \frac{2l_i+1}{n_i^2} f_{(nl)_i,\,(nl)_k} \tag{10}$$

$$S^*_{n_i,\,n_k} = \sum_{l_k,\,l_i} S_{(nl)_i,\,(nl)_k}. \tag{11}$$

These "average" values are applicable to most problems in plasma spectroscopy and astrophysics. This is due to the circumstance that states with the same principal (n), but different orbital (l) quantum numbers fall practically together ("degeneracy"), so that only a single line is observed for all the possible combinations between states of different principal quantum numbers. The only assumption entering into the application of "average" values is that the atomic substates must be occupied according to their statistical weights [45]. The above assumption is fulfilled for any reasonably dense plasma, where the excited atoms undergo many collisions during their lifetimes.

In table B the probabilities for transitions between the various sublevels $(nl)_i - (nl)_k$ are listed. This table should be useful primarily for theoretical applications. Tables C and D, finally, contain the most important fine structure $[(nlj)_i - (nlj)_k]$ and hyperfine structure lines $[(nljf)_i - (nljf)_k]$ of hydrogen (j = inner or total electronic angular momentum quantum number; f = total atomic angular momentum quantum number). For these two special tables we have made a further change by presenting frequencies and energy differences rather than the usual wavelengths and energy levels.

In all other tables, the energy levels are given (in units of cm^{-1}) relative to the ground state with $E_0 = 0$. We have limited the numerical values to six digits which should be more than sufficient for all applications. The same limitation was imposed on the wavelengths.

In a number of cases we have had to calculate wavelengths from energy level differences. These are given in brackets to distinguish them from the presumably more accurate observed material. However, hydrogen is an obvious exception. Also given in brackets are all energy levels which are not derived from the analysis of spectra, but are extrapolated or obtained from approximate wave function calculations. We have included in this category those energy levels derived from observational material that are shifted by an unknown amount indicated by an

---

[5] It should be mentioned, that for allowed transitions the strengths S of lines in a multiplet add up to the total multiplet strength (see also appendix B), and that for forbidden transitions the total transition probability is obtained by adding the electric quadrupole and magnetic dipole probabilities.

"x" or "y" in ref. [43]. Those calculated or extrapolated values which we expect to be quite uncertain have been indicated, in addition to the brackets, by a question mark.

The averaged energy levels for a multiplet have been obtained by weighting the component levels according to their statistical weights, and the multiplet wavelength is calculated from the averaged energy levels, taking the refraction of air into account for wavelengths longer than 2000 Å [42]. These averaged values are indicated by italics.

The statistical weights g have been included in this tabulation because of their importance in applications involving line intensities. They have been obtained from the inner quantum numbers J listed in the "Atomic Energy Levels" by applying the relations given in Appendix B.

The second part of the table contains the data proper. The numerical values contain as many digits as are consistent with the estimated accuracy of the data.[6]

The numbers in the source column refer to the references listed after the individual introductions. If two or more references are listed, we have given each source equal weight in arriving at the averaged value. If the data for all lines of a multiplet are given, then these are either obtained from the relationships listed in Appendix B and from LS-coupling tables [17–19], which is indicated in the source column by "ls", or they are obtained directly from the literature. In the latter case they are sometimes marked "n", if they are *normalized* to a basis which is different from the one chosen originally by the authors. Similarly, the multiplet values sometimes have been renormalized and have been marked "n".

For the forbidden lines, a few small changes in the arrangement have been made. First, we have indicated the type of transition, i.e., we have listed an "m" for magnetic dipole and "e" for electric quadrupole lines. Furthermore, the log gf and f_{ik} columns are omitted, since these units are not used for forbidden lines. (The line strength S, which now has different atomic units (see table III), is also used infrequently). It should be noted that the total transition probabilities of forbidden lines are obtained by adding the magnetic dipole and electric quadrupole values.

We finally would like to mention that we have assembled and explained in Appendix A all abbreviations appearing in the tabulations.

F. FUTURE PLANS AND ACKNOWLEDGEMENTS

It is our plan to extend this critical compilation to all other elements and make revisions whenever necessary. The present tables should therefore be regarded as the first volume of a larger work spanning all elements. However, realization of this large project in a systematic fashion, say, in order of increasing atomic number, does not appear feasible at the present time, since there are relatively few reliable data available for many heavier elements, and essentially none for higher stages of ionization. As an interim solution, we probably shall attempt to assemble, in an irregular fashion, tables of best values for the spectra of those heavier elements and ions for which extensive and worthwhile data are presently at hand. These will be primarily the heavier noble gases, some of the well-known metals, the alkalis, and the alkaline earths. Also, the third period of the periodic table appears to be promising.

---

[6] During the computations and conversions all digits were retained and finally rounded off. Thus, it may sometimes occur that the line strengths do not exactly add up to the multiplet strength.

Finally, it is our wish and hope that this compilation may stimulate further work on the lightest ten elements, since many gaps and unreliable data are evident on closer inspection of the tables. The two areas that merit the highest attention are the higher ions and those lower excited transitions that are subject to the effects of configuration interaction.

It is our pleasure to acknowledge the help and collaboration of many workers in this field. In particular, we would like to thank P. S. Kelly and B. H. Armstrong for sending us preprints of their extensive SCF-calculations on nitrogen and oxygen, H. R. Griem for supplying us with a computer program to calculate Bates-Damgaard values; and R. H. Garstang and A. M. Naqvi for extensive discussions and some re-calculations of transition probabilities for forbidden lines.

We also express our sincere gratitude to the students who have worked during the past summers on the preliminary aspects of this compilation: These are Mary DesJardins, Maureen Zagronic, Berry Cobb, Don Hall, and Paul Voigt.

We would finally like to thank several of our collegues at NBS; especially A.W. Weiss for many useful discussions and for carrying out many SCF-calculations when serious gaps in the data showed up; Mrs. C. E. Moore-Sitterly for generously furnishing us with new material on energy levels and wavelengths; and J. Z. Klose for undertaking a lifetime study for important excited states of Ne I.

It is also a pleasure to acknowledge the competent help of Miss Jean Bates and Mrs. Marilyn Duffany in typing and proofreading the manuscript.

References

[1] Glennon, B. M. and Wiese, W. L., National Bureau of Standards Monograph 50 (1962) (U.S. Government Printing Office, Washington, D.C.).

[2] Bates, D. R. and Damgaard, A., Phil. Trans. Roy. Soc. London **A242**, 101 (1949).

[3] Moore, C. E., "A Multiplet Table of Astrophysical Interest, Revised Edition," National Bureau of Standards Tech. Note 36 (1959) (U.S. Government Printing Office, Washington, D.C.).

[4] Moore, C. E., "An Ultraviolet Multiplet Table," National Bureau of Standards Circular 488, Sec. 1 (1950) (U.S. Government Printing Office, Washington, D.C.).

[5] Wiese, W. L. in "Proceedings Xth Colloq. Spectrosc. Internat.," p. 37, (Spartan Books, Washington, D.C., 1963).

[6] Foster, E. W., Repts. Prog. in Physics, XXVII, 469 (1964).

[7] Berg, H. F., Eckerle, K. L. Burris, R. W., and Wiese, W. L., Astrophys. J. **139**, 751 (1964).

[8] Richter, J., Z. Astrophysik **53**, 262 (1961).

[9] Frie, W. and Maecker, H., Z. Physik **162**, 69 (1961).

[10] Wiese, W. L., Chapter VI in "Plasma Diagnostics," (edited by Huddlestone, R. H. and Leonard, S. L., Academic Press, New York, 1965).

[11] Griem, H. R., Phys. Rev. **128**, 997 (1962).

[12] Shumaker, Jr., J. B., Rev. Sci. Instr. **32**, 65 (1961).

[13] Maecker, H., Z. Naturforsch. **11**, 457 (1956).

[14] Bennett, Jr., W. R., Kindlmann, P. J., and Mercer, G. N., Applied Optics, Supplement 2 of Chemical Lasers, 34 (1965).

[15] Rozhdestvenskii, D., Ann. Physik **39**, 307 (1912).

[16] Penkin, N. P., J. Quant. Spectrosc. Radiat. Transfer **4**, 41 (1964).

[17] Goldberg, L., Astrophys J. **82**, 1 (1935) and **84**, 11 (1936).

[18] White, H. E. and Eliason, A. Y., Phys. Rev. **44**, 753 (1933).

[19] Allen, C. W., "Astrophysical Quantities," 2d Ed. (The Athlone Press, London, 1963).

[20] Hartree, D. R., "The Calculation of Atomic Structures," (John Wiley and Sons, New York, 1956).

[21] Fock, V., Z. Physik **61**, 126 (1930).

[22] Trefftz, E., Schlüter, A., Dettmar, K. H., and Jörgens, K., Z. Astrophysik **44**, 1 (1957).

[23] Biermann, L. and Lübeck, K., Z. Astrophysik **25**, 325 (1948).

[24] Roothaan, C. C. J. and Bagus, P. S., in "Methods in Computational Physics", Vol. II p. 47 (Academic Press, New York, 1963).

[25] Weiss, A. W., Astrophys. J. **138**, 1262 (1963).

[26] Kelly, P. S., J. Quant. Spectrosc. Radiat. Transfer **4**, 117 (1964).
[27] Weiss, A. W., private communication (1964).
[28] Yutsis, A. P., Zhur. Eksptl. i Teoret. Fiz. **23**, 129 (1952).
[29] Boldt, G., Z. Naturforsch. **18A**, 1107 (1963).
[30] Labuhn, F., to be published in Z. Naturforsch.
[31] Garstang, R. H., Monthly Notices Roy. Astron. Soc. **111**, 115 (1951).
[32] Garstang, R. H., Astrophys. J. **115**, 506 (1952).
[33] Garstang, R. H., Monthly Notices Roy. Astron. Soc. **120**, 201 (1960).
[34] Naqvi, A. M., Thesis Harvard (1951).
[35] Seaton, M. J. and Osterbrock, D. E., Astrophys. J. **125**, 66 (1957).
[36] Yamanouchi, T. and Horie, H., J. Phys. Soc. Japan **7**, 52 (1952).
[37] Ufford, C. W. and Gilmour, R. M., Astrophys. J. **111**, 580 (1950).
[38] Shortley, G. H., Aller, L. H., Baker, J. G., and Menzel, D. H., Astrophys. J. **93**, 178 (1941).
[39] Slater, J. C., Phys. Rev. **34**, 1293 (1929).

[40] Garstang, R. H., Proc. Cambridge Phil. Soc. **52**, 107 (1956).
[41] Omholt, A., Geofys. Publikasjoner Norske Videnskaps.—Akad. Oslo **21**, 1 (1959).
[42] Garstang, R. H., Chapter I in "Atomic and Molecular Processes", (edited by Bates, D. R., Academic Press, New York, 1962).
[43] Moore, C. E., "Atomic Energy Levels", National Bureau of Standards Circular 467; Vol. I (1949); Vol. II (1952); Vol. III (1958) (U.S. Government Printing Office, Washington, D.C.).
[44] Reports of the Triple Commission for Spectroscopy, J. Opt. Soc. Am. **52**, 476 (1962); **52**, 583 (1962); **53**, 885 (1963).
[45] Bethe, H. A. and Salpeter, E. E., "Quantum Mechanics of One-and Two-Electron Atoms", (Academic Press, New York, 1957).
[46] Coleman, C. D., Bozman, W. R., and Meggers, W. F., National Bureau of Standards Monograph 3 (1960) (U.S. Government Printing Office, Washington, D.C.).

Table I.

Relationships between the quantities for hydrogen, indicated by H, and hydrogen-like ions of charge Z (the other symbols are explained in Sec. E).

$$f_Z = f_H \qquad S_Z = Z^{-2} S_H \qquad A_Z = Z^4 A_H$$

Table II.

Reference list of additional material which is considered to be quite reliable but not covered in the table because of its very limited use (the quantum numbers are given in their customary notation).

Spectrum	Transitions	Author
H I	$2 \to n$ for $41 \leq n \leq 60$ $n_i l_i \to n_k l_k$ for $5 \leq n_i \leq 20, 6 \leq n_k \leq 20$, and all possible l-values $2l \to nl$ for $21 \leq n \leq 60$	Green, L. C., Rush, P. P., and Chandler, C. D., Astrophys. J. Suppl. Ser. **3**, 37 (1957).
H I	$1s \to np$ for $7 \leq n \leq 50$ $2l \to nl$ for $7 \leq n \leq 50$ and all possible l-values $3l \to nl$ for $7 \leq n \leq 50$ and all possible l-values $4l \to nl$ for $7 \leq n \leq 50$ and all possible l-values	Harriman, J. M., Phys. Rev. **101**, 594 (1956) and Document No. 4705, American Documentation Institute Auxiliary Publications Project, Photoduplication Service, Library of Congress, Washington, D. C.
N I	$s-p$, $p-d$, and $d-f$ for $2 \leq n \leq 11$; with $1s^2 2s^2 2p^2$ core $s-p$, $p-d$, and $d-f$ for $2 \leq n \leq 8$; with $1s^2 2s\, 2p^3$ and $1s^2 2p^4$ cores	Kelly, P. S., J. Quant. Spectrosc. Radiat. Transfer **4**, 117–148 (1964).
N II, O III	$s-p$, $p-d$, and $d-f$ for $2 \leq n \leq 8$; with $1s^2 2s^2 2p$ core	Kelly, P. S., J. Quant. Spectrosc. Radiat. Transfer **4**, 117–148 (1964).
N III, O IV	$s-p$, $p-d$, and $d-f$ for $2 \leq n \leq 8$; with $1s^2 2s^2$ core	Kelly, P. S., J. Quant. Spectrosc. Radiat. Transfer **4**, 117–148 (1964).
N IV, O V	$s-p$, $p-d$, and $d-f$ for $2 \leq n \leq 8$; with $1s^2 2s$ core	Kelly, P. S., J. Quant. Spectrosc. Radiat. Transfer **4**, 117–148 (1964).
N V, O VI	$s-p$, $p-d$, and $d-f$ for $2 \leq n \leq 8$; with $1s^2$ core	Kelly, P. S., J. Quant. Spectrosc. Radiat. Transfer **4**, 117–148 (1964).
O I	$s-p$, $p-d$, and $d-f$ for $2 \leq n \leq 8$; with $1s^2 2s^2 2p^3$ core	Kelly, P. S., J. Quant. Spectrosc. Radiat. Transfer **4**, 117–148 (1964).
O II	$s-p$, $p-d$, and $d-f$ for $2 \leq n \leq 8$; with $1s^2 2s^2 2p^2$ core	Kelly, P. S., J. Quant. Spectrosc. Radiat. Transfer **4**, 117–148 (1964).

Table III.

Conversion factors. The factor in each box converts by multiplication the quantity above it into the one at its left.

	A_{ki}	f_{ik}	S
A_{ki}	1	$\dfrac{6.670_2 \times 10^{15}}{\lambda^2} \dfrac{g_i}{g_k}$	E_d $\dfrac{2.026_1 \times 10^{18}}{g_k \lambda^3}$ E_q $\dfrac{1.679_8 \times 10^{18}}{g_k \lambda^5}$ M_d $\dfrac{2.697_2 \times 10^{13}}{g_k \lambda^3}$
f_{ik}	$1.4992 \times 10^{-16} \lambda^2 \dfrac{g_k}{g_i}$	1	E_d $\dfrac{303.7_5}{g_i \lambda}$ E_q $\dfrac{251.8}{g_i \lambda^3}$ M_d $\dfrac{4.043_6 \times 10^{-3}}{g_i \lambda}$
S	E_d $\ \ 4.935_6 \times 10^{-19} g_k \lambda^3$ E_q $\ \ 5.953 \times 10^{-19} g_k \lambda^5$ M_d $\ \ 3.707_6 \times 10^{-14} g_k \lambda^3$	E_d $\ \ 3.292_1 \times 10^{-3} g_i \lambda$ E_q $\ \ 3.971 \times 10^{-3} g_i \lambda^3$ M_d $\ \ 247.3_0 g_i \lambda$	1

The line strength is given in atomic units, which are:
For electric dipole transitions (allowed — denoted by E_d):

$$a_0^2 e^2 = 6.459_4 \times 10^{-36} \text{ cm}^2 \text{ esu}^2;$$

for electric quadrupole transitions (forbidden — denoted by E_q):

$$a_0^4 e^2 = 1.808_8 \times 10^{-52} \text{ cm}^4 \text{ esu}^2;$$

for magnetic dipole transitions (forbidden — denoted by M_d):

$$e^2 h^2 / 16\pi^2 m_e^2 c^2 = 8.599 \times 10^{-41} \text{ erg}^2 \text{ gauss}^{-2}.$$

The transition probability is in units sec^{-1}, and the f-value is dimensionless. The wavelength λ is given in Angstrom units, and g_i and g_k are the statistical weights of the lower and upper state, respectively.

APPENDIX A

Key to abbreviations and symbols used in the tables

(A) Symbols for indication of accuracy:

AA . . . . uncertainties within   1%
A . . . . do   3%
B . . . . do   10%
C . . . . do   25%
D . . . . do   50%
E . . . . uncertainties larger than   50%

(B) Abbreviations appearing in the source column of allowed transitions

$ls = LS$-coupling
$ca =$ Coulomb approximation
$n =$ normalized to a different scale

(C) Types of forbidden lines

$e =$ electric quadrupole line
$m =$ magnetic dipole line
(Total transition probabilities of forbidden lines are obtained by adding the e- and m-values).

(D) Special symbols used in the wavelength and energy level columns.

Number in parentheses under multiplet notation refers to running number of ref. [3] (Revised Multiplet Table)

If letters "uv" are added, reference is made to running number in ref. [4] (Ultraviolet Multiplet Table)

Numbers in italics indicate multiplet values, i.e., weighted averages of line values.

Numbers in square brackets approximate calculated or extrapolated values.

Question marks indicate rather uncertain values.

APPENDIX B

(A) Statistical Weights:

The statistical weights are related to the inner quantum number J_L (in one-electron spectra j) of a level (initial and final states of a *line*) by

$$g_L = 2J_L + 1,$$

and to the quantum numbers of a term (initial and final states of a *multiplet*) by

$$g_M = (2L + 1)(2S + 1).$$

(The "multiplet" values g_M may also be obtained by summing over all possible "line" values g_L. S is the resultant spin.)

(B) Relations between the strengths of lines and the total multiplet strength:

1. Line strength S:

$$S(i, k) = \sum_{J_i, J_k} S(J_i, J_k)$$

or $S(\text{Multiplet}) = \sum S(\text{line})$

(k denotes the upper and i the lower term).

2. Absorption oscillator strength:

$$f_{ik}^{\text{multiplet}} = \frac{1}{\bar{\lambda}_{ik} \sum_{J_i} (2J_i + 1)} \sum_{J_k, J_i} (2J_i + 1) \times \lambda(J_i, J_k) \times f(J_i, J_k)$$

The mean wavelength for the multiplet $\bar{\lambda}_{ik}$ may be obtained from the *weighted* energy levels. Usually the wavelength differences for the lines within a multiplet are very small, so that the wavelength factors may be neglected.

3. Transition probabilities

$$A_{ki}^{\text{multiplet}} = \frac{1}{(\bar{\lambda}_{ik})^3 \sum_{J_k} (2J_k + 1)} \sum_{J_i, J_k} (2J_k + 1) \times \lambda(J_i, J_k)^3 \times A(J_k, J_i)$$

Relative strengths $S(J_i, J_k)$ of the components of a multiplet are listed in refs. [17–19] for the case of LS-coupling.

766-655 O-66—2

HYDROGEN

H

Ground State $1s\,^2S_{1/2}$

Ionization Potential 13.595 eV $= 109678.758$ cm^{-1}

Allowed Transitions

For hydrogen a special tabular arrangement is used. In Table A the "average" transition probabilities for transitions between lower states of principal quantum number $(n)_i$ to upper states $(n)_k$ are listed. They are taken from extensive calculations by Green, Rush, and Chandler; Harriman; Herdan and Hughes; Karzas and Latter; and Menzel and Pekeris [1]. These values are applicable to most problems in plasma spectroscopy and astrophysics (see general introduction, Sec. E). Table B contains the probabilities for transitions between the various sublevels $(nl)_i$ $- (nl)_k$. This table should be useful primarily for theoretical applications. Both tables include only four significant figures since relativistic effects, which are of the order of α^2, have been neglected in the calculations (α is the fine structure constant). It should be noted that Green, Rush, and Chandler; and Harriman list more transitions, but these, not being of any practical importance, are omitted.

Table C contains the values for nine fine structure lines as calculated from the work of Wild [2]. The effect of the Lamb shift has been taken into account by using his equation (4a) to calculate the line strength and then by using the energy levels given in NBS Circular 467 (Atomic Energy Levels) for conversion into the other quantities.

The values for the transition between the two hyperfine structure components of the $1s\,^2S_{1/2}$ level are also taken from Wild [2] and are given in Table D. This magnetic dipole transition has a statistical weight of $2f+1$, where f is $j \pm 1/2$ for hydrogen.

The metastable $2s\,^2S_{1/2}$ level gives rise to transitions to the ground state only by means of two-photon emission. This process was studied in particular by Shapiro and Breit [3]. Their calculation of the transition probability for the $1s\,^2S_{1/2} - 2s\,^2S_{1/2}$ transition gives a value of 8.23 sec^{-1} with an estimated accuracy of better than 3 percent. The transition itself gives rise to a continuum; hence no f or S values are given.

Finally, it should be mentioned that in the conversion factors used for hydrogen the reduced mass and other appropriate constants are taken into account.

References

[1] Green, L. C., Rush, P. P., and Chandler, C. D., Astrophys. J. Suppl. Ser. **3**, 37–50 (1957); Harriman, J. M., Phys. Rev. **101**, 594–598 (1956) and Document No. 4705, American Documentation Institute Auxiliary Publications Project, Photoduplication Service, Library of Congress, Washington, D. C.; Herdan, R., and Hughes, T. P., Astrophys. J. **133**, 294–298 (1961); Karzas, W. J., and Latter, R., Astrophys. J. Suppl. Ser. **6**, 167–212 (1961); Menzel, D. H., and Pekeris, C. L., Monthly Notices Roy. Astron. Soc. **96**, 77–111 (1935).

[2] Wild, J. P., Astrophys. J. **115**, 206–221 (1952).

[3] Shapiro, J., and Breit, G., Phys. Rev. **113**, 179–181 (1959).

H — Table A. $(n)_i - (n)_k$ Transitions (Average Values)

Transition	$\lambda(\text{Å})$	$E_i(\text{cm}^{-1})$	$E_k(\text{cm}^{-1})$	g_i	g_k	$A_{ki}(\text{sec}^{-1})$	f_{ik}	$S(\text{at.u.})$	$\log gf$	Accuracy	Source
1−2 (L$_\alpha$)	1215.67	0	82259	2	8	4.699×10^8	0.4162	3.330	−0.0797	AA	1
1−3 (L$_\beta$)	1025.72	0	97492	2	18	5.575×10^7	7.910×10^{-2}	0.5339	−0.8008	AA	1
1−4 (L$_\gamma$)	792.537	0	102824	2	32	1.278×10^7	2.899×10^{-2}	0.1855	−1.2367	AA	1
1−5 (L$_\delta$)	949.743	0	105292	2	50	4.125×10^6	1.394×10^{-2}	8.711×10^{-2}	−1.5548	AA	1
1−6 (L$_\epsilon$)	937.803	0	106632	2	72	1.644×10^6	7.799×10^{-3}	4.813×10^{-2}	−1.8069	AA	1
1−7	930.748	0	107440	2	98	7.568×10^5	4.814×10^{-3}	2.948×10^{-2}	−2.0165	AA	1
1−8	926.226	0	107965	2	128	3.869×10^5	3.183×10^{-3}	1.940×10^{-2}	−2.1961	AA	1
1−9	923.150	0	108325	2	162	2.143×10^5	2.216×10^{-3}	1.346×10^{-2}	−2.3534	AA	1
1−10	920.963	0	108582	2	200	1.263×10^5	1.605×10^{-3}	9.729×10^{-3}	−2.4934	AA	1
1−11	919.352	0	108772	2	242	7.834×10^4	1.201×10^{-3}	7.263×10^{-3}	−2.6196	AA	1
1−12	918.129	0	108917	2	288	5.066×10^4	9.214×10^{-4}	5.567×10^{-3}	−2.7345	AA	1
1−13	917.181	0	109030	2	338	3.393×10^4	7.227×10^{-4}	4.362×10^{-3}	−2.8400	AA	1
1−14	916.429	0	109119	2	392	2.341×10^4	5.774×10^{-4}	3.482×10^{-3}	−2.9375	AA	1
1−15	915.824	0	109191	2	450	1.657×10^4	4.686×10^{-4}	2.824×10^{-3}	−3.0281	AA	1
1−16	915.329	0	109250	2	512	1.200×10^4	3.856×10^{-4}	2.323×10^{-3}	−3.1129	AA	1
1−17	914.919	0	109299	2	578	8858	3.211×10^{-4}	1.933×10^{-3}	−3.1924	AA	1
1−18	914.576	0	109340	2	648	6654	2.702×10^{-4}	1.626×10^{-3}	−3.2673	AA	1
1−19	914.286	0	109375	2	722	5077	2.296×10^{-4}	1.381×10^{-3}	−3.3381	AA	1
1−20	914.039	0	109405	2	800	3928	1.967×10^{-4}	1.183×10^{-3}	−3.4052	AA	1
1−21	913.826	0	109430	2	882	3077	1.698×10^{-4}	1.021×10^{-3}	−3.4691	AA	1
1−22	913.641	0	109452	2	968	2438	1.476×10^{-4}	8.874×10^{-4}	−3.5299	AA	1
1−23	913.480	0	109471	2	1058	1952	1.291×10^{-4}	7.761×10^{-4}	−3.5880	AA	1
1−24	913.339	0	109488	2	1152	1578	1.136×10^{-4}	6.827×10^{-4}	−3.6436	AA	1
1−25	913.215	0	109503	2	1250	1286	1.005×10^{-4}	6.037×10^{-4}	−3.6970	AA	1
1−26	913.104	0	109517	2	1352	1057	8.928×10^{-5}	5.364×10^{-4}	−3.7482	AA	1
1−27	913.006	0	109528	2	1458	875.3	7.970×10^{-5}	4.788×10^{-4}	−3.7975	AA	1
1−28	912.918	0	109539	2	1568	729.7	7.144×10^{-5}	4.292×10^{-4}	−3.8450	AA	1
1−29	912.839	0	109548	2	1682	612.2	6.429×10^{-5}	3.862×10^{-4}	−3.8908	AA	1
1−30	912.768	0	109557	2	1800	516.7	5.806×10^{-5}	3.487×10^{-4}	−3.9351	AA	1
1−31	912.703	0	109565	2	1922	438.6	5.261×10^{-5}	3.160×10^{-4}	−3.9779	AA	1
1−32	912.645	0	109572	2	2048	374.2	4.782×10^{-5}	2.872×10^{-4}	−4.0193	AA	1
1−33	912.592	0	109578	2	2178	320.8	4.360×10^{-5}	2.618×10^{-4}	−4.0595	AA	1
1−34	912.543	0	109584	2	2312	276.3	3.986×10^{-5}	2.394×10^{-4}	−4.0985	AA	1
1−35	912.499	0	109589	2	2450	239.0	3.653×10^{-5}	2.194×10^{-4}	−4.1363	AA	1
1−36	912.458	0	109594	2	2592	207.6	3.357×10^{-5}	2.016×10^{-4}	−4.1730	AA	1
1−37	912.420	0	109599	2	2738	181.0	3.092×10^{-5}	1.856×10^{-4}	−4.2088	AA	1
1−38	912.385	0	109603	2	2888	158.4	2.854×10^{-5}	1.713×10^{-4}	−4.2436	AA	1
1−39	912.353	0	109607	2	3042	139.1	2.640×10^{-5}	1.585×10^{-4}	−4.2774	AA	1
1−40	912.324	0	109610	2	3200	122.6	2.446×10^{-5}	1.469×10^{-4}	−4.3105	AA	1
2−3 (H$_\alpha$)	6562.80	82259	97492	8	18	4.410×10^7	0.6407	110.7	0.7098	AA	1
2−4 (H$_\beta$)	4861.32	82259	102824	8	32	8.419×10^6	0.1193	15.27	−0.0202	AA	1
2−5 (H$_\lambda$)	4340.46	82259	105292	8	50	2.530×10^6	4.467×10^{-2}	5.105	−0.4469	AA	1
2−6 (H$_\delta$)	4101.73	82259	106632	8	72	9.732×10^5	2.209×10^{-2}	2.386	−0.7527	AA	1
2−7 (H$_\epsilon$)	3970.07	82259	107440	8	98	4.389×10^5	1.270×10^{-2}	1.328	−0.9929	AA	1
2−8	3889.05	82259	107965	8	128	2.215×10^5	8.036×10^{-3}	0.8228	−1.1919	AA	1
2−9	3835.38	82259	108325	8	162	1.216×10^5	5.429×10^{-3}	0.5482	−1.3622	AA	1
2−10	3797.90	82259	108582	8	200	7.122×10^4	3.851×10^{-3}	0.3851	−1.5114	AA	1
2−11	3770.63	82259	108772	8	242	4.397×10^4	2.835×10^{-3}	0.2815	−1.6443	AA	1
2−12	3750.15	82259	108917	8	288	2.834×10^4	2.151×10^{-3}	0.2124	−1.7643	AA	1
2−13	3734.37	82259	109030	8	338	1.893×10^4	1.672×10^{-3}	0.1644	−1.8737	AA	1
2−14	3721.94	82259	109119	8	392	1.303×10^4	1.326×10^{-3}	0.1300	−1.9743	AA	1
2−15	3711.97	82259	109191	8	450	9210	1.070×10^{-3}	0.1046	−2.0674	AA	1
2−16	3703.85	82259	109250	8	512	6658	8.764×10^{-4}	8.547×10^{-2}	−2.1542	AA	1
2−17	3697.15	82259	109299	8	578	4910	7.270×10^{-4}	7.077×10^{-2}	−2.2354	AA	1

Transition	λ(Å)	E_i(cm⁻¹)	E_k(cm⁻¹)	g_i	g_k	A_{ki}(sec⁻¹)	f_{ik}	S(at.u.)	log gf	Accuracy	Source
2−18	3691.55	82259	109340	8	648	3685	6.099×10^{-4}	5.928×10^{-2}	−2.3117	AA	1
2−19	3686.83	82259	109375	8	722	2809	5.167×10^{-4}	5.016×10^{-2}	−2.3837	AA	1
2−20	3682.81	82259	109405	8	800	2172	4.416×10^{-4}	4.283×10^{-2}	−2.4518	AA	1
2−21	3679.35	82259	109430	8	882	1700	3.805×10^{-4}	3.686×10^{-2}	−2.5165	AA	1
2−22	3676.36	82259	109452	8	968	1347	3.302×10^{-4}	3.196×10^{-2}	−2.5781	AA	1
2−23	3673.76	82259	109471	8	1058	1078	2.884×10^{-4}	2.790×10^{-2}	−2.6369	AA	1
2−24	3671.48	82259	109488	8	1152	870.7	2.534×10^{-4}	2.449×10^{-2}	−2.6931	AA	1
2−25	3669.46	82259	109503	8	1250	709.6	2.238×10^{-4}	2.163×10^{-2}	−2.7470	AA	1
2−26	3667.68	82259	109517	8	1352	583.0	1.987×10^{-4}	1.919×10^{-2}	−2.7987	AA	1
2−27	3666.10	82259	109528	8	1458	482.6	1.772×10^{-4}	1.711×10^{-2}	−2.8484	AA	1
2−28	3664.68	82259	109539	8	1568	402.2	1.587×10^{-4}	1.532×10^{-2}	−2.8962	AA	1
2−29	3663.40	82259	109548	8	1682	337.4	1.427×10^{-4}	1.377×10^{-2}	−2.9424	AA	1
2−30	3662.26	82259	109557	8	1800	284.7	1.288×10^{-4}	1.242×10^{-2}	−2.9869	AA	1
2−31	3661.22	82259	109565	8	1922	241.6	1.167×10^{-4}	1.125×10^{-2}	−3.0300	AA	1
2−32	3660.28	82259	109572	8	2048	206.1	1.060×10^{-4}	1.021×10^{-2}	−3.0717	AA	1
2−33	3659.42	82259	109578	8	2178	176.7	9.658×10^{-5}	9.305×10^{-3}	−3.1120	AA	1
2−34	3658.64	82259	109584	8	2312	152.2	8.825×10^{-5}	8.501×10^{-3}	−3.1512	AA	1
2−35	3657.92	82259	109589	8	2450	131.6	8.086×10^{-5}	7.788×10^{-3}	−3.1892	AA	1
2−36	3657.27	82259	109594	8	2592	114.3	7.427×10^{-5}	7.152×10^{-3}	−3.2261	AA	1
2−37	3656.66	82259	109599	8	2738	99.66	6.837×10^{-5}	6.583×10^{-3}	−3.2620	AA	1
2−38	3656.11	82259	109603	8	2888	87.20	6.309×10^{-5}	6.073×10^{-3}	−3.2969	AA	1
2−39	3655.59	82259	109607	8	3042	76.57	5.834×10^{-5}	5.615×10^{-3}	−3.3310	AA	1
2−40	3655.12	82259	109610	8	3200	67.46	5.405×10^{-5}	5.202×10^{-3}	−3.3641	AA	1
3−4 (P_α)	18751.0	97492	102824	18	32	8.986×10^{6}	0.8421	935.4	1.1806	AA	1
3−5 (P_β)	12818.1	97492	105292	18	50	2.201×10^{6}	0.1506	114.3	0.4331	AA	1
3−6 (P_γ)	10938.1	97492	106632	18	72	7.783×10^{5}	5.584×10^{-2}	36.18	0.0022	AA	1
3−7 (P_δ)	10049.4	97492	107440	18	98	3.358×10^{5}	2.768×10^{-2}	16.48	−0.3025	AA	1
3−8 (P_ϵ)	9545.98	97492	107965	18	128	1.651×10^{5}	1.604×10^{-2}	9.069	−0.5396	AA	1
3−9	9229.02	97492	108325	18	162	8.905×10^{4}	1.023×10^{-2}	5.595	−0.7347	AA	1
3−10	9014.91	97492	108582	18	200	5.156×10^{4}	6.980×10^{-3}	3.728	−0.9009	AA	1
3−11	8862.79	97492	108772	18	242	3.156×10^{4}	4.996×10^{-3}	2.623	−1.0461	AA	1
3−12	8750.47	97492	108917	18	288	2.021×10^{4}	3.711×10^{-3}	1.924	−1.1752	AA	1
3−13	8665.02	97492	109030	18	338	1.343×10^{4}	2.839×10^{-3}	1.457	−1.2916	AA	1
3−14	8598.39	97492	109119	18	392	9211	2.224×10^{-3}	1.133	−1.3977	AA	1
3−15	8545.39	97492	109191	18	450	6490	1.776×10^{-3}	0.8992	−1.4952	AA	1
3−16	8502.49	97492	109250	18	512	4680	1.443×10^{-3}	0.7267	−1.5855	AA	1
3−17	8467.26	97492	109299	18	578	3444	1.188×10^{-3}	0.5963	−1.6696	AA	1
3−18	8437.96	97492	109340	18	648	2580	9.916×10^{-4}	0.4957	−1.7484	AA	1
3−19	8413.32	97492	109375	18	722	1964	8.361×10^{-4}	0.4167	−1.8225	AA	1
3−20	8392.40	97492	109405	18	800	1517	7.118×10^{-4}	0.3539	−1.8924	AA	1
4−5	40512.0	102824	105292	32	50	2.699×10^{6}	1.038	4428	1.5212	AA	1
4−6	26252.0	102824	106632	32	72	7.711×10^{5}	0.1793	495.6	0.7586	AA	1
4−7	21655.0	102824	107440	32	98	3.041×10^{5}	6.549×10^{-2}	149.4	0.3213	AA	1
4−8	19445.6	102824	107965	32	128	1.424×10^{5}	3.230×10^{-2}	66.14	0.0143	AA	1
4−9	18174.1	102824	108325	32	162	7.459×10^{4}	1.870×10^{-2}	35.79	−0.2230	AA	1
4−10	17362.1	102824	108582	32	200	4.235×10^{4}	1.196×10^{-2}	21.87	−0.4171	AA	1
4−11	16806.5	102824	108772	32	242	2.556×10^{4}	8.187×10^{-3}	14.49	−0.5817	AA	1
4−12	16407.2	102824	108917	32	288	1.620×10^{4}	5.886×10^{-3}	10.17	−0.7250	AA	1
4−13	16109.3	102824	109030	32	338	1.069×10^{4}	4.393×10^{-3}	7.452	−0.8521	AA	1
4−14	15880.5	102824	109119	32	392	7288	3.375×10^{-3}	5.645	−0.9665	AA	1
4−15	15700.7	102824	109191	32	450	5110	2.656×10^{-3}	4.392	−1.0706	AA	1
4−16	15556.5	102824	109250	32	512	3671	2.131×10^{-3}	3.492	−1.1662	AA	1
4−17	15438.9	102824	109299	32	578	2693	1.739×10^{-3}	2.827	−1.2547	AA	1
4−18	15341.8	102824	109340	32	648	2013	1.439×10^{-3}	2.324	−1.3370	AA	1
4−19	15260.6	102824	109375	32	722	1529	1.204×10^{-3}	1.936	−1.4141	AA	1
4−20	15191.8	102824	109405	32	800	1178	1.019×10^{-3}	1.631	−1.4865	AA	1

H−Table A. $(n)_i − (n)_k$ Transitions (Average Values)—*Continued*

Transition	$\lambda(\text{Å})$	$E_i(\text{cm}^{-1})$	$E_k(\text{cm}^{-1})$	g_i	g_k	$A_{ki}(\text{sec}^{-1})$	f_{ik}	$S(\text{at.u.})$	log gf	Accuracy	Source
5−6	74578	105292	106632	50	72	1.025×10^6	1.231	1.511×10^4	1.7893	AA	1
5−7	46525	105292	107440	50	98	3.253×10^5	0.2069	1584	1.0147	AA	1
5−8	37395	105292	107965	50	128	1.388×10^5	7.448×10^{-2}	458.3	0.5710	AA	1
5−9	32961	105292	108325	50	162	6.908×10^4	3.645×10^{-2}	197.7	0.2607	AA	1
5−10	30384	105292	108582	50	200	3.800×10^4	2.104×10^{-2}	105.2	0.0219	AA	1
5−11	28722	105292	108772	50	242	2.246×10^4	1.344×10^{-2}	63.55	−0.1725	AA	1
5−12	27575	105292	108917	50	288	1.402×10^4	9.209×10^{-3}	41.79	−0.3368	AA	1
5−13	26744	105292	109030	50	338	9148	6.631×10^{-3}	29.18	−0.4794	AA	1
5−14	26119	105292	109119	50	392	6185	4.959×10^{-3}	21.32	−0.6056	AA	1
5−15	25636	105292	109191	50	450	4308	3.821×10^{-3}	16.12	−0.7189	AA	1
5−16	25254	105292	109250	50	512	3079	3.014×10^{-3}	12.53	−0.8218	AA	1
5−17	24946	105292	109299	50	578	2249	2.425×10^{-3}	9.957	−0.9162	AA	1
5−18	24693	105292	109340	50	648	1675	1.984×10^{-3}	8.062	−1.0035	AA	1
5−19	24483	105292	109375	50	722	1268	1.646×10^{-3}	6.631	−1.0846	AA	1
5−20	24307	105292	109405	50	800	975.1	1.382×10^{-3}	5.528	−1.1605	AA	1
6−7	123680	106632	107440	72	98	4.561×10^5	1.424	4.173×10^4	2.0108	AA	1
6−8	75005	106632	107965	72	128	1.561×10^5	0.2340	4160	1.2266	AA	1
6−9	59066	106632	108325	72	162	7.065×10^4	8.315×10^{-2}	1164	0.7772	AA	1
6−10	51273	106632	108582	72	200	3.688×10^4	4.038×10^{-2}	490.6	0.4635	AA	1
6−11	46712	106632	108772	72	242	2.110×10^4	2.320×10^{-2}	256.8	0.2227	AA	1
6−12	43753	106632	108917	72	288	1.288×10^4	1.479×10^{-2}	153.3	0.0273	AA	1
6−13	41697	106632	109030	72	338	8271	1.012×10^{-2}	100.0	−0.1374	AA	1
6−14	40198	106632	109119	72	392	5526	7.289×10^{-3}	69.43	−0.2800	AA	1
6−15	39065	106632	109191	72	450	3815	5.455×10^{-3}	50.50	−0.4059	AA	1
6−16	38184	106632	109250	72	512	2707	4.207×10^{-3}	38.07	−0.5186	AA	1
6−17	37484	106632	109299	72	578	1966	3.324×10^{-3}	29.53	−0.6209	AA	1
6−18	36916	106632	109340	72	648	1457	2.679×10^{-3}	23.44	−0.7146	AA	1
6−19	36449	106632	109375	72	722	1099	2.196×10^{-3}	18.96	−0.8011	AA	1
6−20	36060	106632	109405	72	800	842.4	1.825×10^{-3}	15.59	−0.8815	AA	1
7−8	190570	107440	107965	98	128	2.272×10^5	1.616	9.931×10^4	2.1996	AA	1
7−9	113060	107440	108325	98	162	8.237×10^4	0.2609	9514	1.4077	AA	1
7−10	87577	107440	108582	98	200	3.905×10^4	9.163×10^{-2}	2588	0.9533	AA	1
7−11	75061	107440	108772	98	242	2.117×10^4	4.416×10^{-2}	1069	0.6363	AA	1
7−12	67701	107440	108917	98	288	1.250×10^4	2.525×10^{-2}	551.3	0.3935	AA	1
7−13	62902	107440	109030	98	338	7845	1.605×10^{-2}	325.7	0.1967	AA	1
7−14	59552	107440	109119	98	392	5156	1.097×10^{-2}	210.6	0.0313	AA	1
7−15	57099	107440	109191	98	450	3516	7.891×10^{-3}	145.3	−0.1116	AA	1
7−16	55237	107440	109250	98	512	2471	5.905×10^{-3}	105.2	−0.2376	AA	1
7−17	53783	107440	109299	98	578	1781	4.556×10^{-3}	79.03	−0.3502	AA	1
7−18	52622.5	107440	109340	98	648	1312	3.602×10^{-3}	61.13	−0.4522	AA	1
7−19	51679	107440	109375	98	722	984.9	2.905×10^{-3}	48.43	−0.5456	AA	1
7−20	50899	107440	109405	98	800	751.7	2.383×10^{-3}	39.13	−0.6316	AA	1
8−9	277960	107965	108325	128	162	1.233×10^5	1.807	2.116×10^5	2.3642	AA	1
8−10	162050	107965	108582	128	200	4.676×10^4	0.2876	1.964×10^4	1.5661	AA	1
8−11	123840	107965	108772	128	242	2.301×10^4	0.1000	5217	1.1072	AA	1
8−12	105010	107965	108917	128	288	1.287×10^4	4.787×10^{-2}	2117	0.7873	AA	1
8−13	93894	107965	109030	128	338	7804	2.724×10^{-2}	1077	0.5424	AA	1
8−14	86621	107965	109119	128	392	5010	1.726×10^{-2}	629.8	0.3442	AA	1
8−15	81527	107965	109191	128	450	3359	1.177×10^{-2}	404.1	0.1778	AA	1
8−16	77782	107965	109250	128	512	2331	8.456×10^{-3}	277.1	0.0344	AA	1
8−17	74930	107965	109299	128	578	1664	6.323×10^{-3}	199.6	−0.0919	AA	1
8−18	72696	107965	109340	128	648	1216	4.877×10^{-3}	149.4	−0.2046	AA	1
8−19	70908	107965	109375	128	722	906.9	3.856×10^{-3}	115.2	−0.3066	AA	1
8−20	69448	107965	109405	128	800	688.6	3.112×10^{-3}	91.04	−0.3998	AA	1

Transition	λ(Å)	E_i(cm^{-1})	E_k(cm^{-1})	g_i	g_k	A_{ki}(sec^{-1})	f_{ik}	S(at.u.)	log gf	Accu-racy	Source
9 — 10	388590	108325	108582	162	200	7.151×10^4	1.999	4.141×10^5	2.5103	AA	1
9 — 11	223340	108325	108772	162	242	2.813×10^4	0.3143	3.742×10^4	1.7068	AA	1
9 — 12	168760	108325	108917	162	288	1.427×10^4	0.1083	9746	1.2442	AA	1
9 — 13	141790	108325	109030	162	338	8192	5.152×10^{-2}	3895	0.9215	AA	1
9 — 14	125840	108325	109119	162	392	5080	2.918×10^{-2}	1958	0.6746	AA	1
9 — 15	115360	108325	109191	162	450	3325	1.843×10^{-2}	1134	0.4750	AA	1
9 — 16	108010	108325	109250	162	512	2268	1.254×10^{-2}	721.9	0.3077	AA	1
9 — 17	102580	108325	109299	162	578	1598	8.995×10^{-3}	492.0	0.1635	AA	1
9 — 18	98443	108325	109340	162	648	1156	6.719×10^{-3}	352.7	0.0368	AA	1
9 — 19	95191	108325	109375	162	722	855.5	5.180×10^{-3}	262.9	−0.0762	AA	1
9 — 20	92579	108325	109405	162	800	645.2	4.094×10^{-3}	202.1	−0.1783	AA	1
10 — 11	525200	108582	108772	200	242	4.377×10^4	2.190	7.571×10^5	2.6415	AA	1
10 — 12	298310	108582	108917	200	288	1.774×10^4	0.3408	6.692×10^4	1.8335	AA	1
10 — 13	223250	108852	109030	200	338	9231	0.1166	1.713×10^4	1.3676	AA	1
10 — 14	186100	108582	109119	200	392	5417	5.513×10^{-2}	6753	1.0424	AA	1
10 — 15	164070	108582	109191	200	450	3424	3.109×10^{-2}	3358	0.7937	AA	1
10 — 16	149580	108582	109250	200	512	2280	1.958×10^{-2}	1927	0.5928	AA	1
10 — 17	139380	108582	109299	200	578	1578	1.328×10^{-2}	1219	0.4243	AA	1
10 — 18	131840	108582	109340	200	648	1127	9.515×10^{-3}	825.8	0.2794	AA	1
10 — 19	126080	108582	109375	200	722	825.2	7.099×10^{-3}	589.2	0.1522	AA	1
10 — 20	121530	108582	109405	200	800	617.3	5.468×10^{-3}	437.4	0.0389	AA	1
11 — 12	690500	108772	108917	242	288	2.799×10^4	2.381	1.310×10^6	2.7606	AA	1
11 — 13	388320	108772	109030	242	338	1.163×10^4	0.3673	1.136×10^5	1.9489	AA	1
11 — 14	288230	108772	109119	242	392	6186	0.1248	2.865×10^4	1.4800	AA	1
11 — 15	238620	108772	109191	242	450	3699	5.872×10^{-2}	1.116×10^4	1.1526	AA	1
11 — 16	209150	108772	109250	242	512	2377	3.298×10^{-2}	5495	0.9021	AA	1
11 — 17	189730	108772	109299	242	578	1606	2.070×10^{-2}	3129	0.6999	AA	1
11 — 18	176030	108772	109340	242	648	1127	1.402×10^{-2}	1965	0.5304	AA	1
11 — 19	165900	108772	109375	242	722	814.1	1.002×10^{-2}	1324	0.3848	AA	1
11 — 20	158120	108772	109405	242	800	602.6	7.468×10^{-3}	940.5	0.2570	AA	1
12 — 13	887300	108917	109030	288	338	1.857×10^4	2.572	2.163×10^6	2.8697	AA	1
12 — 14	494740	108917	109119	288	392	7884	0.3938	1.847×10^5	2.0547	AA	1
12 — 15	364610	108917	109191	288	450	4271	0.1330	4.596×10^4	1.5832	AA	1
12 — 16	300020	108917	109250	288	512	2596	6.228×10^{-2}	1.771×10^4	1.2538	AA	1
12 — 17	261610	108917	109299	288	578	1693	3.486×10^{-2}	8644	1.0017	AA	1
12 — 18	236260	108917	109340	288	648	1159	2.182×10^{-2}	4886	0.7982	AA	1
12 — 19	218360	108917	109375	288	722	822.3	1.474×10^{-2}	3050	0.6278	AA	1
12 — 20	205090	108917	109405	288	800	600.5	1.052×10^{-2}	2045	0.4814	AA	1
13 — 14	1118000	109030	109119	338	392	1.271×10^4	2.763	3.438×10^6	2.9703	AA	1
13 — 15	619000	109030	109191	338	450	5496	0.4202	2.894×10^5	2.1524	AA	1
13 — 16	453290	109030	109250	338	512	3026	0.1412	7.119×10^4	1.6787	AA	1
13 — 17	371000	109030	109299	338	578	1866	6.584×10^{-2}	2.717×10^4	1.3474	AA	1
13 — 18	322000	109030	109340	338	648	1232	3.672×10^{-2}	1.316×10^4	1.0939	AA	1
13 — 19	289640	109030	109375	338	722	853.2	2.292×10^{-2}	7386	0.8892	AA	1
13 — 20	266740	109030	109405	338	800	611.9	1.545×10^{-2}	4584	0.7178	AA	1
14 — 15	1386000	109119	109191	392	450	8933	2.954	5.284×10^6	3.0637	AA	1
14 — 16	762300	109119	109250	392	512	3926	0.4467	4.393×10^5	2.2433	AA	1
14 — 17	555200	109119	109299	392	578	2192	0.1494	1.070×10^5	1.7675	AA	1
14 — 18	452220	109119	109340	392	648	1369	6.938×10^{-2}	4.048×10^4	1.4345	AA	1

Transition	$\lambda(\text{Å})$	$E_i(\text{cm}^{-1})$	$E_k(\text{cm}^{-1})$	g_i	g_k	$A_{ki}(\text{sec}^{-1})$	f_{ik}	$S(\text{at.u.})$	log gf	Accu-racy	Source
14—19	390880	109119	109375	392	722	914.4	3.858×10^{-2}	1.946×10^4	1.1796	AA	1
14—20	350300	109119	109405	392	800	639.7	2.402×10^{-2}	1.086×10^4	0.9738	AA	1
15—16	1694000	109191	109250	450	512	6429	3.145	7.889×10^6	3.1509	AA	1
15—17	926100	109191	109299	450	578	2864	0.4731	6.489×10^5	2.3281	AA	1
15—18	671200	109191	109340	450	648	1620	0.1575	1.566×10^5	1.8505	AA	1
15—19	544400	109191	109375	450	722	1023	7.292×10^{-2}	5.879×10^4	1.5160	AA	1
15—20	468760	109191	109405	450	800	690.3	4.043×10^{-2}	2.807×10^4	1.2599	AA	1
16—17	2044000	109250	109299	512	578	4720	3.336	1.149×10^7	3.2325	AA	1
16—18	1112000	109250	109340	512	648	2130	0.4995	9.358×10^5	2.4078	AA	1
16—19	802300	109250	109375	512	722	1217	0.1657	2.240×10^5	1.9285	AA	1
16—20	648200	109250	109405	512	800	776.7	7.644×10^{-2}	8.349×10^4	1.5926	AA	1
17—18	2438000	109299	109340	578	648	3530	3.527	1.636×10^7	3.3094	AA	1
17—19	1321000	109299	109375	578	722	1610	0.5259	1.321×10^6	2.4828	AA	1
17—20	949200	109299	109405	578	800	929.6	0.1738	3.139×10^5	2.0020	AA	1
18—19	2882000	109340	109375	648	722	2680	3.718	2.285×10^7	3.3819	AA	1
18—20	1554000	109340	109405	648	800	1235	0.5523	1.831×10^6	2.5537	AA	1
19—20	3374000	109375	109405	722	800	2067	3.909	3.134×10^7	3.4506	AA	1

H—Table B. $(nl)_i - (nl)_k$ Transitions

Transition	$\lambda(\text{Å})$	$E_i(\text{cm}^{-1})$	$E_k(\text{cm}^{-1})$	g_i	g_k	$A_{ki}(\text{sec}^{-1})$	f_{ik}	$S(\text{at.u.})$	log gf	Accu-racy	Source
$1s-2p$	1215.67	0	82259	2	6	6.265×10^8	0.4162	3.330	-0.0797	AA	1
$1s-3p$	1025.72	0	97492	2	6	1.672×10^8	7.910×10^{-2}	0.5339	-0.8008	AA	1
$1s-4p$	972.537	0	102824	2	6	6.818×10^7	2.899×10^{-2}	0.1855	-1.2367	AA	1
$1s-5p$	949.743	0	105292	2	6	3.437×10^7	1.394×10^{-2}	8.711×10^{-2}	-1.5548	AA	1
$1s-6p$	937.804	0	106632	2	6	1.973×10^7	7.800×10^{-3}	4.813×10^{-2}	-1.8069	AA	1
$2p-3s$	6562.86	82259	97492	6	2	6.313×10^6	1.359×10^{-2}	1.761	-1.0886	AA	1
$2p-4s$	4861.35	82259	102824	6	2	2.578×10^6	3.045×10^{-3}	0.2923	-1.7383	AA	1
$2p-5s$	4340.48	82259	105292	6	2	1.289×10^6	1.213×10^{-3}	0.1040	-2.1379	AA	1
$2p-6s$	4101.75	82259	106632	6	2	7.350×10^5	6.180×10^{-4}	5.006×10^{-2}	-2.4309	AA	1
$2s-3p$	6562.74	82259	97492	2	6	2.245×10^7	0.4349	18.79	-0.0606	AA	1
$2s-4p$	4861.29	82259	102824	2	6	9.668×10^6	0.1028	3.288	-0.6871	AA	1
$2s-5p$	4340.44	82259	105292	2	6	4.948×10^6	4.193×10^{-2}	1.198	-1.0764	AA	1
$2s-6p$	4101.71	82259	106632	2	6	2.858×10^6	2.163×10^{-2}	0.5840	-1.3639	AA	1
$2p-3d$	6562.81	82259	97492	6	10	6.465×10^7	0.6958	90.17	0.6206	AA	1
$2p-4d$	4861.33	82259	102824	6	10	2.062×10^7	0.1218	11.69	-0.1362	AA	1
$2p-5d$	4340.47	82259	105292	6	10	9.425×10^6	4.437×10^{-2}	3.803	-0.5748	AA	1
$2p-6d$	4101.74	82259	106632	6	10	5.145×10^6	2.163×10^{-2}	1.752	-0.8868	AA	1

Transition	λ(Å)	E_i(cm^{-1})	E_k(cm^{-1})	g_i	g_k	A_{ki}(sec^{-1})	f_{ik}	S(at.u.)	log gf	Accuracy	Source
$3s-4p$	18750.8	97492	102824	2	6	3.065×10^6	0.4847	59.83	-0.0135	AA	1
$3s-5p$	12818.0	97492	105292	2	6	1.638×10^6	0.1210	10.21	-0.6161	AA	1
$3s-6p$	10938.0	97492	106632	2	6	9.551×10^5	5.139×10^{-2}	3.700	-0.9881	AA	1
$3p-4s$	18751.1	97492	102824	6	2	1.835×10^6	3.225×10^{-2}	11.94	-0.7133	AA	1
$3p-5s$	12818.1	97492	105292	6	2	9.046×10^5	7.428×10^{-3}	1.880	-1.3510	AA	1
$3p-6s$	10938.1	97492	106632	6	2	5.071×10^5	3.032×10^{-3}	0.6550	-1.7401	AA	1
$3p-4d$	18750.9	97492	102824	6	10	7.037×10^6	0.6183	228.9	0.5693	AA	1
$3p-5d$	12818.0	97492	105292	6	10	3.391×10^6	0.1392	35.24	-0.0781	AA	1
$3p-6d$	10938.1	97492	106632	6	10	1.878×10^6	5.614×10^{-2}	12.13	-0.4726	AA	1
$3d-4p$	18751.2	97492	102824	10	6	3.475×10^5	1.099×10^{-2}	6.783	-0.9589	AA	1
$3d-5p$	12818.2	97492	105292	10	6	1.495×10^5	2.210×10^{-3}	0.9324	-1.6556	AA	1
$3d-6p$	10938.1	97492	106632	10	6	7.824×10^4	8.420×10^{-4}	0.3031	-2.0747	AA	1
$3d-4f$	18751.1	97492	102824	10	14	1.379×10^7	1.018	628.0	1.0075	AA	1
$3d-5f$	12818.1	97492	105292	10	14	4.542×10^6	0.1566	66.08	0.1949	AA	1
$3d-6f$	10938.1	97492	106632	10	14	2.146×10^6	5.389×10^{-2}	19.40	-0.2685	AA	1
$4s-5p$	40511	102824	105292	2	6	7.372×10^5	0.5442	145.1	0.0368	AA	1
$4s-6p$	26251	102824	106632	2	6	4.456×10^5	0.1381	23.87	-0.5587	AA	1
$4p-5s$	40512	102824	105292	6	2	6.450×10^5	5.291×10^{-2}	42.33	-0.4983	AA	1
$4p-6s$	26251	102824	106632	6	2	3.582×10^5	1.234×10^{-2}	6.396	-1.1306	AA	1
$4p-5d$	40511	102824	105292	6	10	1.486×10^6	0.6093	487.4	0.5630	AA	1
$4p-6d$	26251	102824	106632	6	10	8.622×10^5	0.1485	76.96	-0.0502	AA	1
$4d-5p$	40512	102824	105292	10	6	1.884×10^5	2.782×10^{-2}	37.10	-0.5556	AA	1
$4d-6p$	26252	102824	106632	10	6	9.416×10^4	5.837×10^{-3}	5.044	-1.2338	AA	1
$4d-5f$	40512	102824	105292	10	14	2.584×10^6	0.8903	1187	0.9495	AA	1
$4d-6f$	26252	102824	106632	10	14	1.287×10^6	0.1862	160.8	0.2699	AA	1
$4f-5d$	40512	102824	105292	14	10	5.047×10^4	8.871×10^{-3}	16.56	-0.9059	AA	1
$4f-6d$	26252	102824	106632	14	10	2.145×10^4	1.583×10^{-3}	1.915	-1.6544	AA	1
$4f-5g$	40512	102824	105292	14	18	4.254×10^6	1.346	2512	1.2751	AA	1
$4f-6g$	26252	102824	106632	14	18	1.373×10^6	0.1824	220.6	0.4070	AA	1
$5s-6p$	74577	105292	106632	2	6	2.430×10^5	0.6078	298.4	0.0848	AA	1
$5p-6s$	74578	105292	106632	6	2	2.682×10^5	7.454×10^{-2}	109.8	-0.3495	AA	1
$5p-6d$	74578	105292	106632	6	10	4.495×10^5	0.6247	920.0	0.5738	AA	1
$5d-6p$	74579	105292	106632	10	6	9.593×10^4	4.800×10^{-2}	117.8	-0.3188	AA	1
$5d-6f$	74578	105292	106632	10	14	7.232×10^5	0.8443	2072	0.9265	AA	1
$5f-6d$	74579	105292	106632	14	10	3.908×10^4	2.328×10^{-2}	79.98	-0.4870	AA	1
$5f-6g$	74578	105292	106632	14	18	1.106×10^6	1.185	4073	1.2200	AA	1
$5g-6f$	74579	105292	106632	18	14	1.137×10^4	7.376×10^{-3}	32.59	-0.8769	AA	1
$5g-6h$	74578	105292	106632	18	22	1.645×10^6	1.676	7406	1.4796	AA	1

H — Table C. $(nlj)_i - (nlj)_k$ Transitions (Fine Structure Lines)

Transition	ν(Mc/sec)	ΔE(cm^{-1})	g_i	g_k	A_{ki}(sec^{-1})	f_{ik}	S(at.u.)	$\log gf$	Accuracy	Source
$2s\ ^2S_{1/2} - 2p\ ^2P°_{3/2}$	9884	0.3297	2	4	6.54×10^{-7}	1.80×10^{-5}	36.0	-4.443	A	2
$3s\ ^2S_{1/2} - 3p\ ^2P°_{3/2}$	2944	0.0982	2	4	1.04×10^{-7}	3.22×10^{-5}	216	-4.191	A	2
$3p\ ^2P°_{1/2} - 3d\ ^2D_{3/2}$	3244	0.1082	2	4	8.67×10^{-8}	2.22×10^{-5}	135	-4.353	A	2
$3p\ ^2P°_{3/2} - 3d\ ^2D_{5/2}$	1082	0.0361	4	6	3.86×10^{-9}	6.67×10^{-6}	243	-4.574	A	2
$4s\ ^2S_{1/2} - 4p\ ^2P°_{3/2}$	1247	0.0416	2	4	2.63×10^{-8}	4.55×10^{-5}	720	-4.041	A	2
$4p\ ^2P°_{1/2} - 4d\ ^2D_{3/2}$	1367	0.0456	2	4	2.77×10^{-8}	3.99×10^{-5}	576	-4.098	A	2
$4p\ ^2P°_{3/2} - 4d\ ^2D_{5/2}$	456	0.0152	4	6	1.23×10^{-9}	1.20×10^{-5}	1040	-4.320	A	2
$4d\ ^2D_{3/2} - 4f\ ^2F°_{5/2}$	456	0.0152	4	6	7.18×10^{-10}	6.98×10^{-6}	605	-4.554	A	2
$4d\ ^2D_{5/2} - 4f\ ^2F°_{7/2}$	228	0.0076	6	8	9.61×10^{-11}	3.33×10^{-6}	864	-4.700	A	2

H — Table D. $(nljf)_i - (nljf)_k$ Transition (Hyperfine Structure Line, Magnetic Dipole Transition)

Transition	ν(Mc/sec)	ΔE(cm^{-1})	g_i	g_k	A_{ki}(sec^{-1})	f_{ik}	S(at.u.)	$\log gf$	Accuracy	Source
$1s\ ^2S_{1/2}\ (f=0 \rightarrow f=1)$	1420.4	0.04738	1	3	2.87×10^{-15}	5.75×10^{-12}	3.00	-11.241	A	2

HELIUM

He I

Ground State $1s^2\,{}^1S_0$

Ionization Potential $24.580\ \mathrm{eV} = 198305\ \mathrm{cm}^{-1}$

Allowed Transitions

List of tabulated lines:

Wavelength [Å]	No.	Wavelength [Å]	No.	Wavelength [Å]	No.
506.200	11	4387.93	29	19543	105
506.570	10	4437.55	23	20425	113
507.058	9	4471.5	86	20581.3	12
507.718	8	4713.2	80	21120	97
508.643	7	4921.93	28	21132.0	39
509.998	6	5015.68	13	21494	116
512.098	5	5047.74	22	21608	126
515.617	4	5875.7	85	21617	67
522.213	3	6678.15	27	21841	60
537.030	2	7065.19	79	22284	57
584.334	1	7065.71	79	23063	54
2677.1	78	7281.35	21	24727	120
2696.1	77	8361.77	96	26113	63
2723.2	76	9463.57	95	26185	125
2763.8	75	9603.42	38	26198	66
2829.07	74	9702.66	100	26248	69
2945.10	73	10311	104	26251	128
3187.74	72	10667.6	99	26531	59
3231.27	20	10829.1	70	26671	122
3258.28	19	10830.2	70	26881	115
3296.77	18	10830.3	70	27600	56
3354.55	17	10902.2	48	28542	112
3447.59	16	10912.9	110	33299	53
3554.4	92	10917.0	51	37026	119
3562.95	84	10996.6	107	40053	62
3587.3	91	11013.1	37	40365	124
3613.64	15	11045.0	44	40396	65
3634.2	90	11225.9	41	40536	68
3652.0	83	11969.1	103	40550	127
3705.0	89	12528	94	41216	58
3819.6	88	12755.7	47	42430	121
3833.55	34	12785	109	42497	93
3867.5	82	12790.3	50	46053	55
3871.79	33	12846	98	46936	114
3888.65	71	12968.4	43	74351	35
3926.53	32	12985	106	108800	111
3935.91	26	13411.8	40	180950	52
3964.73	14	15083.7	36	186200	101
4009.27	31	17002	102	439440	118
4023.97	25	18555.6	46	957600	45
4026.2	87	18686	108	2.16×10^6	61
4120.8	81	18696.9	49	1.39×10^7	123
4143.76	30	19063	117	1.82×10^7	64
4168.97	24	19089.4	42		

Aside from hydrogen, extremely precise *f*-values exist only for a few lines of helium. These are the result of extensive variational calculations (up to 220 parameter wave functions) of Schiff and Pekeris, [1] which give an agreement of 1% or less between the dipole length, velocity, and acceleration forms of the transition matrix element. Similar calculations have been undertaken for a few other transitions by Weiss, [2] but are not quite as refined (up to 54 parameter wave functions) and the agreement between the different forms of the matrix element is not quite as good.

For transitions to higher excited states, recourse has to be taken to somewhat less elaborate theoretical approximations. The following work has been used: Calculations by Low and Stewart (unpublished, but results quoted by Dalgarno and Stewart [3]) with variational wave functions for the ground state and modified hydrogenic wave functions for the excited states; similar calculations by Körwien [6]; self-consistent field calculations, including exchange and correlation effects, by Trefftz, Schlüter, Dettmar, and Jörgens [4]; and applications of various sum rules to modify calculated values by Dalgarno and Lynn [5], and Dalgarno and Kingston [7]. Furthermore, the results of Goldberg [8], who employed screened hydrogenic wave functions, and Hylleraas [9], who employed variational wave functions have been used in a few instances. (Hylleraas' work has not been extensively used, since it probably contains quite a number of numerical errors.) Finally, for all other tabulated transitions, the Coulomb approximation (see general introduction) has been employed, and is expected to give reliable results for this simple atom (uncertainties within 10%). It should be noted that all above-mentioned calculations are nonrelativistic.

For some important helium lines reliable experimental data [10–13] are also available. They all result from determinations of lifetimes of excited states and agree generally quite closely, often within 10%, with the tabulated theoretical results, which are considered more accurate in these cases.

References

[1] Schiff, B., and Pekeris, C. L., Phys. Rev. **134,** A638–A640 (1964).

[2] Weiss, A. W., private communication (1962).

[3] Dalgarno, A., and Stewart, A. L., Proc. Phys. Soc. London A **76,** 49–55 (1960).

[4] Trefftz, E., Schlüter, A., Dettmar, K. H., and Jörgens, K., Z. Astrophys. **44,** 1–17 (1957).

[5] Dalgarno, A., and Lynn, N., Proc. Phys. Soc. London A **70,** 802–808 (1957).

[6] Körwien, H., Z. Physik **91,** 1–36 (1934).

[7] Dalgarno, A., and Kingston, A. E., Proc. Phys. Soc. London A **72,** 1053–1060 (1958).

[8] Goldberg, L., Astrophys. J. **90,** 414–428 (1939).

[9] Hylleraas, E. A., Z. Physik **106,** 395–404 (1937).

[10] Heron, S., McWhirter, R. W. P., and Rhoderick, E. H., Proc. Roy. Soc. London A **234,** 565–582 (1956).

[11] Osherovich, A. L., and Savich, J. G., Optika i Spektroskopiya **4,** 715–718 (1958) (Translated in "Optical Transition Probabilities," Office of Technical Services, U.S. Department of Commerce, Washington, D.C.)

[12] Bennett, R. G., and Dalby, F. W., J. Chem. Phys. **31,** 434–441 (1959).

[13] Kindlmann, P. J., and Bennett, W. R., Jr., Bull. Am. Phys. Soc. II **8,** 87 (1963).

He I. Allowed Transitions

No.	Transition Array	Multiplet	$\lambda(\text{Å})$	$E_i(\text{cm}^{-1})$	$E_k(\text{cm}^{-1})$	g_i	g_k	$A_{ki}(10^8\ \text{sec}^{-1})$	f_{ik}	$S(\text{at.u.})$	$\log gf$	Accuracy	Source
1	$1s^2 - 1s2p$	$^1S - {}^1P°$ (2 uv)	584.334	0	171135	1	3	17.99	0.2762	0.5313	-0.5588	AA	1
2	$1s^2 - 1s3p$	$^1S - {}^1P°$ (3 uv)	537.030	0	186210	1	3	5.66	0.0734	0.1298	-1.1343	AA	1
3	$1s^2 - 1s4p$	$^1S - {}^1P°$ (4 uv)	522.213	0	191493	1	3	2.46	0.0302	0.0519	-1.520	A	2
4	$1s^2 - 1s5p$	$^1S - {}^1P°$ (5 uv)	515.617	0	193943	1	3	1.28	0.0153	0.0260	-1.815	B$^+$	3
5	$1s^2 - 1s6p$	$^1S - {}^1P°$ (6 uv)	512.098	0	195275	1	3	0.719	0.00848	0.0143	-2.072	B$^+$	3, 4
6	$1s^2 - 1s7p$	$^1S - {}^1P°$ (7 uv)	509.998	0	196079	1	3	0.507	0.00593	0.00995	-2.227	B	5, 6
7	$1s^2 - 1s8p$	$^1S - {}^1P°$ (8 uv)	508.643	0	196602	1	3	0.343	0.00399	0.00668	-2.399	B	5, 6
8	$1s^2 - 1s9p$	$^1S - {}^1P°$ (9 uv)	507.718	0	196960	1	3	0.237	0.00275	0.00459	-2.561	B	5, 6
9	$1s^2 - 1s10p$	$^1S - {}^1P°$ (10 uv)	507.058	0	197216	1	3	0.181	0.00209	0.00349	-2.680	B	5, 6
10	$1s^2 - 1s11p$	$^1S - {}^1P°$	506.570	0	197406	1	3	0.130	0.00150	0.00250	-2.824	B	6
11	$1s^2 - 1s12p$	$^1S - {}^1P°$	506.200	0	197550	1	3	0.104	0.00119	0.00199	-2.923	B	6
12	$1s2s - 1s2p$	$^1S - {}^1P°$	20581.3	166278	171135	1	3	0.01976	0.3764	25.50	-0.4244	AA	1
13	$1s2s - 1s3p$	$^1S - {}^1P°$ (4)	5015.68	166278	186210	1	3	0.1338	0.1514	2.500	-0.8199	AA	1
14	$1s2s - 1s4p$	$^1S - {}^1P°$ (5)	3964.73	166278	191493	1	3	0.0717	0.0507	0.662	-1.295	A	2
15	$1s2s - 1s5p$	$^1S - {}^1P°$ (6)	3613.64	166278	193943	1	3	0.0376	0.0221	0.263	-1.656	B	7
16	$1s2s - 1s6p$	$^1S - {}^1P°$ (7)	3447.59	166278	195275	1	3	0.0239	0.0128	0.145	-1.894	A	4
17	$1s2s - 1s7p$	$^1S - {}^1P°$ (8)	3354.55	166278	196079	1	3	0.0130	0.00660	0.0729	-2.180	B	7
18	$1s2s - 1s8p$	$^1S - {}^1P°$ (9)	3296.77	166278	196602	1	3	0.00901	0.00440	0.0478	-2.356	B	7
19	$1s2s - 1s9p$	$^1S - {}^1P°$	3258.28	166278	196960	1	3	0.00650	0.00310	0.0333	-2.508	B	7
20	$1s2s - 1s10p$	$^1S - {}^1P°$	3231.27	166278	197216	1	3	0.00490	0.00230	0.0245	-2.638	B	7
21	$1s2p - 1s3s$	$^1P° - {}^1S$ (45)	7281.35	171135	184865	3	1	0.181	0.0480	3.45	-0.842	A	2
22	$1s2p - 1s4s$	$^1P° - {}^1S$ (47)	5047.74	171135	190940	3	1	0.0655	0.00834	0.416	-1.602	A	4
23	$1s2p - 1s5s$	$^1P° - {}^1S$ (50)	4437.55	171135	193663	3	1	0.0313	0.00308	0.135	-2.034	B	ca
24	$1s2p - 1s6s$	$^1P° - {}^1S$ (52)	4168.97	171135	195115	3	1	0.0176	0.00153	0.0630	-2.338	A	4

No.	Transition Array	Multiplet	$\lambda(\text{Å})$	$E_i(\text{cm}^{-1})$	$E_k(\text{cm}^{-1})$	g_i	g_k	$A_{ki}(10^8 \text{ sec}^{-1})$	f_{ik}	$S(\text{at.u.})$	$\log gf$	Accuracy	Source
25	$1s2p - 1s7s$	$^1P^\circ - ^1S$ (54)	4023.97	171135	195979	3	1	0.0109	8.81×10^{-4}	0.0350	-2.578	B$^+$	4
26	$1s2p - 1s8s$	$^1P^\circ - ^1S$ (57)	3935.91	171135	196535	3	1	0.00718	5.56×10^{-4}	0.0216	-2.778	B$^+$	4
27	$1s2p - 1s3d$	$^1P^\circ - ^1D$ (46)	6678.15	171135	186105	3	5	0.638	0.711	46.9	0.329	A	2
28	$1s2p - 1s4d$	$^1P^\circ - ^1D$ (48)	4921.93	171135	191447	3	5	0.202	0.122	5.95	-0.435	A	4
29	$1s2p - 1s5d$	$^1P^\circ - ^1D$ (51)	4387.93	171135	193918	3	5	0.0907	0.0436	1.89	-0.883	A	4
30	$1s2p - 1s6d$	$^1P^\circ - ^1D$ (53)	4143.76	171135	195261	3	5	0.0495	0.0213	0.870	-1.195	B	ca
31	$1s2p - 1s7d$	$^1P^\circ - ^1D$ (55)	4009.27	171135	196070	3	5	0.0279	0.0112	0.444	-1.473	C$^+$	8
32	$1s2p - 1s8d$	$^1P^\circ - ^1D$ (58)	3926.53	171135	196596	3	5	0.0195	0.00750	0.291	-1.648	A	4
33	$1s2p - 1s9d$	$^1P^\circ - ^1D$ (60)	3871.79	171135	196956	3	5	0.0126	0.00471	0.180	-1.850	C$^+$	8
34	$1s2p - 1s10d$	$^1P^\circ - ^1D$ (62)	3833.55	171135	197213	3	5	0.00971	0.00357	0.135	-1.971	A	4
35	$1s3s - 1s3p$	$^1S - ^1P^\circ$	[74351]	184865	186210	1	3	0.00253	0.629	154	-0.201	A	2
36	$1s3s - 1s4p$	$^1S - ^1P^\circ$	15083.7	184865	191493	1	3	0.0137	0.140	6.95	-0.854	B	2
37	$1s3s - 1s5p$	$^1S - ^1P^\circ$ (70)	11013.1	184865	193943	1	3	0.00956	0.0521	1.89	-1.283	B	ca
38	$1s3s - 1s6p$	$^1S - ^1P^\circ$ (71)	9603.42	184865	195275	1	3	0.00564	0.0234	0.739	-1.631	B	9
39	$1s3p - 1s4s$	$^1P^\circ - ^1S$	21132.0	186210	190940	3	1	0.0459	0.103	21.4	-0.512	B	ca
40	$1s3p - 1s5s$	$^1P^\circ - ^1S$	[13411.8]	186210	193664	3	1	0.0202	0.0182	2.41	-1.263	B	ca
41	$1s3p - 1s6s$	$^1P^\circ - ^1S$ (87)	11225.9	186210	195115	3	1	0.0110	0.00690	0.765	-1.684	B	ca
42	$1s3p - 1s4d$	$^1P^\circ - ^1D$	19089.4	186210	191447	3	5	0.0711	0.647	122	0.288	B	ca
43	$1s3p - 1s5d$	$^1P^\circ - ^1D$	12968.4	186210	193918	3	5	0.0331	0.139	17.8	-0.380	B	ca
44	$1s3p - 1s6d$	$^1P^\circ - ^1D$ (88)	11045.0	186210	195261	3	5	0.0181	0.0553	6.03	-0.780	B	ca
45	$1s3d - 1s3p$	$^1D - ^1P^\circ$	[957600]	186105	186210	5	3	1.68×10^{-6}	0.0139	219	-1.158	B	2
46	$1s3d - 1s4p$	$^1D - ^1P^\circ$	18555.6	186105	191447	5	3	0.00277	0.00858	2.62	-1.368	C$^+$	2
47	$1s3d - 1s5p$	$^1D - ^1P^\circ$	12755.7	186105	193943	5	3	0.00127	0.00186	0.390	-2.032	B	ca
48	$1s3d - 1s6p$	$^1D - ^1P^\circ$	10902.2	186105	195275	5	3	9.23×10^{-4}	9.86×10^{-4}	0.177	-2.307	B	9
49	$1s3d - 1s4f$	$^1D - ^1F^\circ$	18696.9	186105	191452	5	7	0.138	1.01	312	0.705	B	ca
50	$1s3d - 1s5f$	$^1D - ^1F^\circ$	12790.3	186105	193921	5	7	0.0461	0.158	33.3	-0.102	B	ca
51	$1s3d - 1s6f$	$^1D - ^1F^\circ$ (84)	10917.0	186105	195263	5	7	0.0212	0.0529	9.51	-0.577	B	ca

No.	Transition Array	Multiplet	λ(Å)	E_i(cm⁻¹)	E_k(cm⁻¹)	g_i	g_k	A_{ki}(10⁸ sec⁻¹)	f_{ik}	S(at.u.)	log gf	Accuracy	Source
52	$1s4s-1s4p$	$^1S-^1P°$	[180950]	190940	191493	1	3	5.79×10^{-4}	0.853	508	-0.069	B	ca
53	$1s4s-1s5p$	$^1S-^1P°$	[33299]	190940	193943	1	3	0.00302	0.151	16.5	-0.822	B	ca
54	$1s4s-1s6p$	$^1S-^1P°$	[23063]	190940	195275	1	3	0.00250	0.0599	4.55	-1.222	B	ca
55	$1s4p-1s5s$	$^1P°-^1S$	[46053]	191493	193664	3	1	0.0150	0.159	72.2	-0.322	B	ca
56	$1s4p-1s6s$	$^1P°-^1S$	[27600]	191493	195115	3	1	0.00721	0.0274	7.48	-1.085	B	ca
57	$1s4p-1s7s$	$^1P°-^1S$	[22284]	191493	195979	3	1	0.00438	0.0109	2.39	-1.487	B	ca
58	$1s4p-1s5d$	$^1P°-^1D$	[41216]	191493	193918	3	5	0.0153	0.649	264	0.289	B	ca
59	$1s4p-1s6d$	$^1P°-^1D$	[26531]	191493	195261	3	5	0.00861	0.152	39.7	-0.342	B	ca
60	$1s4p-1s7d$	$^1P°-^1D$	[21841]	191493	196070	3	5	0.00533	0.0635	13.7	-0.720	B	ca
61	$1s4d-1s4p$	$^1D-^1P°$	[2.16×10^6]	191447	191493	5	3	5.70×10^{-7}	0.0240	856	-0.920	B	ca
62	$1s4d-1s5p$	$^1D-^1P°$	[40053]	191447	193943	5	3	0.00166	0.0240	15.8	-0.922	B	ca
63	$1s4d-1s6p$	$^1D-^1P°$	[26113]	191447	195275	5	3	7.85×10^{-4}	0.00482	2.07	-1.618	B	ca
64	$1s4d-1s4f$	$^1D-^1F°$	[1.82×10^7]	191447	191452	5	7	3.63×10^{-10}	0.00253	757	-1.899	B	ca
65	$1s4d-1s5f$	$^1D-^1F°$	[40396]	191447	193921	5	7	0.0259	0.887	590	0.647	B	ca
66	$1s4d-1s6f$	$^1D-^1F°$	[26198]	191447	195263	5	7	0.0130	0.187	80.7	-0.029	B	ca
67	$1s4d-1s7f$	$^1D-^1F°$	[21617]	191447	196071	5	7	0.00734	0.0719	25.6	-0.444	B	ca
68	$1s4f-1s5d$	$^1F°-^1D$	[40536]	191452	193918	7	5	5.20×10^{-4}	0.00915	8.55	-1.193	B	ca
69	$1s4f-1s6d$	$^1F°-^1D$	[26248]	191452	195261	7	5	2.49×10^{-4}	0.00184	1.11	-1.891	B	ca
70	$1s2s-1s2p$	$^3S-^3P°$ (1)	10830	159856	169087	3	9	0.1022	0.5391	57.66	0.2088	AA	1
			10830.3	159856	169087	3	5	0.1022	0.2994	32.03	-0.0466	AA	ls
			10830.2	159856	169087	3	3	0.1022	0.1797	19.22	-0.2684	AA	ls
			10829.1	159856	169088	3	1	0.1022	0.05990	6.407	-0.7454	AA	ls
71	$1s2s-1s3p$	$^3S-^3P°$ (2)	3888.65	159856	185565	3	9	0.09478	0.06446	2.476	-0.7136	AA	1
72	$1s2s-1s4p$	$^3S-^3P°$ (3)	3187.74	159856	191217	3	9	0.0505	0.0231	0.727	-1.159	B	2
73	$1s2s-1s5p$	$^3S-^3P°$ (11 uv)	2945.10	159856	193801	3	9	0.0293	0.0114	0.332	-1.465	B	7
74	$1s2s-1s6p$	$^3S-^3P°$ (12 uv)	2829.07	159856	195193	3	9	0.0169	0.00608	0.170	-1.739	B	7
75	$1s2s-1s7p$	$^3S-^3P°$	2763.8	159856	196027	3	9	0.0111	0.00381	0.104	-1.942	B	7
76	$1s2s-1s8p$	$^3S-^3P°$	2723.2	159856	196567	3	9	0.00780	0.00260	0.0700	-2.108	B	7
77	$1s2s-1s9p$	$^3S-^3P°$	2696.1	159856	196935	3	9	0.00550	0.00180	0.0479	-2.268	B	7
78	$1s2s-1s10p$	$^3S-^3P°$	2677.1	159856	197198	3	9	0.00404	0.00130	0.0344	-2.409	B	7
79	$1s2p-1s3s$	$^3P°-^3S$ (10)	7065.3	169087	183237	9	3	0.278	0.0693	14.5	-0.205	A	2
			7065.19	169087	183237	5	3	0.154	0.0693	8.06	-0.460	A	ls
			7065.19	169087	183237	3	3	0.0925	0.0692	4.83	-0.683	A	ls
			7065.71	169088	183237	1	3	0.0308	0.0692	1.61	-1.160	A	ls

No.	Transition Array	Multiplet	λ(Å)	E_i(cm^{-1})	E_k(cm^{-1})	g_i	g_k	A_{ki}(10^8 sec^{-1})	f_{ik}	S(at.u.)	log gf	Accuracy	Source
80	1s2p − 1s4s	^{3}P° − ^{3}S (12)	4713.2	169087	190298	9	3	0.106	0.0118	1.65	−0.973	B	4
81	1s2p − 1s5s	^{3}P° − ^{3}S (16)	4120.8	169087	193347	9	3	0.0430	0.00365	0.446	−1.483	B	ca
82	1s2p − 1s6s	^{3}P° − ^{3}S (20)	3867.5	169087	194936	9	3	0.0236	0.00176	0.202	−1.800	B	ca
83	1s2p − 1s8s	^{3}P° − ^{3}S (27)	3652.0	169087	196461	9	3	0.0108	7.21 × 10^{-4}	0.0780	−2.188	B	4
84	1s2p − 1s10s	^{3}P° − ^{3}S (33)	3562.95	169087	197145	9	3	0.00543	3.45 × 10^{-4}	0.0364	−2.508	B	4
85	1s2p − 1s3d	^{3}P° − ^{3}D (11)	5875.7	169087	186102	9	15	0.706	0.609	106	0.739	A	2
86	1s2p − 1s4d	^{3}P° − ^{3}D (14)	4471.5	169087	191445	9	15	0.251	0.125	16.6	0.052	A	4
87	1s2p − 1s5d	^{3}P° − ^{3}D (18)	4026.2	169087	193917	9	15	0.117	0.0474	5.66	−0.370	A	4
88	1s2p − 1s6d	^{3}P° − ^{3}D (22)	3819.6	169087	195260	9	15	0.0589	0.0215	2.43	−0.714	B	ca
89	1s2p − 1s7d	^{3}P° − ^{3}D (25)	3705.0	169087	196070	9	15	0.0444	0.0152	1.67	−0.864	C$^+$	8
90	1s2p − 1s8d	^{3}P° − ^{3}D (28)	3634.2	169087	196595	9	15	0.0261	0.00862	0.928	−1.110	A	4
91	1s2p − 1s9d	^{3}P° − ^{3}D (31)	3587.3	169087	196955	9	15	0.0205	0.00660	0.702	−1.226	C$^+$	8
92	1s2p − 1s10d	^{3}P° − ^{3}D (34)	3554.4	169087	197213	9	15	0.0131	0.00414	0.436	−1.429	A	4
93	1s3s − 1s3p	^{3}S − ^{3}P°	[42947]	183237	185565	3	9	0.0108	0.896	380	0.429	A	2
94	1s3s − 1s4p	^{3}S − ^{3}P°	12528	183237	191217	3	9	0.00608	0.0429	5.31	−0.890	B	2
95	1s3s − 1s5p	^{3}S − ^{3}P° (67)	9463.57	183237	193801	3	9	0.00608	0.0245	2.29	−1.134	B	ca
96	1s3s − 1s6p	^{3}S − ^{3}P° (68)	8361.77	183237	195193	3	9	7.16 × 10^{-4}	0.00225	0.186	−2.170	B	9
97	1s3p − 1s4s	^{3}P° − ^{3}S	21120	185565	190298	9	3	0.0652	0.145	91.0	0.117	B	ca
98	1s3p − 1s5s	^{3}P° − ^{3}S	12846	185565	193347	9	3	0.0269	0.0222	8.45	−0.699	B	ca
99	1s3p − 1s6s	^{3}P° − ^{3}S (73)	10667.6	185565	194936	9	3	0.0142	0.00810	2.56	−1.137	B	ca
100	1s3p − 1s7s	^{3}P° − ^{3}S (75)	9702.66	185565	195868	9	3	0.00858	0.00404	1.16	−1.440	B	ca
101	1s3p − 1s3d	^{3}P° − ^{3}D	[186200]	185565	186102	9	15	1.28 × 10^{-4}	0.111	613	0.000	A	2
102	1s3p − 1s4d	^{3}P° − ^{3}D	17002	185565	191445	9	15	0.0668	0.482	243	0.638	B	ca
103	1s3p − 1s5d	^{3}P° − ^{3}D (72)	11969.1	185565	193917	9	15	0.0343	0.123	43.5	0.043	B	ca

No.	Transition Array	Multiplet	λ(Å)	E_i(cm^{-1})	E_k(cm^{-1})	g_i	g_k	A_{ki}(10^8 sec^{-1})	f_{ik}	S(at.u.)	log gf	Accuracy	Source
104	$1s3p-1s6d$	^{3}P° — ^{3}D (74)	10311	185565	195260	9	15	0.0197	0.0524	16.0	−0.327	B	ca
105	$1s3d-1s4p$	^{3}D — ^{3}P°	19543	186102	191217	15	9	0.00597	0.0205	19.8	−0.512	C$^+$	2
106	$1s3d-1s5p$	^{3}D — ^{3}P°	12985	186102	193801	15	9	0.00274	0.00415	2.66	−1.206	B	ca
107	$1s3d-1s6p$	^{3}D — ^{3}P° (78)	10996.6	186102	195193	15	9	5.67×10^{-4}	6.17×10^{-4}	0.335	−2.034	B	9
108	$1s3d-1s4f$	^{3}D — ^{3}F°	18686	186102	191452	15	21	0.139	1.02	937	1.183	B	ca
109	$1s3d-1s5f$	^{3}D — ^{3}F°	12785	186102	193921	15	21	0.0462	0.158	100	0.376	B	ca
110	$1s3d-1s6f$	^{3}D — ^{3}F° (79)	10912.9	186102	195263	15	21	0.0212	0.0531	28.6	−0.099	B	ca
111	$1s4s-1s4p$	^{3}S — ^{3}P°	[108800]	190298	191217	3	9	0.00227	1.21	1300	0.560	B	ca
112	$1s4s-1s5p$	^{3}S — ^{3}P°	[28542]	190298	193801	3	9	0.00128	0.0468	13.2	−0.852	B	ca
113	$1s4s-1s6p$	^{3}S — ^{3}P°	[20425]	190298	195193	3	9	0.00147	0.0276	5.57	−1.082	B	ca
114	$1s4p-1s5s$	^{3}P° — ^{3}S	[46936]	191217	193347	9	3	0.0202	0.223	310	0.302	B	ca
115	$1s4p-1s6s$	^{3}P° — ^{3}S	[26881]	191217	194936	9	3	0.00925	0.0334	26.6	−0.522	B	ca
116	$1s4p-1s7s$	^{3}P° — ^{3}S	[21494]	191217	195868	9	3	0.00543	0.0125	7.99	−0.947	B	ca
117	$1s4p-1s8s$	^{3}P° — ^{3}S	[19063]	191217	196461	9	3	0.00340	0.00618	3.49	−1.255	B	ca
118	$1s4p-1s4d$	^{3}P° — ^{3}D	[439440]	191217	191445	9	15	4.15×10^{-5}	0.200	2610	0.256	B	ca
119	$1s4p-1s5d$	^{3}P° — ^{3}D	[37026]	191217	193917	9	15	0.0129	0.442	485	0.600	B	ca
120	$1s4p-1s6d$	^{3}P° — ^{3}D	[24727]	191217	195260	9	15	0.00795	0.121	89.0	0.039	B	ca
121	$1s4d-1s5p$	^{3}D — ^{3}P°	[42430]	191445	193801	15	9	0.00333	0.0539	113	−0.092	B	ca
122	$1s4d-1s6p$	^{3}D — ^{3}P°	[26671]	191445	195193	15	9	0.00160	0.0102	13.5	−0.813	B	ca
123	$1s4d-1s4f$	^{3}D — ^{3}F°	[1.39×10^7]	191445	191452	15	21	8.15×10^{-10}	0.00331	2270	−1.305	B	ca
124	$1s4d-1s5f$	^{3}D — ^{3}F°	[40365]	191445	193921	15	21	0.0260	0.888	1770	1.125	B	ca
125	$1s4d-1s6f$	^{3}D — ^{3}F°	[26185]	191445	195263	15	21	0.0130	0.187	242	0.448	B	ca
126	$1s4d-1s7f$	^{3}D — ^{3}F°	[21608]	191445	196071	15	21	0.00734	0.0720	76.8	0.033	B	ca
127	$1s4f-1s5d$	^{3}F° — ^{3}D	[40550]	191452	193917	21	15	5.25×10^{-4}	0.00924	25.9	−0.712	B	ca
128	$1s4f-1s6d$	^{3}F° — ^{3}D	[26251]	191452	195260	21	15	2.51×10^{-4}	0.00185	3.36	−1.410	B	ca

LITHIUM

Li I

Ground State $1s^2 2s\ ^2S_{1/2}$

Ionization Potential $5.390\ eV = 43487.19\ cm^{-1}$

Allowed Transitions

List of tabulated lines:

Wavelength [Å]	No.	Wavelength [Å]	No.	Wavelength [Å]	No.
2333.94	12	10510.6	28	28417	38
2340.16	11	10792.1	21	38081	40
2348.22	10	10919.1	33	40294	45
2358.92	9	11032.1	24	40562	47
2373.55	8	12237.7	27	41791	42
2394.36	7	12793.3	32	47804	50
2425.41	6	12928.9	30	54633	37
2475.06	5	13557.8	23	68592	34
2562.31	4	17546.1	26	70319	53
2741.19	3	18586.8	36	74379	56
3232.63	2	18703.1	31	75010	57
3985.5	16	19274.8	29	77145	54
4132.6	19	24464.7	22	102850	51
4273.1	15	24971	35	139610	49
4602.9	18	25197	41	279490	25
4971.7	14	26201	46	650000	39
6103.6	17	26260	48	1261000	52
6707.8	1	26536	43	1.04×10^7	55
8126.4	13	26877.8	20	1.47×10^7	44

The transition probabilities for the $2s-2p$, $2p-3s$, $2p-3d$, $3s-3p$, and $3p-3d$ transitions are taken from the dipole length calculations of Weiss [1]. The values for the $2s-np\,(n=3\ .\ .\ .\ 13)$ transitions are selected from the anomalous dispersion measurements of Filippov [2] normalized to Weiss' f-value for the resonance transition $2s-2p$. For this series, preference is given to Filippov's experimental values since the theoretical methods show strong cancellation effects in the transition integral. Uncertainties of not more than 10% are indicated by the very good agreement of the selected material with other determinations.

References

[1] Weiss, A. W., Astrophys. J. **138**, 1262–1276 (1963).
[2] Filippov, A. N., Ž. Physik **69**, 526–547 (1931); Zhur. Eksptl. i Teoret. Fiz. **2**, 24–41 (1932) (translated in "Optical Transition Probabilities," Office of Technical Services, U.S. Department of Commerce, Washington, D.C.).

Li I. Allowed Transitions

No.	Transition Array	Multiplet	λ(Å)	$E_i(\text{cm}^{-1})$	$E_k(\text{cm}^{-1})$	g_i	g_k	$A_{ki}(\text{sec}^{-1})$	f_{ik}	S(at.u.)	log gf	Accuracy	Source
1	2s − 2p	²S − ²P° (1)	6707.8	0.00	14903.9	2	6	3.72×10^7	0.753	33.3	0.178	A	1
2	2s − 3p	²S − ²P° (2)	3232.63	0.00	30925.4	2	6	1.17×10^6	0.00552	0.117	−1.957	B	2
3	2s − 4p	²S − ²P° (1 uv)	2741.19	0.00	36469.6	2	6	1.42×10^6	0.00480	0.0866	−2.018	B	2
4	2s − 5p	²S − ²P° (2 uv)	2562.31	0.00	39015.6	2	6	1.07×10^6	0.00316	0.0533	−2.199	B	2
5	2s − 6p	²S − ²P° (3 uv)	2475.06	0.00	40390.8	2	6	6.97×10^5	0.00192	0.0313	−2.416	B	2
6	2s − 7p	²S − ²P° (4 uv)	2425.41	0.00	41217.4	2	6	4.84×10^5	0.00128	0.0204	−2.592	B	2
7	2s − 8p	²S − ²P° (5 uv)	2394.36	0.00	41751.6	2	6	3.55×10^5	9.16×10^{-4}	0.0144	−2.737	B	2
8	2s − 9p	²S − ²P°	2373.55	0.00	42118.3	2	6	2.68×10^5	6.79×10^{-4}	0.0106	−2.867	B	2
9	2s − 10p	²S − ²P°	2358.92	0.00	42379.2	2	6	2.09×10^5	5.22×10^{-4}	0.00811	−2.981	B	2
10	2s − 11p	²S − ²P°	2348.22	0.00	42569.1	2	6	1.65×10^5	4.08×10^{-4}	0.00631	−3.088	B	2
11	2s − 12p	²S − ²P°	2340.16	0.00	42719.1	2	6	1.34×10^5	3.29×10^{-4}	0.00507	−3.182	B	2
12	2s − 13p	²S − ²P°	2333.94	0.00	42832.9	2	6	1.09×10^5	2.67×10^{-4}	0.00410	−3.273	B	2
13	2p − 3s	²P° − ²S (3)	8126.4	14903.9	27206.1	6	2	3.49×10^7	0.115	18.5	−0.160	B+	1
14	2p − 4s	²P° − ²S (5)	4971.7	14903.9	35012.1	6	2	1.01×10^7	0.0125	1.23	−1.126	B	ca
15	2p − 5s	²P° − ²S	4273.1	14903.9	38299.5	6	2	4.60×10^6	0.00420	0.355	−1.599	B	ca
16	2p − 6s	²P° − ²S	3985.5	14903.9	39987.6	6	2	2.50×10^6	0.00198	0.156	−1.924	B	ca
17	2p − 3d	²P° − ²D (4)	6103.6	14903.9	31283.1	6	10	7.16×10^7	0.667	80.4	0.602	B+	1
18	2p − 4d	²P° − ²D (6)	4602.9	14903.9	36623.4	6	10	2.30×10^7	0.122	11.1	−0.137	B	ca
19	2p − 5d	²P° − ²D	4132.6	14903.9	39094.9	6	10	1.06×10^7	0.0453	3.70	−0.566	B	ca
20	3s − 3p	²S − ²P°	26877.8	27206.1	30925.4	2	6	3.77×10^6	1.23	217	0.389	B+	1
21	3s − 4p	²S − ²P°	[10792.1]	27206.1	36469.6	2	6	3.69×10^3	1.93×10^{-4}	0.0137	−3.413	B	ca
22	3p − 4s	²P° − ²S	24464.7	30925.4	35012.1	6	2	7.46×10^6	0.223	108	0.127	B	ca
23	3p − 5s	²P° − ²S	13557.8	30925.4	38299.5	6	2	2.76×10^6	0.0254	6.80	−0.817	B	ca
24	3p − 6s	²P° − ²S	11032.1	30925.4	39987.6	6	2	1.44×10^6	0.00874	1.90	−1.280	B	ca
25	3p − 3d	²P° − ²D	[279490]	30925.4	31283.1	6	10	3.81×10^3	0.0743	410	−0.351	B	1
26	3p − 4d	²P° − ²D	17546.1	30925.4	36623.4	6	10	6.85×10^6	0.527	183	0.500	B	ca
27	3p − 5d	²P° − ²D	12237.7	30925.4	39094.9	6	10	3.41×10^6	0.128	30.9	−0.116	B	ca
28	3p − 6d	²P° − ²D	10510.6	30925.4	40437.3	6	10	1.94×10^6	0.0534	11.1	−0.494	B	ca

Li I. Allowed Transitions—*Continued*

No.	Transition Array	Multiplet	$\lambda(\text{Å})$	$E_i(\text{cm}^{-1})$	$E_k(\text{cm}^{-1})$	g_i	g_k	$A_{ki}(\text{sec}^{-1})$	f_{ik}	$S(\text{at.u.})$	$\log gf$	Accuracy	Source
29	$3d-4p$	$^2\text{D}-^2\text{P}°$	19274.8	31283.1	36469.6	10	6	5.52×10^5	0.0184	11.7	-0.734	B	*ca*
30	$3d-5p$	$^2\text{D}-^2\text{P}°$	[12928.9]	31283.1	39015.6	10	6	2.31×10^5	0.00348	1.48	-1.459	B	*ca*
31	$3d-4f$	$^2\text{D}-^2\text{F}°$	18703.1	31283.1	36630.2	10	14	1.38×10^7	1.01	625	1.006	B	*ca*
32	$3d-5f$	$^2\text{D}-^2\text{F}°$	12793.3	31283.1	39104.5	10	14	4.63×10^6	0.159	67.0	0.201	B	*ca*
33	$3d-6f$	$^2\text{D}-^2\text{F}°$	[10919.1]	31283.1	[40439.0]	10	14	2.11×10^6	0.0529	19.0	-0.277	B	*ca*
34	$4s-4p$	$^2\text{S}-^2\text{P}°$	[68592]	35012.1	36469.6	2	6	7.72×10^5	1.63	737	0.514	B	*ca*
35	$4s-5p$	$^2\text{S}-^2\text{P}°$	[24971]	35012.1	39015.6	2	6	2.07×10^3	5.81×10^{-4}	0.0955	-2.935	B	*ca*
36	$4s-6p$	$^2\text{S}-^2\text{P}°$	[18586.8]	35012.1	40390.8	2	6	8.38×10^3	0.00130	0.159	-2.585	B	*ca*
37	$4p-5s$	$^2\text{P}°-^2\text{S}$	[54633]	36469.6	38299.5	6	2	2.25×10^6	0.335	362	0.303	B	*ca*
38	$4p-6s$	$^2\text{P}°-^2\text{S}$	[28417]	36469.6	39987.6	6	2	9.22×10^5	0.0372	20.9	-0.651	B	*ca*
39	$4p-4d$	$^2\text{P}°-^2\text{D}$	[650000]	36469.6	36623.4	6	10	1.28×10^3	0.135	1740	-0.091	B	*ca*
40	$4p-5d$	$^2\text{P}°-^2\text{D}$	[38081]	36469.6	39094.9	6	10	1.36×10^6	0.494	372	0.472	B	*ca*
41	$4p-6d$	$^2\text{P}°-^2\text{D}$	[25197]	36469.6	40437.3	6	10	8.19×10^5	0.130	64.6	-0.108	B	*ca*
42	$4d-5p$	$^2\text{D}-^2\text{P}°$	[41791]	36623.4	39015.6	10	6	2.86×10^5	0.0450	61.9	-0.347	B	*ca*
43	$4d-6p$	$^2\text{D}-^2\text{P}°$	[26536]	36623.4	40390.8	10	6	1.39×10^5	0.00879	7.67	-1.056	B	*ca*
44	$4d-4f$	$^2\text{D}-^2\text{F}°$	[1.47×10^7]	36623.4	36630.2	10	14	6.90×10^{-2}	0.00313	1520	-1.504	B	*ca*
45	$4d-5f$	$^2\text{D}-^2\text{F}°$	[40294]	36623.4	39104.5	10	14	2.58×10^6	0.878	1160	0.944	B	*ca*
46	$4d-6f$	$^2\text{D}-^2\text{F}°$	[26201]	36623.4	[40439.0]	10	14	1.30×10^6	0.187	161	0.272	B	*ca*
47	$4f-5d$	$^2\text{F}°-^2\text{D}$	[40562]	36630.2	39094.9	14	10	5.23×10^4	0.00922	17.2	-0.889	B	*ca*
48	$4f-6d$	$^2\text{F}°-^2\text{D}$	[26260]	36630.2	40437.3	14	10	2.50×10^4	0.00185	2.24	-1.587	B	*ca*
49	$5s-5p$	$^2\text{S}-^2\text{P}°$	[139610]	38299.5	39015.6	2	6	2.33×10^5	2.05	1880	0.612	B	*ca*
50	$5s-6p$	$^2\text{S}-^2\text{P}°$	[47804]	38299.5	40390.8	2	6	1.72×10^3	0.00177	0.557	-2.451	B	*ca*
51	$5p-6s$	$^2\text{P}°-^2\text{S}$	[102850]	39015.6	39987.6	6	2	8.48×10^5	0.448	911	0.430	B	*ca*
52	$5p-5d$	$^2\text{P}°-^2\text{D}$	[1261000]	39015.6	39094.9	6	10	4.78×10^2	0.190	4730	0.057	B	*ca*
53	$5p-6d$	$^2\text{P}°-^2\text{D}$	[70319]	39015.6	40437.3	6	10	3.98×10^5	0.491	683	0.470	B	*ca*
54	$5d-6p$	$^2\text{D}-^2\text{P}°$	[77145]	39094.9	40390.8	10	6	1.42×10^5	0.0758	192	-0.121	B	*ca*
55	$5d-5f$	$^2\text{D}-^2\text{F}°$	[1.04×10^7]	39094.9	39104.5	10	14	0.696	0.0159	5440	-0.800	B	*ca*
56	$5d-6f$	$^2\text{D}-^2\text{F}°$	[74379]	39094.9	[40439.0]	10	14	7.22×10^5	0.838	2050	0.924	B	*ca*
57	$5f-6d$	$^2\text{F}°-^2\text{D}$	[75010]	39104.5	40437.3	14	10	4.19×10^4	0.0252	87.3	-0.452	B	*ca*

Li II

Ground State $1s^2 \, {}^1S_0$

Ionization Potential   75.619 eV $=610079$ cm^{-1}

Allowed Transitions

List of tabulated lines:

Wavelength [Å]	No.	Wavelength [Å]	No.	Wavelength [Å]	No.
178.015	2	1653.2	31	3306.5	17
199.282	1	1681.8	10	3684.1	39
861.36	30	1755.5	6	4156.3	14
944.72	29	2605.1	47	4325.7	45
972.30	34	2657.3	43	4637.8	23
1018.0	37	2674.43	40	4671.8	50
1031.9	33	2728.4	52	4678.4	24
1044.3	9	2730.7	26	4787.5	19
1093.2	5	2767.1	21	4840.8	48
1102.6	12	2790.5	18	4881.3	41
1109.0	8	2952.5	15	5038.7	16
1132.0	36	3029.1	46	5484.8	27
1166.7	32	3155.4	42	9562.2	3
1198.3	28	3195.8	51	21091	38
1237.4	11	3199.4	25	33661	13
1253.5	7	3235.7	49	57324	44
1420.7	4	3250.1	20	211360	22
1493.2	35				

The values are selected from Weiss' calculations [1] or, when not available, from the Coulomb approximation. The transition probabilities determined by Weiss are the result of extensive non-relativistic variational calculations. Values have been determined in both the dipole length and dipole velocity approximations and agree to within 1%, except for the $3p \, {}^1P^\circ - 3d \, {}^1D$ transition where agreement is not as good. The average of the two approximations is adopted [1].

Reference

[1] Weiss, A. W., private communication (1964).

Li II. Allowed Transitions

No.	Transition Array	Multiplet	λ(Å)	E_i(cm^{-1})	E_k(cm^{-1})	g_i	g_k	A_{ki}(sec^{-1})	f_{ik}	S(at.u.)	log gf	Accuracy	Source
1	$1s^2 - 1s2p$	$^1S - ^1P°$ (1 uv)	199.282	0	501816	1	3	256	0.457	0.300	-0.340	A	1
2	$1s^2 - 1s3p$	$^1S - ^1P°$ (2 uv)	178.015	0	561749	1	3	77.9	0.111	0.0651	-0.955	A	1
3	$1s2s - 1s2p$	$^1S - ^1P°$	[9562.2]	491361	501816	1	3	0.0518	0.213	6.71	-0.672	A	1
4	$1s2s - 1s3p$	$^1S - ^1P°$	[1420.7]	491361	561749	1	3	2.82	0.256	1.20	-0.592	A	1
5	$1s2s - 1s4p$	$^1S - ^1P°$	[1093.2]	491361	582832	1	3	1.32	0.0712	0.256	-1.147	B	ca
6	$1s2p - 1s3s$	$^1P° - ^1S$	[1755.5]	501816	558779	3	1	2.04	0.0314	0.544	-1.026	B	ca
7	$1s2p - 1s4s$	$^1P° - ^1S$	[1253.5]	501816	581590	3	1	0.776	0.00609	0.0754	-1.738	B	ca
8	$1s2p - 1s5s$	$^1P° - ^1S$	[1109.0]	501816	591984	3	1	0.382	0.00235	0.0257	-2.152	B	ca
9	$1s2p - 1s6s$	$^1P° - ^1S$	[1044.3]	501816	597574	3	1	0.214	0.00117	0.0120	-2.456	B	ca
10	$1s2p - 1s3d$	$^1P° - ^1D$	[1681.8]	501816	561276	3	5	10.1	0.714	11.9	0.331	A	1
11	$1s2p - 1s4d$	$^1P° - ^1D$	[1237.4]	501816	582631	3	5	3.10	0.119	1.45	-0.448	B	ca
12	$1s2p - 1s5d$	$^1P° - ^1D$	[1102.6]	501816	592508	3	5	1.37	0.0415	0.452	-0.905	B	ca
13	$1s3s - 1s3p$	$^1S - ^1P°$	[33661]	558779	561749	1	3	0.00710	0.362	40.1	-0.442	B	ca
14	$1s3s - 1s4p$	$^1S - ^1P°$ (3)	4156.3	558779	582832	1	3	0.343	0.267	3.65	-0.574	B	ca
15	$1s3s - 1s5p$	$^1S - ^1P°$	[2952.5]	558779	592639	1	3	0.202	0.0791	0.769	-1.102	B	ca
16	$1s3p - 1s4s$	$^1P° - ^1S$	[5038.7]	561749	581590	3	1	0.541	0.0687	3.42	-0.686	B	ca
17	$1s3p - 1s5s$	$^1P° - ^1S$	[3306.5]	561749	591984	3	1	0.252	0.0138	0.449	-1.384	B	ca
18	$1s3p - 1s6s$	$^1P° - ^1S$	[2790.5]	561749	597574	3	1	0.139	0.00542	0.149	-1.789	B	ca
19	$1s3p - 1s4d$	$^1P° - ^1D$	[4787.5]	561749	582631	3	5	1.14	0.654	30.9	0.293	B	ca
20	$1s3p - 1s5d$	$^1P° - ^1D$	[3250.1]	561749	592508	3	5	0.528	0.139	4.48	-0.379	B	ca
21	$1s3p - 1s6d$	$^1P° - ^1D$	[2767.1]	561749	597877	3	5	0.289	0.0552	1.51	-0.781	B	ca
22	$1s3d - 1s3p$	$^1D - ^1P°$	[211360]	561276	561749	5	3	3.98×10^{-5}	0.0160	55.7	-1.097	B	1
23	$1s3d - 1s4p$	$^1D - ^1P°$	[4637.8]	561276	582832	5	3	0.0471	0.00911	0.695	-1.342	B	ca
24	$1s3d - 1s4f$	$^1D - ^1F°$	[4678.4]	561276	582645	5	7	2.21	1.02	78.2	0.706	B	ca
25	$1s3d - 1s5f$	$^1D - ^1F°$	[3199.4]	561276	592523	5	7	0.736	0.158	8.33	-0.102	B	ca
26	$1s3d - 1s6f$	$^1D - ^1F°$	[2730.7]	561276	597886	5	7	0.338	0.0528	2.38	-0.578	B	ca
27	$1s2s - 1s2p$	$^3S - ^3P°$ (1)	5484.8	476046	494273	3	9	0.228	0.308	16.7	-0.034	A	1
28	$1s2s - 1s3p$	$^3S - ^3P°$	[1198.3]	476046	559501	3	9	2.88	0.186	2.20	-0.253	A	1
29	$1s2s - 1s4p$	$^3S - ^3P°$	[944.72]	476046	581897	3	9	1.39	0.0558	0.521	-0.776	B	ca
30	$1s2s - 1s5p$	$^3S - ^3P°$	[861.36]	476046	592141	3	9	0.722	0.0241	0.205	-1.141	B	ca
31	$1s2p - 1s3s$	$^3P° - ^3S$	[1653.2]	494273	554761	9	3	2.85	0.0390	1.91	-0.455	B	ca
32	$1s2p - 1s4s$	$^3P° - ^3S$	[1166.7]	494273	579982	9	3	1.02	0.00697	0.241	-1.202	B	ca

No.	Transition Array	Multiplet	λ(Å)	E_i(cm^{-1})	E_k(cm^{-1})	g_i	g_k	A_{ki}(sec^{-1})	f_{ik}	S(at.u.)	log gf	Accuracy	Source
33	1s2p − 1s5s	³P° − ¹³S	[1031.9]	494273	591184	9	3	0.490	0.00261	0.0797	−1.630	B	ca
34	1s2p − 1s6s	³P° − ³S	[972.30]	494273	597122	9	3	0.270	0.00128	0.0368	−1.939	B	ca
35	1s2p − 1s3d	³P° − ³D	[1493.2]	494273	561245	9	15	11.2	0.625	27.7	0.750	A	1
36	1s2p − 1s4d	³P° − ³D	[1132.0]	494273	582612	9	15	3.80	0.122	4.08	0.039	B	ca
37	1s2p − 1s5d	³P° − ³D	[1018.0]	494273	592505	9	15	1.78	0.0461	1.39	−0.382	B	ca
38	1s3s − 1s3p	³S − ³P°	[21091]	554761	559501	3	9	0.0254	0.509	106	0.184	B	ca
39	1s3s − 1s4p	³S − ³P° (2)	3684.1	554761	581897	3	9	0.309	0.189	6.86	−0.248	B	ca
40	1s3s − 1s5p	³S − ³P° (4 uv)	2674.43	554761	592141	3	9	0.192	0.0617	1.63	−0.733	B	ca
41	1s3p − 1s4s	³P° − ³S (4)	4881.3	559501	579982	9	3	0.714	0.0850	12.3	−0.116	B	ca
42	1s3p − 1s5s	³P° − ³S	[3155.4]	559501	591184	9	3	0.318	0.0158	1.48	−0.846	B	ca
43	1s3p − 1s6s	³P° − ³S	[2657.3]	559501	597122	9	3	0.172	0.00606	0.477	−1.263	B	ca
44	1s3p − 1s3d	³P° − ³D	[57324]	559501	561245	9	15	0.00110	0.0904	154	−0.090	A	1
45	1s3p − 1s4d	³P° − ³D (5)	4325.7	559501	582612	9	15	1.09	0.508	65.1	0.660	B	ca
46	1s3p − 1s5d	³P° − ³D	[3029.1]	559501	592505	9	15	0.549	0.126	11.3	0.054	B	ca
47	1s3p − 1s6d	³P° − ³D	[2605.1]	559501	597876	9	15	0.312	0.0530	4.09	−0.322	B	ca
48	1s3d − 1s4p	³D − ³P°	[4840.8]	561245	581897	15	9	0.0941	0.0198	4.74	−0.527	B	ca
49	1s3d − 1s5p	³D − ³P°	[3235.7]	561245	592141	15	9	0.0391	0.00369	0.589	−1.257	B	ca
50	1s3d − 1s4f	³D − ³F°	[4671.8]	561245	582644	15	21	2.21	1.01	234	1.182	B	ca
51	1s3d − 1s5f	³D − ³F°	[3195.8]	561245	592527	15	21	0.739	0.158	25.0	0.376	B	ca
52	1s3d − 1s6f	³D − ³F°	[2728.4]	561245	597886	15	21	0.339	0.0530	7.14	−0.100	B	ca

BERYLLIUM

Be I

Ground State $1s^2 2s^2 \, {}^1S_0$

Ionization Potential $9.320 \text{ eV} = 75192.29 \text{ cm}^{-1}$

Allowed Transitions

The results taken from Weiss' self-consistent field calculations [1] are estimated to be accurate to 10–25 percent because of the good agreement between the dipole length and velocity approximations and because of the inclusion of configuration interaction. The average of the two approximations is adopted [1]. For the resonance line the adopted value is within 10 percent of the result of calculations of Bolotin and Yutsis [2], who include configuration interaction in a more limited way. The Coulomb approximation, employed for the other transitions, is not considered to be very reliable here since the lower state has the same principal quantum number as the ground state.

References

[1] Weiss, A. W., private communication (1964).
[2] Bolotin, A. B., and Yutsis, A. P., Zhur. Eksptl. i Teoret. Fiz. **24**, 537–543 (1953) (Translated in "Optical Transition Probabilities," Office of Technical Services, U.S. Department of Commerce, Washington, D.C.).

Be I. Allowed Transitions

No.	Transition Array	Multiplet	$\lambda(\text{Å})$	$E_i(\text{cm}^{-1})$	$E_k(\text{cm}^{-1})$	g_i	g_k	$A_{ki}(10^8 \text{ sec}^{-1})$	f_{ik}	$S(\text{at.u.})$	$\log gf$	Accuracy	Source
1	$2s^2 - 2s2p(^2S)2p$	$^1S - {}^1P°$ (1 uv)	2348.61	0.0	42565.3	1	3	5.47	1.36	10.5	0.133	C+	1
2	$2s2p - 2p^2$	$^3P° - {}^3P$ (2 uv)	2650.6	21980.1	59695.8	9	9	4.42	0.466	36.6	0.623	C+	1
3		$^1P° - {}^1S$	[3455.2]	42565.3	71498.9	3	1	2.21	0.132	4.50	−0.403	C	1
4	$2s2p - 2s(^2S)3s$	$^3P° - {}^3S$ (1)	3321.2	21980.1	52080.9	9	3	0.62	0.034	3.4	−0.51	D	ca
5		$^1P° - {}^1S$ (2)	8254.10	42565.3	54677.2	3	1	0.38	0.13	11	−0.41	D	ca
6	$2s2p - 2s(^2S)3d$	$^3P° - {}^3D$ (3 uv)	2494.6	21980.1	62053.6	9	15	1.0	0.16	12	0.15	D	ca
7		$^1P° - {}^1D$ (3)	4572.67	42565.3	64428.2	3	5	0.37	0.19	8.6	−0.24	D	ca
8	$2s2p - 2s(^2S)4s$	$^1P° - {}^1S$ (4)	4407.91	42565.3	65245.4	3	1	0.090	0.0087	0.38	−1.58	D	ca
9	$2s2p - 2s(^2S)4d$	$^1P° - {}^1D$ (5)	3813.40	42565.3	68781.2	3	5	0.23	0.084	3.2	−0.60	D	ca
10	$2s2p - 2s(^2S)5s$	$^1P° - {}^1S$ (6)	3736.28	42565.3	69322.3	3	1	0.038	0.0027	0.099	−2.10	D	ca
11	$2s2p - 2s(^2S)5d$	$^1P° - {}^1D$ (7)	3515.54	42565.3	71002.3	3	5	0.13	0.041	1.4	−0.91	D	ca

Forbidden Transitions

Naqvi's calculations [1] are the only available source. The results for the $^3P° - ^3P°$ transitions are essentially independent of the choice of the interaction parameters. For the $^3P° - ^1P°$ transitions, Naqvi uses empirical term intervals, i.e., the effects of configuration interaction should be partially included.

Reference

[1] Naqvi, A. M., Thesis Harvard (1951).

Be I. Forbidden Transitions

No.	Transition Array	Multiplet	$\lambda(\text{Å})$	$E_i(\text{cm}^{-1})$	$E_k(\text{cm}^{-1})$	g_i	g_k	Type of Transition	$A_{ki}(\text{sec}^{-1})$	$S(\text{at.u.})$	Accuracy	Source
1	$2s2p - 2s(^2S)2p$	$^3P° - ^3P°$										
			$[14.7 \times 10^7]$	21978.25	21979.93	1	3	m	5.66×10^{-12}	2.00	B	1
			$[42.6 \times 10^6]$	21979.93	21981.28	3	5	m	1.74×10^{-10}	2.50	B	1
2		$^3P° - ^1P°$										
			$[4856.1]$	21978.3	42565.3	1	3	m	9.6×10^{-7}	1.22×10^{-8}	C	1
			$[4856.5]$	21979.9	42565.3	3	3	m	0.0092	1.17×10^{-4}	C	1
			$[4856.8]$	21981.3	42565.3	5	3	m	1.19×10^{-6}	1.52×10^{-8}	C	1

Be II

Ground State $\hspace{8cm}$ $1s^2 2s\ ^2S_{1/2}$

Ionization Potential $\hspace{5cm}$ $18.206\ \text{eV} = 146881.7\ \text{cm}^{-1}$

Allowed Transitions

The values taken from Weiss' calculations [1] are estimated to be accurate to within 10 percent because of the very close agreement between his dipole length and dipole velocity approximations, except for the case of the $3p - 3d$ transition where somewhat larger divergencies occur. The values calculated with the dipole length approximation are adopted.

Reference

[1] Weiss, A. W., Astrophys. J. **138**, 1262–1276 (1963).

Be II. Allowed Transitions

No.	Transition Array	Multiplet	$\lambda(\text{Å})$	$E_i(\text{cm}^{-1})$	$E_k(\text{cm}^{-1})$	g_i	g_k	$A_{ki}(10^8 \text{ sec}^{-1})$	f_{ik}	$S(\text{at.u.})$	$\log gf$	Accuracy	Source
1	$2s-2p$	$^2\text{S}-^2\text{P}°$ (1)	3130.6	0.0	31933.2	2	6	1.15	0.505	10.4	0.004	A	1
2	$2s-3p$	$^2\text{S}-^2\text{P}°$ (1 uv)	1036.27	0.0	96497.6	2	6	1.66	0.0804	0.549	-0.794	B	1
3	$2p-3s$	$^2\text{P}°-^2\text{S}$ (3 uv)	1776.2	31933.2	88231.2	6	2	4.22	0.0665	2.33	-0.399	B+	1
4	$2p-3d$	$^2\text{P}°-^2\text{D}$ (4 uv)	1512.4	31933.2	98053.2	6	10	11.4	0.652	19.5	0.592	B+	1
5	$3s-3p$	$^2\text{S}-^2\text{P}°$	12094	88231.2	96497.6	2	6	0.128	0.839	66.8	0.225	B	1
6	$3s-4p$	$^2\text{S}-^2\text{P}°$ (2)	3274.64	88231.2	118760	2	6	0.143	0.0691	1.49	-0.860	B	ca
7	$3p-4s$	$^2\text{P}°-^2\text{S}$ (3)	5270.7	96497.6	115465	6	2	0.969	0.134	14.0	-0.093	B	ca
8	$3p-5s$	$^2\text{P}°-^2\text{S}$ (5)	3247.7	96497.6	127336	6	2	0.410	0.0216	1.38	-0.888	B	ca
9	$3p-3d$	$^2\text{P}°-^2\text{D}$	64266	96497.6	98053.2	6	10	7.83×10^{-4}	0.0808	103	-0.314	B	1
10	$3p-4d$	$^2\text{P}°-^2\text{D}$ (4)	4360.9	96497.6	119422	6	10	1.09	0.519	44.7	0.493	B	ca
11	$3d-4f$	$^2\text{D}-^2\text{F}°$ (6)	4673.46	98053.2	119445	10	14	2.21	1.01	156	1.006	B	ca

Be III

Ground State $1s^2\,^1\text{S}_0$

Ionization Potential $153.850 \text{ eV} = 1241255 \text{ cm}^{-1}$

Allowed Transitions

The results of extensive non-relativistic variational calculations by Weiss [1] are chosen. Values have been calculated in both the dipole length and dipole velocity approximations and agree to within 1 percent, except for the $3p\,^1\text{P}°-3d\,^1\text{D}$ transition where agreement is not as good. The average of the two approximations is adopted [1].

Reference

[1] Weiss, A. W., private communication (1964).

Be III. Allowed Transitions

No.	Transition Array	Multiplet	$\lambda(\text{Å})$	$E_i(\text{cm}^{-1})$	$E_k(\text{cm}^{-1})$	g_i	g_k	$A_{ki}(10^8 \text{ sec}^{-1})$	f_{ik}	$S(\text{at.u.})$	$\log gf$	Accuracy	Source
1	$1s^2 - 1s2p$	$^1S - ^1P°$	[100.25]	0	997466	1	3	1220	0.552	0.182	−0.258	A	1
2	$1s^2 - 1s3p$	$^1S - ^1P°$	[88.314]	0	1132323	1	3	362	0.127	0.0369	−0.896	A	1
3	$1s2s - 1s2p$	$^1S - ^1P°$	[6141.2]	981187	997466	1	3	0.0877	0.149	3.02	−0.827	A	1
4	$1s2s - 1s3p$	$^1S - ^1P°$	[398.19]	981187	1132323	1	3	42.8	0.305	0.400	−0.516	A	1
5	$1s2p - 1s3d$	$^1P° - ^1D$	[746.70]	997466	[1131389]	3	5	51.0	0.711	5.24	0.329	A	1
6	$1s3d - 1s3p$	$^1D - ^1P°$	[107000]?	[1131389]	1132323	5	3	1.32×10^{-4}	0.0136	24.0	−1.168	C +	1
7	$1s2s - 1s2p$	$^3S - ^3P°$	[3721.8]	[956496]	[983357]	3	9	0.342	0.213	7.83	−0.195	A	1
8	$1s2s - 1s3p$	$^3S - ^3P°$	[583.01]	[956496]	[1128020]	3	9	16.5	0.252	1.45	−0.122	A	1
9	$1s2p - 1s3d$	$^3P° - ^3D$	[675.66]	[983357]	[1131360]	9	15	56.1	0.640	12.8	0.760	A	1
10	$1s3p - 1s3d$	$^3P° - ^3D$	[29930]?	[1128020]	[1131360]	9	15	0.00318	0.0712	63.1	−0.193	A	1

BORON

B I

Ground State $1s^2 2s^2 2p$ $^2P°_{1/2}$

Ionization Potential   8.296 eV = 66930 cm^{-1}

Allowed Transitions

The values for the $2s^2 2p - 2s2p^2$ ($^2P° - ^2D$, ^2S, ^2P) transitions are taken from the calculations of Bolotin and Yutsis [1], who employ analytical one-electron wave functions. Self-consistent field calculations of Tsiunaitis and Yutsis [2] have been adopted for the $2p$ $^2P° - 3s$ ^2S transition. Since both determinations take into account the important effects of configuration interaction only in a limited way, large uncertainties are expected.

References

[1] Bolotin, A. B., and Yutsis, A. P., Zhur. Eksptl. i Teoret. Fiz. **24**, 537–543 (1953) (Translated in "Optical Transition Probabilities," Office of Technical Services, U.S. Department of Commerce, Washington, D.C.).
[2] Tsiunaitis, G. K., and Yutsis, A. P., Soviet Phys.—JETP **1**, 358–363 (1955).

B I.   Allowed Transitions

No.	Transition Array	Multiplet	λ(Å)	E_i(cm^{-1})	E_k(cm^{-1})	g_i	g_k	A_{ki}(10^8 sec^{-1})	f_{ik}	S(at.u.)	log gf	Accuracy	Source
1	$2s^2 2p-2s2p^2$	^{2}P$^\circ$ − ^{2}D (2 uv)	2089.3	10	47857	6	10	2.2	0.24	9.7	0.15	E	1
			2089.57	15	47857	4	6	2.1	0.21	5.8	−0.07	E	ls
			2088.84	0	47857	2	4	1.8	0.23	3.2	−0.33	E	ls
			[2089.6]	15	47857	4	4	0.36	0.024	0.65	−1.02	E	ls
2		^{2}P$^\circ$ − ^{2}S	1573.5	10	63561	6	2	13	0.16	5.1	−0.01	E	1
			[1573.7]	15	63561	4	2	8.8	0.16	3.4	−0.18	E	ls
			[1573.3]	0	63561	2	2	4.4	0.16	1.7	−0.48	E	ls
3		^{2}P$^\circ$ − ^{2}P	1378.7	10	72543	6	6	23	0.66	18	0.60	E	1
			[1378.7]	15	72547	4	4	19	0.55	10	0.34	E	ls
			[1378.6]	0	72535	2	2	15	0.44	4.0	−0.05	E	ls
			[1378.9]	15	72535	4	2	7.7	0.11	2.0	−0.36	E	ls
			[1378.4]	0	72547	2	4	3.9	0.22	2.0	−0.36	E	ls
4	$2p-(^1$S)$3s$	^{2}P$^\circ$ − ^{2}S (1 uv)	2497.4	10	40040	6	2	3.6	0.11	5.5	−0.17	D	2
			2497.72	15	40040	4	2	2.4	0.11	3.7	−0.35	D	ls
			2496.77	0	40040	2	2	1.2	0.11	1.8	−0.66	D	ls
5	$3s-(^1$S)$3p$	^{2}S − ^{2}P$^\circ$	11661	40040	48613	2	6	0.174	1.07	82	0.330	C	ca
			11660	40040	48613	2	4	0.174	0.71	54	0.152	C	ls
			11662	40040	48612	2	2	0.174	0.355	27.2	−0.149	C	ls
6	$3p-(^1$S)$3d$	^{2}P$^\circ$ − ^{2}D	16243	48613	54768	6	10	0.138	0.90	291	0.73	C	ca
			16245	48613	54768	4	6	0.138	0.82	175	0.51	C	ls
			16240	48612	54768	2	4	0.115	0.91	97	0.259	C	ls
			16245	48613	54768	4	4	0.0230	0.091	19.4	−0.440	C	ls
7	$3p-(^1$S)$4s$	^{2}P$^\circ$ − ^{2}S	15628	48613	55010	6	2	0.154	0.188	58	0.052	C	ca
			15629	48613	55010	4	2	0.103	0.188	38.8	−0.123	C	ls
			15625	48612	55010	2	2	0.051	0.188	19.4	−0.424	C	ls
8	$3p-(^1$S)$5s$	^{2}P$^\circ$ − ^{2}S	8668.1	48613	60146	6	2	0.0486	0.0182	3.12	−0.96	C	ca
			8668.6	48613	60146	4	2	0.0324	0.0182	2.08	−1.137	C	ls
			8667.2	48612	60146	2	2	0.0162	0.0182	1.04	−1.438	C	ls

Forbidden Transitions

Naqvi's calculation [1] of the one possible transition in the ground state configuration $2p$ is the only available source. The line strength should be quite accurate, since it does not sensitively depend on the choice of the interaction parameters.

Reference

[1] Naqvi, A. M., Thesis Harvard (1951).

B I.   Forbidden Transitions

No.	Transition Array	Multiplet	λ(Å)	E_i(cm^{-1})	E_k(cm^{-1})	g_i	g_k	Type of Transition	A_{ki}(sec^{-1})	S(at.u.)	Accuracy	Source
1	$2p-2p$	^{2}P$^\circ$ − ^{2}P$^\circ$	[66.0×10^5]	0	15.15	2	4	m	3.15 × 10^{-8}	1.33	C	1

BII

Ground State $\qquad$ $1s^2 2s^2\ {}^1S_0$

Ionization Potential $\qquad$ $25.149\ \text{eV} = 202895\ \text{cm}^{-1}$

Allowed Transitions

Except for the $2s3d\ {}^3D - 2s4f\ {}^3F°$ transition, for which a Coulomb approximation is employed, the values are taken from Weiss' self-consistent field calculations [1]. The length and velocity approximations disagree noticeably—for the $2s2p\ {}^1P° - 2p^2\ {}^1D$ transition by as much as a factor of three. The average of the two approximations is adopted [1]. Accuracies within 50 percent are indicated by the following comparison: Weiss [1] has undertaken refined calculations, including configuration interaction, for the same transitions in Be I—the first member of this isoelectronic sequence—in addition to calculations of the type done for this ion. In all cases the agreement with the average of the dipole length and velocity approximations is close.

Reference

[1] Weiss, A. W., private communication (1964).

BII.   Allowed Transitions

No.	Transition Array	Multiplet	$\lambda(\text{Å})$	$E_i(\text{cm}^{-1})$	$E_k(\text{cm}^{-1})$	g_i	g_k	$A_{ki}(10^8\ \text{sec}^{-1})$	f_{ik}	$S(\text{at.u.})$	$\log gf$	Accuracy	Source
1	$2s^2 -$ $2s(^2S)2p$	${}^1S - {}^1P°$ (1 uv)	1362.46	0.0	73396.7	1	3	13	1.1	4.9	0.04	D	1
2	$2s2p - 2p^2$	${}^3P° - {}^3P$ (3 uv)	[1624.0]	[37350.9]	[98925.5]	9	9	8.4	0.33	16	0.48	D	1
			1623.99	[37356.4]	[98932.7]	5	5	6.3	0.25	6.7	0.10	D	ls
			1623.99	[37340.0]	[98918.7]	3	3	2.0	0.081	1.3	−0.61	D	ls
			1624.37	[37356.4]	[98918.7]	5	3	3.5	0.082	2.2	−0.39	D	ls
			[1624.2]	[37340.0]	[98910.3]	3	1	8.5	0.11	1.8	−0.47	D	ls
			1623.57	[37340.0]	[98932.7]	3	5	2.1	0.14	2.2	−0.39	D	ls
			[1623.8]	[37333.6]	[98918.7]	1	3	2.8	0.34	1.8	−0.47	D	ls
3		${}^1P° - {}^1D$ (1)	3451.41	73396.7	102362	3	5	2.2	0.65	22	0.29	E	1
4		${}^1P° - {}^1S$	[1842.8]	73396.7	127662	3	1	6.8	0.12	2.1	−0.46	D	1
5	$2s3d -$ $2s(^2S)4f$	${}^3D - {}^3F°$ (2)	4121.95	[150649]	[174903]	15	21	2.55	0.91	185	1.135	C	ca

Forbidden Transitions

Naqvi's calculations [1] are the only available source. The results for the ${}^3P° - {}^3P°$ transitions are essentially independent of the choice of the interaction parameters. For the ${}^3P° - {}^1P°$ transitions, Naqvi uses empirical term intervals, i.e., the effects of configuration interaction should be partially included.

Reference

[1] Naqvi, A. M., Thesis Harvard (1951).

BII. Forbidden Transitions

No.	Transition Array	Multiplet	λ(Å)	E_i(cm^{-1})	E_k(cm^{-1})	g_i	g_k	Type of Transition	A_{ki}(sec^{-1})	S(at.u.)	Accuracy	Source
1	$2s2p-2s(^2S)2p$	$^3P°-^3P°$	[15.6 × 10^6]	[37333.6]	[37340.0]	1	3	m	4.74 × 10^{-9}	2.00	C	1
			[61.0 × 10^5]	[37340.0]	[37356.4]	3	5	m	5.94 × 10^{-8}	2.50	B	1
2		$^3P°-^1P°$										
			[2772.1]	[37333.6]	73396.7	1	3	m	8.5 × 10^{-5}	2.02 × 10^{-7}	C	1
			[2772.5]	[37340.0]	73396.7	3	3	m	0.201	4.77 × 10^{-4}	C	1
			[2773.9]	[37356.4]	73396.7	5	3	m	1.07 × 10^{-4}	2.53 × 10^{-7}	C	1

BIII

Ground State $1s^2 2s\ ^2S_{1/2}$

Ionization Potential   37.920 eV = 305931.1 cm^{-1}

Allowed Transitions

The values taken from Weiss' calculations [1] are estimated to be accurate to within 10 percent because of the very close agreement between his dipole length and dipole velocity approximations, except for the case of the $3p-3d$ transition where somewhat larger divergencies occur. The values calculated with the dipole length approximation are adopted.

Reference

[1] Weiss, A. W., Astrophys. J. **138,** 1262–1276 (1963).

BIII. Allowed Transitions

No.	Transition Array	Multiplet	λ(Å)	E_i(cm^{-1})	E_k(cm^{-1})	g_i	g_k	A_{ki}(10^8 sec^{-1})	f_{ik}	S(at.u.)	log gf	Accuracy	Source
1	$2s-2p$	$^2S-^2P°$	2066.3	0.0	48381.2	2	6	1.91	0.366	4.98	−0.136	A	1
2	$2s-3p$	$^2S-^2P°$	518.25	0.0	192956	2	6	12.5	0.151	0.515	−0.520	B	1
3	$2p-3s$	$^2P°-^2S$	758.60	48381.2	180202	6	2	16.3	0.0470	0.704	−0.550	B+	1
4	$2p-3d$	$^2P°-^2D$	677.09	48381.2	196071	6	10	56.8	0.651	8.71	0.592	B+	1
5	$3s-3p$	$^2S-^2P°$	7838.5	180202	192956	2	6	0.222	0.614	31.7	0.089	B	1
6	$3p-3d$	$^2P°-^2D$	32094	192956	196071	6	10	0.00279	0.0719	45.6	−0.365	B	1
7	$4p-5d$	$^2P°-^2D$ (1)	4243.60	242832	266390	6	10	1.11	0.501	42.0	0.478	B	ca
8	$4d-5f$	$^2D-^2F°$ (2)	4487.46	244139	266417	10	14	2.10	0.887	131	0.948	B	ca

B IV

Ground State $1s^2\ ^1S_0$

Ionization Potential $259.298\ \text{eV} = 2091960\ \text{cm}^{-1}$

Allowed Transitions

The results of extensive non-relativistic variational calculations by Weiss [1] are chosen. Values have been calculated in both the dipole length and dipole velocity approximations and agree to within 1 percent, except for the $3p\,^1P° - 3d\,^1D$ transition, where agreement is not as good. The average of the two approximations is adopted [1].

Reference

[1] Weiss, A. W., private communication (1964).

B IV.   Allowed Transitions

No.	Transition Array	Multiplet	$\lambda(\text{Å})$	$E_i(\text{cm}^{-1})$	$E_k(\text{cm}^{-1})$	g_i	g_k	$A_{ki}(10^8\ \text{sec}^{-1})$	f_{ik}	$S(\text{at.u.})$	$\log gf$	Accuracy	Source
1	$1s^2 - 1s2p$	$^1S - ^1P°$	[60.313]	0	1658020	1	3	3720	0.609	0.121	-0.215	A	1
2	$1s^2 - 1s3p$	$^1S - ^1P°$	[52.682]	0	1898180	1	3	1080	0.135	0.0234	-0.870	A	1
3	$1s2s - 1s2p$	$^1S - ^1P°$	[4499.4]	[1635801]	1658020	1	3	0.125	0.114	1.69	-0.943	A	1
4	$1s2s - 1s3p$	$^1S - ^1P°$	[381.13]	[1635801]	1898180	1	3	51.0	0.333	0.418	-0.478	A	1
5	$1s2p - 1s3d$	$^1P° - ^1D$	[418.83]	1658020	[1896780]	3	5	162	0.709	2.93	0.328	A	1
6	$1s3d - 1s3p$	$^1D - ^1P°$	[71410]?	[1896780]	1898180	5	3	2.62×10^{-4}	0.0120	14.1	-1.222	C +	1
7	$1s2s - 1s2p$	$^3S - ^3P°$	2823.4	1601505	*1636913*	3	9	0.455	0.163	4.55	-0.311	A	1
8	$1s2s - 1s3p$	$^3S - ^3P°$	[344.19]	1601505	[1892046]	3	9	54.6	0.291	0.989	-0.059	A	1
9	$1s2p - 1s3d$	$^3P° - ^3D$	[385.05]	*1636913*	[1896618]	9	15	175	0.650	7.42	0.767	A	1
10	$1s3p - 1s3d$	$^3P° - ^3D$	[21870]?	[1892046]	[1896618]	9	15	0.00484	0.0578	37.5	-0.284	A	1

CARBON

C I

Ground State $1s^2 2s^2 2p^2\ ^3P_0$

Ionization Potential   11.264 eV = 90878.3 cm^{-1}

Allowed Transitions

List of tabulated lines:

Wavelength [Å]	No.	Wavelength [Å]	No.	Wavelength [Å]	No.
945.193	4	1657.00	5	9078.32	29
945.336	4	1657.37	5	9088.57	29
945.566	4	1657.89	5	9094.89	29
1260.75	13	1658.11	5	9111.85	29
1260.9	13	1751.9	20	9603.09	28
1260.96	13	1764	24	9620.86	28
1261.12	13	1765	19	9658.49	28
1261.4	13	1930.93	6	10124	42
1261.56	13	2478.56	8	10548.0	48
1274.13	12	2582.90	7	10683.1	27
1277.15	11	2902.1	26	10685.3	27
1277.27	11	2903.1	26	10691.2	27
1277.4	11	2904.9	26	10707.3	27
1277.62	11	2964.85	1	10729.5	27
1277.77	11	2967.22	1	10754.0	27
1277.8	11	4268.99	39	11330.3	30
1279.25	10	4371.33	38	11330.4	41
1279.90	21	4762.41	34	11602.9	44
1280.15	21	4766.62	34	11609.9	44
1280.34	21	4770.00	34	11619.0	44
1280.65	21	4771.72	34	11631.6	44
1280.89	21	4775.87	34	11638.6	44
1328.82	3	4812.84	33	11653	45
1329.10	3	4817.33	33	11656.0	45
1329.58	3	4826.73	33	11667.1	45
1364.14	25	4932.00	37	11667.1	44
1431.60	9	5039.05	32	11677.0	44
1432.12	9	5041.66	32	11747.5	43
1432.54	9	5044.0	32	11754.0	43
1459.05	18	5049.6	32	11778.0	43
1463.33	17	5052.12	36	11801.8	43
1467.45	23	5054.5	32	11820	49
1469	16	5380.24	35	11824	43
1470.20	15	5793.51	40	11849.3	49
1472	22	5794.46	40	11863.0	49
1481.77	14	5794.8	40	11880.4	49
1560.31	2	5800.33	40	11894.9	49
1560.70	2	5801.17	40	12551.0	46
1561.29	2	5805.76	40	12565.0	46
1561.3	2	6587.75	50	12582.3	46
1561.40	2	8335.19	31	12602.6	46
1656.26	5	9061.48	29	12614.8	46
1656.92	5	9062.53	29	16890	47

The largest part of the data is from emission measurements with stabilized arc sources [2, 5, 6, 7]. In the vacuum ultraviolet, recent measurements by Boldt [2] are given preference over theoretical determinations by Weiss [4] and Bolotin et al. [3], with which the experiment is in marked disagreement (factors of 2–3). At present there are strong indications that the principal source of the disagreement is the relatively crude theoretical treatment of configuration interaction, which is very critical for these transitions. Thus, the theoretical results [3, 4] have been employed only for a few strong transitions for which no experimental data are available. But it should be noted that some experimental values may be quite unreliable due to uncertainties in the identification of the lines.

For the higher excited transitions in the visible several experimental investigations are available. Richter's work with a carbon dioxide plasma [6] is regarded as the most advanced one and his results are principally used. However, from an analysis of his method it appears very likely that the absolute scale is shifted due to a demixing effect in the arc source (see general introduction). This is further substantiated by a disagreement with the Coulomb approximation by an almost constant factor. Since the Coulomb approximation has given very reliable results for $3p-3d$ transitions of atoms of analogous structure, Richter's absolute values are renormalized to give the best agreement with the Coulomb approximation for these latter type transitions. The normalization factor of 1.30 is then applied to all of his other transitions. The work of Maecker [5] and Foster [7], which is used for a few transitions not covered by Richter, is expected to be also subject to demixing effects of the same order of magnitude or higher, since these authors have used more complicated gas mixtures. Thus, their results have been also fitted to the scale established by the Coulomb approximation. Normalization factors of 2.50 and 1.40 are used, respectively.

Finally, two intercombination lines are taken from a recent paper by Garstang [1], who performed intermediate coupling calculations and normalized the values to a scale obtained from the Coulomb approximation.

References

[1] Garstang, R. H., The Observatory **82**, 50–51 (1962).
[2] Boldt, G., Z. Naturforsch. **18a**, 1107–1116 (1963).
[3] Bolotin, A. B., Levinson, I. B., and Levin, L. I., Soviet Phys.—JETP **2**, 391–395 (1956).
[4] Weiss, A. W., private communication (1964).
[5] Maecker, H., Z. Physik **135**, 13–22 (1953).
[6] Richter, J., Z. Physik **151**, 114–123 (1958).
[7] Foster, E. W., Proc. Phys. Soc. London A **80**, 882–893 (1962).

C I. Allowed Transitions

No.	Transition Array	Multiplet	$\lambda(\text{Å})$	$E_i(\text{cm}^{-1})$	$E_k(\text{cm}^{-1})$	g_i	g_k	$A_{ki}(10^8\ \text{sec}^{-1})$	f_{ik}	$S(\text{at.u.})$	$\log gf$	Accuracy	Source
1	$2s^2 2p^2 -$ $2s2p^3$	$^3P - {}^5S^\circ$ (1 uv)											
			2967.22	44	33735	5	5	2.4×10^{-7}	3.2×10^{-8}	1.6×10^{-6}	-6.80	E	1
			2964.85	16	33735	3	5	8.2×10^{-8}	1.8×10^{-8}	5.3×10^{-7}	-7.27	E	1
2		$^3P - {}^3D^\circ$ (3 uv)	*1561.0*	*30*	*64091*	*9*	*15*	*1.5*	*0.091*	*4.2*	*-0.09*	*D*	*2*
			1561.40	44	64089	5	7	1.5	0.078	2.0	-0.41	D	ls
			1560.70	16	64093	3	5	1.1	0.065	1.0	-0.71	D	ls
			1560.31	0	64092	1	3	0.84	0.091	0.47	-1.04	D	ls
			1561.29	44	64093	5	5	0.37	0.014	0.35	-1.67	D	ls
			1560.70	16	64092	3	3	0.62	0.023	0.35	-1.67	D	ls
			[1561.3]	44	64092	5	3	0.041	8.9×10^{-4}	0.023	-2.35	D	ls

766–655 O–66–4

No.	Transition Array	Multiplet	λ(Å)	E_i(cm^{-1})	E_k(cm^{-1})	g_i	g_k	A_{ki}(10^8 sec^{-1})	f_{ik}	S(at.u.)	log gf	Accuracy	Source
3		^{3}P — ^{3}P° (4 uv)	*1329.3*	*30*	*75256*	9	9	1.4	0.038	1.5	−0.47	D	2
			1329.58	44	75256	5	5	1.1	0.029	0.63	−0.84	D	ls
			1329.10	16	75256	3	3	0.37	0.0099	0.13	−1.53	D	ls
			1329.58	44	75256	5	3	0.60	0.0096	0.21	−1.32	D	ls
			1329.10	16	75256	3	1	1.5	0.013	0.17	−1.41	D	ls
			1329.10	16	75256	3	5	0.36	0.016	0.21	−1.32	D	ls
			1328.82	0	75256	1	3	0.49	0.039	0.17	−1.41	D	ls
4		^{3}P — ^{3}S° (31 uv)	*945.44*	*30*	*105801*	9	3	61	0.27	7.6	0.39	E	3
			945.566	44	105801	5	3	34	0.27	4.2	0.13	E	ls
			945.336	16	105801	3	3	20	0.27	2.5	−0.10	E	ls
			945.193	0	105801	1	3	6.7	0.27	0.84	−0.57	E	ls
5	$2p^2$ — $2p(^2P°)3s$	^{3}P — ^{3}P° (2 uv)	*1657.2*	*30*	*60374*	9	9	4.1	0.17	8.3	0.18	D	2
			1657.00	44	60394	5	5	3.1	0.13	3.5	−0.19	D	ls
			1657.37	16	60353	3	3	1.0	0.042	0.69	−0.90	D	ls
			1658.11	44	60353	5	3	1.8	0.044	1.2	−0.66	D	ls
			1657.89	16	60334	3	1	4.1	0.056	0.92	−0.77	D	ls
			1656.26	16	60394	3	5	1.1	0.073	1.2	−0.66	D	ls
			1656.92	0	60353	1	3	1.4	0.17	0.92	−0.77	D	ls
6		^{1}D — ^{1}P° (33 uv)	1930.93	10194	61982	5	3	2.4	0.082	2.6	−0.39	E	4
7		^{1}S — ^{3}P° (60 uv)											
			2582.90	21648	60353	1	3	8.6×10^{-5}	2.6×10^{-5}	2.2×10^{-4}	−4.59	D	5n
8		^{1}S — ^{1}P° (61 uv)	2478.56	21648	61982	1	3	0.34	0.094	0.77	−1.03	E	4
9	$2s2p^3$ — $2s2p^2(^4P)3s$	^{5}S° — ^{5}P (65 uv)	*1431.9*	33735	*103570*	5	15	1.4	0.13	3.1	−0.19	D	2
			1431.60	33735	103587	5	7	1.5	0.064	1.5	−0.49	D	2
			1432.12	33735	103563	5	5	1.4	0.043	1.0	−0.67	D	2
			1432.54	33735	103542	5	3	1.3	0.024	0.57	−0.92	D	2
10	$2p^2$ — $2p(^2P°)3d$	^{3}P — ^{3}F° (6 uv)											
			1279.25	44	78216	5	7	0.11	0.0038	0.080	−1.72	D	2
11		^{3}P — ^{3}D° (7 uv)	*1277.5*	*30*	*78310*	9	15	1.6	0.063	2.4	−0.24	D	2
			1277.62	44	78316	5	7	1.5	0.052	1.1	−0.58	D	ls
			1277.27	16	78307	3	5	1.2	0.048	0.60	−0.85	D	ls
			1277.15	0	78301	1	3	0.88	0.064	0.27	−1.19	D	ls
			1277.77	44	78307	5	5	0.39	0.0095	0.20	−1.32	D	ls
			[1277.4]	16	78301	3	3	0.65	0.016	0.20	−1.32	D	ls
			[1277.8]	44	78301	5	3	0.042	6.2×10^{-4}	0.013	−2.51	D	ls
12		^{3}P — ^{1}F° (8 uv)											
			1274.13	44	78531	5	7	0.0068	2.3×10^{-4}	0.0048	−2.94	D	2
13		^{3}P — ^{3}P° (9 uv)	*1261.3*	*30*	*79315*	9	9	1.2	0.029	1.1	−0.58	D	2
			1261.56	44	79311	5	5	0.93	0.022	0.46	−0.96	D	ls
			1260.96	16	79319	3	3	0.31	0.0074	0.092	−1.65	D	ls
			[1261.4]	44	79319	5	3	0.50	0.0072	0.15	−1.44	D	ls
			[1260.9]	16	79323	3	1	1.2	0.0096	0.12	−1.54	D	ls
			1261.12	16	79311	3	5	0.30	0.012	0.15	−1.44	D	ls
			1260.75	0	79319	1	3	0.40	0.029	0.12	−1.54	D	ls

No.	Transition Array	Multiplet	λ(Å)	E_i(cm⁻¹)	E_k(cm⁻¹)	g_i	g_k	A_{ki}(10⁸ sec⁻¹)	f_{ik}	S(at.u.)	log gf	Accuracy	Source
14		¹D — ¹D° (34 uv)	1481.77	10194	77681	5	5	0.33	0.011	0.27	−1.26	D	2
15		¹D — ³F° (35 uv)	1470.20	10194	78216	5	7	0.0088	4.0 × 10⁻⁴	0.0097	−2.70	D	2
16		¹D — ³D°	1469	10194	78301	5	3	0.019	3.6 × 10⁻⁴	0.0087	−2.74	D	2
17		¹D — ¹F° (37 uv)	1463.33	10194	78531	5	7	2.1	0.093	2.2	−0.33	D	2
18		¹D — ¹P° (38 uv)	1459.05	10194	78728	5	3	0.37	0.0070	0.17	−1.46	D	2
19		¹S — ³D°	1765	21648	78301	1	3	0.0071	0.0010	0.0058	−3.00	D	2
20		¹S — ¹P° (62 uv)	1751.9	21648	78728	1	3	0.87	0.12	0.69	−0.92	D	2
21	2p² — 2p(²P°)4s	³P — ³P° (5 uv)	*1280.4*	*30*	*78133*	9	9	0.82	0.020	0.76	−0.74	D	2
			1280.34	44	78148	5	5	0.62	0.015	0.32	−1.12	D	ls
			1280.34	16	78117	3	3	0.20	0.0050	0.063	−1.83	D	ls
			1280.89	44	78117	5	3	0.35	0.0052	0.11	−1.58	D	ls
			1280.65	16	78105	3	1	0.81	0.0066	0.084	−1.70	D	ls
			1279.90	16	78148	3	5	0.21	0.0087	0.11	−1.58	D	ls
			1280.15	0	78117	1	3	0.27	0.020	0.084	−1.70	D	ls
22		¹D — ³P°	1472	10194	78117	5	3	0.0051	1.0 × 10⁻⁴	0.0024	−3.30	D	2
23		¹D — ¹P° (36 uv)	1467.45	10194	78338	5	3	0.46	0.0089	0.21	−1.35	D	2
24		¹S — ¹P°	1764	21648	78338	1	3	0.022	0.0031	0.018	−2.51	D	2
25	2p² — 2p(²P°)4d	¹D — ¹D° (39 uv)	1364.14	10194	83500	5	5	0.047	0.0013	0.029	−2.19	D	2
26	2s²2p3p — 2s2p³	³P — ³S°	*2903.9*	*71375*	*105801*	9	3	0.044	0.0019	0.16	−1.78	D	5n
			[2904.9]	71386	105801	5	3	0.022	0.0017	0.079	−2.08	D	5n
			[2903.1]	71365	105801	3	3	0.017	0.0021	0.061	−2.20	D	5n
			[2902.1]	71353	105801	1	3	0.0066	0.0025	0.024	−2.60	D	5n
27	2p3s — 2p(²P°)3p	³P° — ³D (1)	*10695*	*60374*	*69722*	9	15	0.18	0.50	160	0.66	D	6n
			10691.2	60394	69744	5	7	0.18	0.43	75	0.33	D	ls
			10683.1	60353	69711	3	5	0.13	0.38	40	0.06	D	ls
			10685.3	60334	69690	1	3	0.10	0.51	18	−0.29	D	ls
			10729.5	60394	69711	5	5	0.043	0.074	13	−0.43	D	ls
			10707.3	60353	69690	3	3	0.072	0.12	13	−0.43	D	ls
			10754.0	60394	69690	5	3	0.0048	0.0050	0.89	−1.60	D	ls
28		³P° — ³S (2)	*9640.6*	*60374*	*70744*	9	3	0.22	0.10	29	−0.04	D	6n
			9658.49	60394	70744	5	3	0.12	0.10	16	−0.30	D	ls
			9620.86	60353	70744	3	3	0.074	0.10	9.7	−0.51	D	ls
			9603.09	60334	70744	1	3	0.024	0.10	3.2	−0.99	D	ls

No.	Transition Array	Multiplet	$\lambda(\text{Å})$	$E_i(\text{cm}^{-1})$	$E_k(\text{cm}^{-1})$	g_i	g_k	$A_{ki}(10^8\ \text{sec}^{-1})$	f_{ik}	$S(\text{at.u.})$	$\log gf$	Accuracy	Source
29		$^3P° - {}^3P$ (3)	9087.6	60374	71375	9	9	0.25	0.31	83	0.44	D	6n
			9094.89	60394	71386	5	5	0.19	0.23	35	0.07	D	ls
			9078.32	60353	71365	3	3	0.062	0.077	6.9	−0.64	D	ls
			9111.85	60394	71365	5	3	0.11	0.080	12	−0.40	D	ls
			9088.57	60353	71353	3	1	0.25	0.10	9.2	−0.51	D	ls
			9061.48	60353	71386	3	5	0.065	0.13	12	−0.40	D	ls
			9062.53	60334	71365	1	3	0.083	0.31	9.2	−0.51	D	ls
30		$^1P° - {}^1D$ (9)	11330.3	61982	72611	3	5	0.13	0.42	47	0.10	D	6n
31		$^1P° - {}^1S$ (10)	8335.19	61982	73976	3	1	0.32	0.11	9.1	−0.48	D	6n
32	$2p3s -$ $2p(^2P°)4p$	$^3P° - {}^3D$ (4)	5041.7	60374	80203	9	15	0.0039	0.0025	0.37	−1.65	D	6n
			5041.66	60394	80223	5	7	0.0038	0.0020	0.17	−1.99	D	ls
			5039.05	60353	80192	3	5	0.0029	0.0018	0.092	−2.26	D	ls
			5039.05	60334	80173	1	3	0.0022	0.0025	0.041	−2.61	D	ls
			[5049.6]	60394	80192	5	5	9.8×10^{-4}	3.7×10^{-4}	0.031	−2.73	D	ls
			[5044.0]	60353	80173	3	3	0.0016	6.2×10^{-4}	0.031	−2.73	D	ls
			[5054.5]	60394	80173	5	3	1.1×10^{-4}	2.5×10^{-5}	0.0021	−3.90	D	ls
33		$^3P° - {}^3S$ (5)	4822.1	60374	81106	9	3	0.0084	9.8×10^{-4}	0.14	−2.05	D	7n
			4826.73	60394	81106	5	3	0.0047	9.8×10^{-4}	0.078	−2.31	D	ls
			4817.33	60353	81106	3	3	0.0028	9.9×10^{-4}	0.047	−2.53	D	ls
			4812.84	60334	81106	1	3	9.7×10^{-4}	0.0010	0.016	−2.99	D	ls
34		$^3P° - {}^3P$ (6)	4769.7	60374	81334	9	9	0.016	0.0053	0.75	−1.32	D	6n
			4771.72	60394	81344	5	5	0.012	0.0039	0.31	−1.70	D	ls
			4766.62	60353	81326	3	3	0.0039	0.0013	0.063	−2.40	D	ls
			4775.87	60394	81326	5	3	0.0062	0.0013	0.10	−2.20	D	ls
			4770.00	60353	81312	3	1	0.015	0.0018	0.083	−2.28	D	ls
			4762.41	60353	81344	3	5	0.0038	0.0021	0.10	−2.20	D	ls
			4762.41	60334	81326	1	3	0.0052	0.0053	0.083	−2.28	D	ls
35		$^1P° - {}^1P$ (11)	5380.24	61982	80564	3	3	0.016	0.0070	0.37	−1.68	D	6n
36		$^1P° - {}^1D$ (12)	5052.12	61982	81770	3	5	0.017	0.011	0.54	−1.49	D	6n
37		$^1P° - {}^1S$ (13)	4932.00	61982	82252	3	1	0.046	0.0055	0.27	−1.78	D	6n
38	$2p3s -$ $2p(^2P°)5p$	$^1P° - {}^1P$ (14)	4371.33	61982	84852	3	3	0.0097	0.0028	0.12	−2.08	D−	ca
39		$^1P° - {}^1D$ (16)	4268.99	61982	85400	3	5	0.0032	0.0015	0.062	−2.36	D	7n
40	$2s2p^3 -$ $2s^22p(^2P°)4p$	$^3D° - {}^3P$ (18)	5797.8	64091	81334	15	9	0.0039	0.0012	0.34	−1.75	D	6n
			5793.51	64089	81344	7	5	0.0033	0.0012	0.16	−2.08	D	ls
			5801.17	64093	81326	5	3	0.0029	8.9×10^{-4}	0.085	−2.35	D	ls
			5805.76	64092	81312	3	1	0.0039	6.6×10^{-4}	0.038	−2.70	D	ls
			5794.46	64093	81344	5	5	5.8×10^{-4}	2.9×10^{-4}	0.028	−2.83	D	ls
			5800.23	64092	81326	3	3	9.7×10^{-4}	4.9×10^{-4}	0.028	−2.83	D	ls
			[5794.8]	64092	81344	3	5	4.0×10^{-5}	3.3×10^{-5}	0.0019	−4.00	D	ls
41	$2p3p -$ $2p(^2P°)3d$	$^1P - {}^1D°$ (19)	11330.4	68858	77681	3	5	0.198	0.63	71	0.280	C	6n, ca

No.	Transition Array	Multiplet	λ(Å)	E_i(cm⁻¹)	E_k(cm⁻¹)	g_i	g_k	A_{ki}(10⁸ sec⁻¹)	f_{ik}	S(at.u.)	log gf	Accuracy	Source
42		¹P—¹P°	10124	68858	78728	3	3	0.171	0.262	26.2	−0.105	C	6n, ca
43		³D—³F° (24)	*11755*	69722	*78227*	15	21	0.242	0.70	407	1.022	C	6n, ca
			11754.0	69744	78250	7	9	0.241	0.64	174	0.65	C	ls
			11754.0	69711	78216	5	7	0.216	0.63	121	0.495	C	ls
			11747.5	69690	78199	3	5	0.202	0.70	81	0.321	C	ls
			11801.8	69744	78216	7	7	0.0266	0.056	15.1	−0.411	C	ls
			[11778]	69711	78199	5	5	0.0375	0.078	15.1	−0.410	C	ls
			[11824]	69744	78199	7	5	0.00104	0.00156	0.426	−1.96	C	ls
44		³D—³D° (25)	*11641*	69722	*78310*	15	15	0.065	0.132	76	0.297	C	6n, ca
			11667.1	69744	78316	7	7	0.057	0.117	31.5	−0.086	C	ls
			11631.6	69711	78307	5	5	0.0453	0.092	17.6	−0.338	C	ls
			11609.9	69690	78301	3	3	0.0492	0.099	11.4	−0.53	C	ls
			11677.0	69744	78307	7	5	0.0101	0.0147	3.95	−0.99	C	ls
			11638.6	69711	78301	5	3	0.0163	0.0198	3.80	−1.004	C	ls
			11619.0	69711	78316	5	7	0.0073	0.0207	3.95	−0.99	C	ls
			11602.9	69690	78307	3	5	0.0099	0.0332	3.80	−1.002	C	ls
45		³S—³P° (29)	*11664*	70744	*79315*	3	9	0.157	0.96	111	0.461	C	6n, ca
			11667.1	70744	79311	3	5	0.158	0.54	62	0.208	C	ls
			11656.0	70744	79319	3	3	0.158	0.321	37.0	−0.016	C	ls
			[11653]	70744	79323	3	1	0.157	0.107	12.3	−0.494	C	ls
46		³P—³P° (30)	*12591*	71375	*79315*	9	9	0.105	0.249	93	0.351	C	6n, ca
			12614.8	71386	79311	5	5	0.078	0.186	38.7	−0.031	C	ls
			12565.0	71365	79319	3	3	0.0262	0.062	7.7	−0.73	C	ls
			12602.6	71386	79319	5	3	0.0435	0.062	12.9	−0.51	C	ls
			12565.0	71365	79323	3	1	0.105	0.083	10.3	−0.60	C	ls
			12582.3	71365	79311	3	5	0.0262	0.104	12.9	−0.51	C	ls
			12551.0	71353	79319	1	3	0.0352	0.249	10.3	−0.60	C	ls
47		¹D—¹F°	16890	72611	78531	5	7	0.123	0.74	205	0.57	C	6n, ca
48	2p3p — 2p(²P°)4s	¹P—¹P° (20)	10548.0	68858	78338	3	3	0.010	0.017	1.8	−1.29	D	6n
49		³D—³P° (23)	*11886*	69722	*78133*	15	9	0.11	0.14	85	0.34	D	6n
			11894.9	69744	78148	7	5	0.096	0.15	40	0.01	D	ls
			11894.9	69711	78117	5	3	0.084	0.11	21	−0.27	D	ls
			11880.4	69690	78105	3	1	0.11	0.080	9.4	−0.62	D	ls
			11849.3	69711	78148	5	5	0.017	0.036	7.1	−0.74	D	ls
			11863.0	69690	78117	3	3	0.029	0.061	7.1	−0.74	D	ls
			[11820]	69690	78148	3	5	0.0012	0.0040	0.47	−1.92	D	ls
50	2p3p — 2p(²P°)4d	¹P—¹P° (22)	6587.75	68858	84032	3	3	0.024	0.015	1.0	−1.34	D	ca

Forbidden Transitions

The adopted values are selected from calculations by Garstang [1], Naqvi [2], and Yamanouchi and Horie [3], which are very similar in character. All electric quadrupole values are taken from Garstang [1], since his estimate of s_q appears to be the most advanced one. For most magnetic dipole lines, values could be taken from Garstang [1], as well as from Naqvi [2], and Yamanouchi and Horie [3], who all arrive at identical results. Only for the ³P—¹S transition, for which configuration interaction is important, a difference occurs. In this case the results of Garstang [1], and Yamanouchi and Horie [3] are selected, since they represent, according to a later study by Garstang [4], the best available approximation (see also the general introduction).

References

[1] Garstang, R. H., Monthly Notices Roy. Astron. Soc. **111**, 115–124 (1951).
[2] Naqvi, A. M,. Thesis Harvard (1951).
[3] Yamanouchi, T. and Horie, H., J. Phys. Soc. Japan **7**, 52–56 (1952).
[4] Garstang, R. H., Proc. Cambridge Phil. Soc. **52**, 107–113 (1956).

C I.   Forbidden Transitions

No.	Transition Array	Multiplet	$\lambda(\text{Å})$	$E_i(\text{cm}^{-1})$	$E_k(\text{cm}^{-1})$	g_i	g_k	Type of Transition	$A_{ki}(\text{sec}^{-1})$	$S(\text{at.u.})$	Accuracy	Source
1	$2p^2 - 2p^2$	³P — ³P										
			$[61.0 \times 10^5]$	0.0	16.4	1	3	m	7.93×10^{-8}	2.00	B	1, 2, 3
			$[23.0 \times 10^5]$	0.0	43.5	1	5	e	2.00×10^{-14}	3.82	C	1
			$[36.9 \times 10^5]$	16.4	43.5	3	5	m	2.68×10^{-7}	2.50	B	1, 2, 3
			$[36.9 \times 10^5]$	16.4	43.5	3	5	e	4.20×10^{-15}	8.6	C	1
2		³P — ¹D (1 F)										
			9808.9	0.0	10193.7	1	5	e	5.5×10^{-8}	1.5×10^{-5}	D	1
			9823.4	16.4	10193.7	3	5	m	7.8×10^{-5}	1.37×10^{-5}	C	1, 2, 3
			9823.4	16.4	10193.7	3	5	e	1.7×10^{-7}	4.6×10^{-5}	D	1
			9849.5	43.5	10193.7	5	5	m	2.30×10^{-4}	4.08×10^{-5}	C	1, 2, 3
			9849.5	43.5	10193.7	5	5	e	1.2×10^{-6}	3.3×10^{-4}	D	1
3		³P — ¹S (2 F)										
			4621.5	16.4	21648.4	3	1	m	0.00260	9.5×10^{-6}	C	1, 3
			4627.3	43.5	21648.4	5	1	e	1.9×10^{-5}	2.4×10^{-5}	D	1
4		¹D — ¹S (3 F)										
			8727.4	10193.7	21648.4	5	1	e	0.50	15.1	C	1

C II

Ionization Potential $24.376\ \text{eV} = 196659.0\ \text{cm}^{-1}$

Allowed Transitions

List of tabulated lines:

Wavelength [Å]	No.	Wavelength [Å]	No.	Wavelength [Å]	No.
687.059	10	3360.9	27	4413.2	24
687.35	10	3361.09	27	4618.9	26
687.355	10	3361.75	27	4628.1	26
858.092	9	3581.80	18	5132.96	14
858.559	9	3584.98	18	5133.29	14
903.624	3	3585.83	18	5137.26	14
903.962	3	3587.68	18	5139.21	14
904.142	3	3588.92	18	5143.49	14
904.480	3	3589.67	18	5145.16	14
1009.85	4	3590.87	18	5151.08	14
1010.07	4	3876.05	22	5640.50	13
1010.37	4	3876.19	22	5648.08	13
1010.37	4	3876.41	22	5662.51	13
1036.34	2	3876.67	22	5889.4	20
1037.02	2	3878.22	22	5889.97	20
1065.88	6				
1065.9	6	3879.60	22	5891.65	20
1066.12	6	3880.59	22	6578.03	11
1323.9	5	3881.2	22	6582.85	11
1334.53	1	3883.8	22	6779.74	12
1335.66	1	3918.98	17	6780.27	12
1335.71	1	3920.68	17	6783.75	12
2173.8	15	4074.53	23	6787.09	12
2174.1	15	4076.00	23	6791.30	12
2509.11	7	4267.02	21	6798.04	12
2511.71	7	4267.2	21	6800.50	12
2512.03	7	4267.27	21	6812.19	12
2746.50	19	4371.59	25	7231.12	16
2747.3	19	4372.49	25	7236.19	16
2747.31	19	4374.28	25	7236.2	16
2836.71	8	4411.20	24	18895	29
2837.60	8	4411.52	24	18916	29
2992.6	28				

Self-consistent field calculations by Weiss [1], and Biermann and Lübeck [3], and a high current arc experiment by Maecker [2] are utilized for the tabulation. The results for the lower and moderately excited transitions should be quite uncertain because in the calculations the strong effects of configuration interaction are essentially neglected, and the experimental work is subject to large systematic uncertainties.

References

[1] Weiss, A. W., private communication (1964).
[2] Maecker, H., Z. Physik **135**, 13–22 (1953).
[3] Biermann, L. and Lübeck, K., Z. Astrophys. **25**, 325–339 (1948).

CII. Allowed Transitions

No.	Transition Array	Multiplet	λ(Å)	E_i(cm^{-1})	E_k(cm^{-1})	g_i	g_k	A_{ki}(10^8 sec^{-1})	f_{ik}	S(at.u.)	log gf	Accuracy	Source
1	$2s^2 2p - 2s 2p^2$	^{2}P° $-$ ^{2}D (1 uv)	_1335.3_	_43_	_74932_	6	10	6.0	0.27	7.0	0.20	E	1
			1335.71	64	74931	4	6	6.0	0.24	4.2	-0.02	E	ls
			1334.53	0	74933	2	4	4.9	0.26	2.3	-0.28	E	ls
			1335.66	64	74933	4	4	1.0	0.027	0.47	-0.97	E	ls
2		^{2}P° $-$ ^{2}S (2 uv)	_1036.8_	_43_	_96494_	6	2	11	0.059	1.2	-0.45	E	1
			1037.02	64	96494	4	2	7.3	0.059	0.80	-0.63	E	ls
			1036.34	0	96494	2	2	3.6	0.059	0.40	-0.93	E	ls
3		^{2}P° $-$ ^{2}P (3 uv)	_904.09_	_43_	_110652_	6	6	42	0.52	9.2	0.49	E	1
			904.142	64	110666	4	4	35	0.43	5.1	0.23	E	ls
			903.962	0	110625	2	2	27	0.34	2.0	-0.17	E	ls
			904.480	64	110625	4	2	14	0.084	1.0	-0.47	E	ls
			903.624	0	110666	2	4	6.9	0.17	1.0	-0.47	E	ls
4	$2s 2p^2 - 2p^3$	^{4}P $-$ ^{4}S° (7 uv)	_1010.2_	_43033_	_142024_	12	4	32	0.16	6.5	0.29	E	1
			1010.37	43051	142024	6	4	16	0.17	3.3	0.00	E	ls
			1010.07	43022	142024	4	4	11	0.17	2.2	-0.18	E	ls
			1009.85	43000	142024	2	4	5.4	0.17	1.1	-0.48	E	ls
5		^{2}D $-$ ^{2}D° (11 uv)	_1323.9_	_74932_	_150465_	10	10	8.7	0.23	10	0.36	E	1
6		^{2}D $-$ ^{2}P° (12 uv)	_1066.0_	_74932_	_168744_	10	6	8.1	0.083	2.9	-0.08	E	1
			1065.88	74931	168750	6	4	7.1	0.081	1.7	-0.31	E	ls
			1066.12	74933	168732	4	2	8.1	0.069	0.97	-0.56	E	ls
			[1065.9]	74933	168750	4	4	0.79	0.014	0.19	-1.27	E	ls
7		^{2}P $-$ ^{2}D° (14 uv)	_2511.0_	_110652_	_150465_	6	10	0.97	0.15	7.6	-0.04	E	2
			2512.03	110666	150463	4	6	0.96	0.14	4.5	-0.26	E	ls
			2509.11	110625	150468	2	4	0.83	0.16	2.6	-0.50	E	ls
			2511.71	110666	150468	4	4	0.17	0.016	0.52	-1.20	E	ls
8	$2s 2p^2 -$ $2s^2(^1$S$)3p$	^{2}S $-$ ^{2}P° (13 uv)	_2837.0_	_96494_	_131732_	2	6	0.35	0.13	2.4	-0.59	E	2
			2836.71	96494	131736	2	4	0.36	0.086	1.6	-0.77	E	ls
			2837.60	96494	131725	2	2	0.35	0.043	0.80	-1.07	E	ls
9	$2p - (^1$S$)3s$	^{2}P° $-$ ^{2}S (4 uv)	_858.41_	_43_	_116538_	6	2	12	0.046	0.78	-0.56	D	1
			858.559	64	116538	4	2	8.3	0.046	0.52	-0.74	D	ls
			858.092	0	116538	2	2	4.2	0.046	0.26	-1.04	D	ls
10	$2p - (^1$S$)3d$	^{2}P° $-$ ^{2}D (5 uv)	_687.25_	_43_	_145551_	6	10	22	0.26	3.5	0.19	D	1
			687.355	64	145551	4	6	22	0.23	2.1	-0.03	D	ls
			687.059	0	145550	2	4	19	0.27	1.2	-0.28	D	ls
			[687.35]	64	145550	4	4	3.6	0.025	0.23	-0.99	D	ls
11	$3s - (^1$S$)3p$	^{2}S $-$ ^{2}P° (2)	_6579.7_	_116538_	_131732_	2	6	0.480	0.93	40.5	0.272	C	1, 3
			6578.03	116538	131736	2	4	0.480	0.62	27.0	0.096	C	ls
			6582.85	116538	131725	2	2	0.479	0.311	13.5	-0.206	C	ls
12	$2s 2p 3s -$ $2s 2p(^3$P°$)3p$	^{4}P° $-$ ^{4}D (14)	_6785.6_	_167007_	_181740_	12	20	0.369	0.424	114	0.71	C	ca
			6783.75	167033	181770	6	8	0.370	0.340	45.6	0.310	C	ls
			6779.74	166988	181734	4	6	0.258	0.267	23.8	0.029	C	ls
			6780.27	166965	181709	2	4	0.154	0.212	9.5	-0.373	C	ls
			6800.50	167033	181734	6	6	0.110	0.076	10.2	-0.341	C	ls

No.	Transition Array	Multiplet	λ(Å)	E_i(cm^{-1})	E_k(cm^{-1})	g_i	g_k	A_{ki}(10^8 sec^{-1})	f_{ik}	S(at.u.)	log gf	Accuracy	Source
			6791.30	166988	181709	4	4	0.195	0.135	12.1	−0.268	C	*ls*
			6787.09	166965	181695	2	2	0.307	0.212	9.5	−0.373	C	*ls*
			6812.19	167033	181709	6	4	0.0183	0.0085	1.14	−1.292	C	*ls*
			6798.04	166988	181695	4	2	0.061	0.0211	1.89	−1.074	C	*ls*
13		^{4}P$^\circ$ − ^{4}S (15)	*5653.9*	*167007*	*184689*	12	4	0.65	0.104	23.2	0.096	C	*ca*
			5662.51	167033	184689	6	4	0.325	0.104	11.6	−0.205	C	*ls*
			5648.08	166988	184689	4	4	0.217	0.104	7.7	−0.381	C	*ls*
			5640.50	166965	184689	2	4	0.109	0.104	3.86	−0.68	C	*ls*
14		^{4}P$^\circ$ − ^{4}P (16)	*5141.8*	*167007*	*186450*	12	12	0.86	0.342	69	0.61	C	*ca*
			5145.16	167033	186464	6	6	0.60	0.239	24.3	0.157	C	*ls*
			5139.21	166988	186441	4	4	0.115	0.0456	3.09	−0.74	C	*ls*
			5137.26	166965	186425	2	2	0.144	0.057	1.93	−0.94	C	*ls*
			5151.08	167033	186441	6	4	0.385	0.102	10.4	−0.213	C	*ls*
			5143.49	166988	186425	4	2	0.72	0.142	9.6	−0.246	C	*ls*
			5133.29	166988	186464	4	6	0.260	0.154	10.4	−0.210	C	*ls*
			5132.96	166965	186441	2	4	0.361	0.285	9.6	−0.244	C	*ls*
15	3s − (^{1}S)4p	^{2}S − ^{2}P$^\circ$	*2173.9*	*116538*	*162523*	2	6	0.253	0.054	0.77	−0.97	C	3
			[2173.8]	116538	162525	2	4	0.251	0.0356	0.51	−1.147	C	*ls*
			[2174.1]	116538	162519	2	2	0.252	0.0179	0.256	−1.447	C	*ls*
16	3p − (^{1}S)3d	^{2}P$^\circ$ − ^{2}D (3)	*7234.4*	*131732*	*145551*	6	10	0.450	0.59	84	0.55	C	1
			7236.19	131736	145551	4	6	0.446	0.52	50	0.322	C	*ls*
			7231.12	131725	145550	2	4	0.375	0.59	28.0	0.071	C	*ls*
			[7236.2]	131736	145550	4	4	0.075	0.059	5.6	−0.63	C	*ls*
17	3p − (^{1}S)4s	^{2}P$^\circ$ − ^{2}S (4)	*3920.2*	*131732*	*157234*	6	2	1.87	0.143	11.1	−0.066	C	3
			3920.68	131736	157234	4	2	1.24	0.143	7.4	−0.242	C	*ls*
			3918.98	131725	157234	2	2	0.62	0.143	3.70	−0.54	C	*ls*
18	2s2p3p − 2s2p(^{3}P$^\circ$)4s	^{4}D − ^{4}P$^\circ$ (23)	*3589.3*	*181740*	*209593*	20	12	0.92	0.107	25.3	0.330	C	*ca*
			3589.67	181770	209620	8	6	0.74	0.107	10.1	−0.068	C	*ls*
			3590.87	181734	209574	6	4	0.58	0.075	5.3	−0.347	C	*ls*
			3590.87	181709	209550	4	2	0.465	0.0449	2.12	−0.75	C	*ls*
			3584.98	181734	209620	6	6	0.166	0.0319	2.26	−0.72	C	*ls*
			3587.68	181709	209574	4	4	0.295	0.057	2.69	−0.64	C	*ls*
			3588.92	181695	209550	2	2	0.466	0.090	2.13	−0.74	C	*ls*
			3581.80	181709	209620	4	6	0.0184	0.0053	0.250	−1.67	C	*ls*
			3585.83	181695	209574	2	4	0.0426	0.0178	0.420	−1.450	C	*ls*
19	3p − (^{1}S)4d	^{2}P$^\circ$ − ^{2}D (15 uv)	*2747.0*	*131732*	*168124*	6	10	0.466	0.088	4.77	−0.278	C	*ca*
			2747.31	131736	168124	4	6	0.466	0.079	2.86	−0.50	C	*ls*
			2746.50	131725	168124	2	4	0.389	0.088	1.59	−0.75	C	*ls*
			[2747.3]	131736	168124	4	4	0.078	0.0088	0.318	−1.454	C	*ls*
20	3d − (^{1}S)4p	^{2}D − ^{2}P$^\circ$ (5)	*5890.4*	*145551*	*162523*	10	6	0.337	0.105	20.4	0.022	C	*ca*
			5889.97	145551	162525	6	4	0.302	0.105	12.2	−0.201	C	*ls*
			5891.65	145550	162519	4	2	0.337	0.088	6.8	−0.455	C	*ls*
			[5889.4]	145550	162525	4	4	0.0337	0.0175	1.36	−1.154	C	*ls*
21	3d − (^{1}S)4f	^{2}D − ^{2}F$^\circ$ (6)	*4267.2*	*145551*	*168979*	10	14	2.46	0.94	132	0.97	C	*ca*
			4267.27	145551	168979	6	8	2.44	0.89	75	0.73	C	*ls*
			4267.02	145550	168979	4	6	2.30	0.94	53	0.58	C	*ls*
			[4267.2]	145551	168979	6	6	0.164	0.0447	3.77	−0.57	C	*ls*

No.	Transition Array	Multiplet	λ(Å)	E_i(cm^{-1})	E_k(cm^{-1})	g_i	g_k	A_{ki}(10^8 sec^{-1})	f_{ik}	S(at.u.)	log gf	Accu-racy	Source
22	2s2p3d— 2s2p(^{3}P°)4f	^{4}F°—^{4}G (33)	3876.7	195786	221574	28	36	2.66	0.77	275	1.333	C	ca
			3876.19	195812	221604	10	12	2.67	0.72	92	0.86	C	ls
			3876.41	195785	221575	8	10	2.43	0.69	70	0.74	C	ls
			3876.67	195765	221553	6	8	2.30	0.69	53	0.62	C	ls
			3876.05	195751	221543	4	6	2.28	0.77	39.3	0.489	C	ls
			3880.59	195812	221575	10	10	0.218	0.0493	6.3	−0.307	C	ls
			3879.60	195785	221553	8	8	0.360	0.081	8.3	−0.187	C	ls
			3878.22	195765	221543	6	6	0.365	0.082	6.3	−0.307	C	ls
			[3883.8]	195812	221553	10	8	0.0080	0.00145	0.186	−1.84	C	ls
			[3881.2]	195785	221543	8	6	0.0132	0.00224	0.229	−1.75	C	ls
23		^{4}D°—^{4}F (36)											
			4076.00	196581	221107	8	10	2.28	0.71	76	0.75	C	ca, ls
			4074.53	196571	221106	6	8	1.96	0.65	52	0.59	C	ca, ls
24		^{2}D°—^{2}F (39)	4411.4	198433	221095	10	14	2.11	0.86	125	0.93	C	ca
			4411.52	198437	221099	6	8	2.09	0.81	71	0.69	C	ls
			4411.20	198426	221090	4	6	1.97	0.86	50	0.54	C	ls
			[4413.2]	198437	221090	6	6	0.140	0.0410	3.57	−0.61	C	ls
25		^{4}P°—^{4}D (45)											
			4374.28	198842	221697	6	8	1.99	0.76	66	0.66	C	ca, ls
			4372.49	198864	221727	4	6	1.40	0.60	34.5	0.380	C	ca, ls
			4371.59	198878	221746	2	4	0.83	0.475	13.7	−0.022	C	ca, ls
26		^{2}F°—^{2}G (50)	4619.1	199966	221609	14	18	2.24	0.92	196	1.110	C	ca
			[4618.9]	199984	221628	8	10	2.24	0.90	109	0.86	C	ls
			[4618.9]	199941	221585	6	8	2.16	0.92	84	0.74	C	ls
			[4628.1]	199984	221585	8	8	0.079	0.0255	3.11	−0.69	C	ls
27	3d—(^{1}S)5p	^{2}D—^{2}P° (7)	3361.3	145551	175293	10	6	0.121	0.0123	1.36	−0.91	C	ca
			3361.09	145551	175295	6	4	0.109	0.0124	0.82	−1.130	C	ls
			3361.75	145550	175288	4	2	0.121	0.0102	0.453	−1.388	C	ls
			[3360.9]	145550	175295	4	4	0.0121	0.00206	0.091	−2.085	C	ls
28	3d—(^{1}S)5f	^{2}D—^{2}F° (8)	2992.6	145551	178956	10	14	0.90	0.169	16.6	0.227	C	ca
29	4s—(^{1}S)4p	^{2}S—^{2}P°	18902	157234	162523	2	6	0.074	1.18	147	0.373	C	3
			[18895]	157234	162525	2	4	0.074	0.79	98	0.197	C	ls
			[18916]	157234	162519	2	2	0.073	0.393	49.0	−0.104	C	ls

Forbidden Transitions

Naqvi's calculation [1] of the one possible transition in the ground state configuration 2p is the only available source. The line strength should be quite accurate, since it does not sensitively depend on the choice of the interaction parameters.

Reference

[1] Naqvi, A. M., Thesis Harvard (1951).

C II. Forbidden Transitions

No.	Transition Array	Multiplet	λ(Å)	E_i(cm^{-1})	E_k(cm^{-1})	g_i	g_k	Type of Transition	A_{ki}(sec^{-1})	S(at.u.)	Accu-racy	Source
1	2p—2p	^{2}P°—^{2}P°	[15.6×10^5]	0	64	2	4	m	2.36×10^{-6}	1.33	C	1

C III

Ground State $1s^22s^2\ {}^1S_0$

Ionization Potential $47.864\ \text{eV} = 386213.9\ \text{cm}^{-1}$

Allowed Transitions

List of tabulated lines:

Wavelength [Å]	No.	Wavelength [Å]	No.	Wavelength [Å]	No.
310.171	3	3609.96	23	4673.91	15
371.694	11	3609.61	23	5244.5	14
371.72	11	3703.52	18	5249.6	26
371.747	11	3883.80	27	5253.55	14
371.784	11	3885.99	27	5272.56	14
371.80	11	3886.2	27	5696.0	17
386.203	2	3889.18	27	5857.9	20
459.462	9	3889.7	27	5862.8	20
459.521	9	3889.8	27	5871.6	20
459.633	9	4056.06	28	5871.8	20
459.64	9	4122.05	24	5880.4	20
538.075	7	4325.70	16	5894.1	20
538.150	7	4379.97	25	6727.1	13
538.312	7	4383.24	25	6730.7	13
574.279	10	4388.24	25	6742.1	13
690.526	8	4516.02	22	6744.2	13
977.026	1	4516.93	22	6762.2	13
1174.92	4	4647.40	12	6773.7	13
1175.25	4	4650.16	12	6851.2	19
1175.57	4	4650.9	15	6853.1	19
1175.70	4	4651.35	12	6857.3	19
1175.97	4	4651.8	15	6862.9	19
1176.35	4	4659.0	15	6869.1	19
1247.37	6	4663.53	15	6871.7	19
2296.89	5	4665.90	15	6881.4	19
3170.16	21				

Values for the $2s^2 - 2s2p$ and $2s2p - 2p^2$ transition arrays are taken from the self-consistent field calculations of Weiss [1]. These calculations do not include the important effects of configuration interaction; hence fairly large uncertainties must be expected. The average of the dipole length and velocity approximations is adopted [I]. Accuracies within 50 percent are indicated by the following comparison: Weiss [1] has undertaken refined calculations, including configuration interaction, for the same transitions in Be I—the first member of this isoelectronic sequence—in addition to calculations of the type done for this ion. In all cases the agreement with the average of the dipole length and velocity approximations is close.

Reference

[1] Weiss, A. W., private communication (1964).

C III. Allowed Transitions

No.	Transition Array	Multiplet	$\lambda(\text{Å})$	$E_i(\text{cm}^{-1})$	$E_k(\text{cm}^{-1})$	g_i	g_k	$A_{ki}(10^8\,\text{sec}^{-1})$	f_{ik}	$S(\text{at.u.})$	$\log gf$	Accuracy	Source
1	$2s^2-2s(^2S)2p$	$^1S-^1P°$ (1 uv)	977.026	0.0	102351	1	3	19	0.81	2.6	-0.09	D	1
2	$2s^2-2s(^2S)3p$	$^1S-^1P°$ (2 uv)	386.203	0.0	258931	1	3	38	0.26	0.32	-0.59	D	ca
3	$2s^2-2s(^2S)4p$	$^1S-^1P°$ (3 uv)	310.171	0.0	322403	1	3	3.7	0.016	0.017	-1.79	D	ca
4	$2s2p-2p^2$	$^3P°-^3P$ (4 uv)	1175.7	52419	137478	9	9	13	0.26	9.1	0.37	D	1
			1175.70	52447	137502	5	5	9.4	0.20	3.8	-0.01	D	ls
			1175.57	52390	137455	3	3	3.1	0.065	0.76	-0.71	D	ls
			1176.35	52447	137455	5	3	5.2	0.065	1.3	-0.49	D	ls
			1175.97	52390	137426	3	1	13	0.087	1.0	-0.58	D	ls
			1174.92	52390	137502	3	5	3.1	0.11	1.3	-0.49	D	ls
			1175.25	52367	137455	1	3	4.2	0.26	1.0	-0.58	D	ls
5		$^1P°-^1D$ (8 uv)	2296.89	102351	145875	3	5	3.6	0.47	11	0.15	D	1
6		$^1P°-^1S$ (9 uv)	1247.37	102351	182520	3	1	12	0.090	1.1	-0.57	D	1
7	$2s2p-2s(^2S)3s$	$^3P°-^3S$ (5 uv)	538.23	52419	238212	9	3	21	0.031	0.49	-0.55	D	ca
			538.312	52447	238212	5	3	12	0.031	0.27	-0.81	D	ls
			538.150	52390	238212	3	3	7.1	0.031	0.16	-1.04	D	ls
			538.075	52367	238212	1	3	2.3	0.031	0.054	-1.51	D	ls
8		$^1P°-^1S$ (10 uv)	690.526	102351	247170	3	1	22	0.053	0.36	-0.80	D	ca
9	$2s2p-2s(^2S)3d$	$^3P°-^3D$ (6 uv)	459.57	52419	270013	9	15	79	0.42	5.7	0.57	D	ca
			459.633	52447	270015	5	7	79	0.35	2.7	0.24	D	ls
			459.521	52390	270011	3	5	59	0.31	1.4	-0.03	D	ls
			459.462	52367	270009	1	3	44	0.42	0.63	-0.38	D	ls
			459.633	52447	270011	5	5	20	0.063	0.47	-0.51	D	ls
			459.521	52390	270009	3	3	33	0.10	0.47	-0.50	D	ls
			[459.64]	52447	270009	5	3	2.2	0.0042	0.032	-1.68	D	ls
10		$^1P°-^1D$ (11 uv)	574.279	102351	276483	3	5	63	0.52	2.9	0.19	D	ca
11	$2s2p-2s(^2S)4d$	$^3P°-^3D$ (7 uv)	371.73	52419	321435	9	15	34	0.12	1.3	0.03	D	ca
			371.747	52447	321450	5	7	34	0.10	0.61	-0.30	D	ls
			371.694	52390	321427	3	5	26	0.089	0.33	-0.57	D	ls
			371.694	52367	321411	1	3	19	0.12	0.15	-0.92	D	ls
			371.784	52447	321427	5	5	8.6	0.018	0.11	-1.05	D	ls
			[371.72]	52390	321411	3	3	14	0.030	0.11	-1.05	D	ls
			[371.80]	52447	321411	5	3	0.96	0.0012	0.0073	-2.23	D	ls
12	$2s3s-2s(^2S)3p$	$^3S-^3P°$ (1)	4648.8	238212	259718	3	9	0.78	0.76	34.9	0.358	C	ca
			4647.40	238212	259724	3	5	0.78	0.423	19.4	0.103	C	ls
			4650.16	238212	259711	3	3	0.78	0.253	11.6	-0.121	C	ls
			4651.35	238212	259706	3	1	0.78	0.084	3.88	-0.60	C	ls
13	$2p3s-2p(^2P°)3p$	$^3P°-^3D$ (3)	6740.8	308283	323114	9	15	0.267	0.303	61	0.436	C	ca
			6744.2	308317	323140	5	7	0.266	0.254	28.2	0.104	C	ls
			6730.7	308248	323101	3	5	0.201	0.227	15.1	-0.167	C	ls
			6727.1	308215	323076	1	3	0.149	0.303	6.7	-0.52	C	ls
			[6762.2]	308317	323101	5	5	0.066	0.0453	5.0	-0.65	C	ls
			[6742.1]	308248	323076	3	3	0.111	0.076	5.0	-0.64	C	ls
			[6773.7]	308317	323076	5	3	0.0073	0.00301	0.336	-1.82	C	ls

No.	Transition Array	Multiplet	λ(Å)	E_i(cm⁻¹)	E_k(cm⁻¹)	g_i	g_k	A_{ki}(10⁸ sec⁻¹)	f_{ik}	S(at.u.)	log gf	Accuracy	Source
14		³P°—³S (4)	*5263.1*	*308283*	*327277*	9	3	0.58	0.080	12.5	−0.142	C	*ca*
			5272.56	308317	327277	5	3	0.320	0.080	7.0	−0.398	C	*ls*
			5253.55	308248	327277	3	3	0.194	0.080	4.17	−0.62	C	*ls*
			5244.5	308215	327277	1	3	0.065	0.081	1.39	−1.094	C	*ls*
15		³P°—³P (5)	*4662.7*	*308283*	*329724*	9	9	0.84	0.273	37.7	0.390	C	*ca*
			4665.90	308317	329743	5	5	0.63	0.204	15.7	0.010	C	*ls*
			[4659.0]	308248	329706	3	3	0.210	0.068	3.14	−0.69	C	*ls*
			4673.91	308317	329706	5	3	0.347	0.068	5.2	−0.468	C	*ls*
			4663.53	308248	329685	3	1	0.84	0.091	4.19	−0.56	C	*ls*
			[4650.9]	308248	329743	3	5	0.211	0.114	5.2	−0.466	C	*ls*
			[4651.8]	308215	329706	1	3	0.281	0.274	4.19	−0.56	C	*ls*
16		¹P°—¹D (7)	4325.70	310005	333116	3	5	1.08	0.50	21.6	0.181	C	*ca*
17	2s3p— 2s(²S)3d	¹P°—¹D (2)	5696.0	258931	276483	3	5	0.50	0.407	22.9	0.087	C	*ca*
18	2p3p— 2p(²P°)3d	¹P—¹P° (12)	3703.52	319719	346713	3	3	0.320	0.066	2.41	−0.70	C	*ca*
19		³D—³D° (19)	*6865.8*	*323114*	*337675*	15	15	0.066	0.0469	15.9	−0.153	C	*ca*
			6871.7	323140	337688	7	7	0.059	0.0416	6.6	−0.54	C	*ls*
			6862.9	323101	337668	5	5	0.0463	0.0327	3.69	−0.79	C	*ls*
			6857.3	323076	337655	3	3	0.050	0.0352	2.39	−0.98	C	*ls*
			[6881.4]	323140	337668	7	5	0.0103	0.0052	0.83	−1.438	C	*ls*
			[6869.1]	323101	337655	5	3	0.0166	0.0070	0.80	−1.450	C	*ls*
			[6853.1]	323101	337688	5	7	0.0074	0.0073	0.83	−1.436	C	*ls*
			[6851.2]	323076	337668	3	5	0.0100	0.0117	0.80	−1.453	C	*ls*
20		³D—³P° (20)	*5880.4*	*323114*	*340115*	15	9	0.0124	0.00385	1.12	−1.238	C	*ca*
			5894.1	323140	340101	7	5	0.0104	0.00385	0.52	−1.57	C	*ls*
			5871.6	323101	340128	5	3	0.0093	0.00290	0.280	−1.84	C	*ls*
			5857.9	323076	340142	3	1	0.0126	0.00216	0.125	−2.188	C	*ls*
			[5880.4]	323101	340101	5	5	0.00186	9.6×10⁻⁴	0.093	−2.317	C	*ls*
			[5862.8]	323076	340128	3	3	0.00313	0.00161	0.093	−2.315	C	*ls*
			[5871.8]	323076	340101	3	5	1.25×10⁻⁴	1.07×10⁻⁴	0.0062	−3.492	C	*ls*
21	2s4s— 2s(²S)5p	¹S—¹P° (8)	3170.16	311721	343256	1	3	0.325	0.147	1.53	−0.83	C	*ca*
22	2s4p— 2s(²S)5s	³P°—³S (9)	*4516.5*	*317798*	*339933*	9	3	1.66	0.169	22.6	0.182	C	*ca*
			4516.93	317800	339933	5	3	0.92	0.169	12.6	−0.072	C	*ls*
			4516.02	317795	339933	3	3	0.55	0.169	7.5	−0.295	C	*ls*
			4516.02	317795	339933	1	3	0.184	0.169	2.51	−0.77	C	*ls*
23	2s4p— 2s(²S)5d	³P°—³D (10)	*3609.3*	*317798*	*345496*	9	15	0.95	0.308	32.9	0.442	C	*ca*
			3609.61	317800	345496	5	7	0.95	0.259	15.4	0.113	C	*ls*
			3608.96	317795	345496	3	5	0.71	0.231	8.2	−0.160	C	*ls*
			3608.96	317795	345496	1	3	0.53	0.308	3.66	−0.51	C	*ls*
			3609.61	317800	345496	5	5	0.236	0.0461	2.74	−0.64	C	*ls*
			3608.96	317795	345496	3	3	0.394	0.077	2.74	−0.64	C	*ls*
			3608.96	317795	345496	3	5	0.0158	0.0051	0.183	−1.81	C	*ls*
24		¹P°—¹D (17)	4122.05	322403	346656	3	5	1.04	0.443	18.0	0.124	C	*ca*

No.	Transition Array	Multiplet	λ(Å)	E_i(cm^{-1})	E_k(cm^{-1})	g_i	g_k	A_{ki}(10^8 sec^{-1})	f_{ik}	S(at.u.)	log gf	Accuracy	Source
25	$2s4d -$ $2s(^2S)5p$	$^3D - ^3P°$ (14)	4385.1	321435	344233	15	9	0.267	0.0463	10.0	−0.160	C	ca
			4388.24	321450	344233	7	5	0.224	0.0462	4.67	−0.491	C	ls
			4383.24	321427	344233	5	3	0.200	0.0346	2.50	−0.76	C	ls
			4379.97	321411	344233	3	1	0.268	0.0257	1.11	−1.114	C	ls
			4383.24	321427	344233	5	5	0.0401	0.0115	0.83	−1.239	C	ls
			4379.97	321411	344233	3	3	0.067	0.0193	0.83	−1.238	C	ls
			4379.97	321411	344233	3	5	0.00268	0.00129	0.056	−2.414	C	ls
26		$^1D - ^1P°$ (23)	5249.6	324212	343256	5	3	0.52	0.128	11.1	−0.194	C	ca
27	$2s4d -$ $2s(^2S)5f$	$^3D - ^3F°$ (15)	3887.1	321435	347154	15	21	1.81	0.58	110	0.93	C	ca
			3889.18	321450	347155	7	9	1.81	0.53	47.2	0.57	C	ls
			3885.99	321427	347153	5	7	1.61	0.51	32.6	0.406	C	ls
			3883.80	321411	347151	3	5	1.52	0.57	22.0	0.236	C	ls
			[3889.7]	321450	347153	7	7	0.201	0.0456	4.09	−0.496	C	ls
			[3886.2]	321427	347151	5	5	0.282	0.064	4.09	−0.495	C	ls
			[3889.8]	321450	347151	7	5	0.0079	0.00128	0.115	−2.047	C	ls
28		$^1D - ^1F°$ (24)	4056.06	324212	348860	5	7	1.45	0.50	33.4	0.398	C	ca

Forbidden Transitions

Naqvi's calculations [1] are the only available source. The results for the $^3P° - ^3P°$ transitions are essentially independent of the choice of the interaction parameters. For the $^3P° - ^1P°$ transitions, Naqvi uses empirical term intervals, i.e., the effects of configuration interaction should be partially included.

Reference

[1] Naqvi, A. M., Thesis Harvard (1951).

C III. Forbidden Transitions

No.	Transition Array	Multiplet	λ(Å)	E_i(cm^{-1})	E_k(cm^{-1})	g_i	g_k	Type of Transition	A_{ki}(sec^{-1})	S(at.u.)	Accuracy	Source
1	$2s2p - 2s(^2S)2p$	$^3P° - ^3P°$										
			[43.5 × 10^5]	52366.7	52389.7	1	3	m	2.18 × 10^{-7}	2.00	B	1
			[17.6 × 10^5]	52389.7	52446.5	3	5	m	2.47 × 10^{-6}	2.50	B	1
2		$^3P° - ^1P°$										
			[2000.0]	52366.7	102351	1	3	m	0.00142	1.26 × 10^{-6}	C	1
			[2000.9]	52389.7	102351	3	3	m	1.35	0.00120	C	1
			[2003.2]	52446.5	102351	5	3	m	0.00179	1.60 × 10^{-6}	C	1

C IV

Ground State $1s^2 2s\ ^2S_{1/2}$

Ionization Potential $64.476 \text{ eV} = 520177.8 \text{ cm}^{-1}$

Allowed Transitions

List of tabulated lines:

Wavelength [Å]	No.	Wavelength [Å]	No.	Wavelength [Å]	No.
222.791	4	384.19	6	4647	19
244.907	3	419.525	5	4665	20
259.471	9	419.714	5	4737	22
259.542	9	1548.20	1	4789	18
289.143	8	1550.77	1	5021	16
289.230	8	2524.40	14	5023	16
296.857	7	2595.14	13	5801.51	10
296.951	7	2697.73	12	5812.14	10
312.418	2	2698.70	12	6592	21
312.455	2	3936	15	20694	11
384.032	6	4440.4	17	20780	11
384.178	6	4441.8	17	20828	11

The values taken from Weiss' calculations [1] are estimated to be accurate to within 10 percent because of the very close agreement between his dipole length and dipole velocity approximations. The values calculated with the length approximation are adopted.

Reference

[1] Weiss, A. W., Astrophys. J. **138,** 1262–1276 (1963).

C IV.   Allowed Transitions

No.	Transition Array	Multiplet	λ(Å)	E_i(cm^{-1})	E_k(cm^{-1})	g_i	g_k	A_{ki}(10^8 sec^{-1})	f_{ik}	S(at.u.)	log gf	Accuracy	Source
1	2s – 2p	^{2}S – ^{2}P° (1 uv)	1549.1	0.0	64555	2	6	2.65	0.286	2.91	−0.243	A	1
			1548.20	0.0	64591	2	4	2.65	0.190	1.94	−0.420	A	ls
			1550.77	0.0	64484	2	2	2.63	0.0950	0.970	−0.721	A	ls
2	2s – 3p	^{2}S – ^{2}P° (2 uv)	312.43	0.0	320070	2	6	45.6	0.200	0.412	−0.397	B+	1
			312.418	0.0	320080	2	4	45.7	0.134	0.275	−0.573	B+	ls
			312.455	0.0	320049	2	2	45.5	0.0666	0.137	−0.876	B+	ls
3	2s – 4p	^{2}S – ^{2}P° (3 uv)	244.907	0.0	408318	2	6	22.1	0.0597	0.0963	−0.923	B	ca
4	2s – 5p	^{2}S – ^{2}P° (4 uv)	222.791	0.0	448859	2	6	11.8	0.0263	0.0385	−1.280	B	ca
5	2p – 3s	^{2}P° – ^{2}S (6 uv)	419.65	64555	302848	6	2	42.7	0.0376	0.312	−0.647	B+	1
			419.714	64591	302848	4	2	28.5	0.0376	0.208	−0.822	B+	ls
			419.525	64484	302848	2	2	14.3	0.0376	0.104	−1.123	B+	ls
6	2p – 3d	^{2}P° – ^{2}D (7 uv)	384.12	64555	324887	6	10	177	0.654	4.96	0.594	B+	1
			384.178	64591	324891	4	6	177	0.589	2.98	0.372	B+	ls
			384.032	64484	324880	2	4	148	0.653	1.65	0.116	B+	ls
			[384.19]	64591	324880	4	4	29.6	0.0654	0.331	−0.582	B+	ls

No.	Transition Array	Multiplet	λ(Å)	E_i(cm^{-1})	E_k(cm^{-1})	g_i	g_k	A_{ki}(10^8 sec^{-1})	f_{ik}	S(at.u.)	log gf	Accuracy	Source
7	2p–4s	^{2}P°–^{2}S (8 uv)	296.92	64555	401347	6	2	17.5	0.00772	0.0453	−1.334	B	ca
			296.951	64591	401347	4	2	11.7	0.00772	0.0302	−1.510	B	ls
			296.857	64484	401347	2	2	5.85	0.00773	0.0151	−1.811	B	ls
8	2p–4d	^{2}P°–^{2}D (9 uv)	289.20	64555	410336	6	10	58.1	0.121	0.694	−0.137	B	ca
			289.230	64591	410338	4	6	58.2	0.109	0.417	−0.359	B	ls
			289.143	64484	410334	2	4	48.5	0.122	0.231	−0.614	B	ls
			[289.23]	64591	410334	4	4	9.69	0.0122	0.0463	−1.313	B	ls
9	2p–5d	^{2}P°–^{2}D (10 uv)	259.52	64555	449887	6	10	22.8	0.0383	0.196	−0.639	B	ca
			259.542	64591	449887	4	6	22.8	0.0345	0.118	−0.860	B	ls
			259.471	64484	449887	2	4	18.9	0.0382	0.0653	−1.117	B	ls
			259.542	64591	449887	4	4	3.80	0.00383	0.0131	−1.814	B	ls
10	3s–3p	^{2}S–^{2}P° (1)	5804.9	302848	320070	2	6	0.318	0.481	18.4	−0.017	B	1
			5801.51	302848	320080	2	4	0.319	0.322	12.3	−0.191	B	ls
			5812.14	302848	320049	2	2	0.316	0.160	6.13	−0.494	B	ls
11	3p–3d	^{2}P°–^{2}D	20754	320070	324887	6	10	0.00579	0.0623	25.5	−0.427	B	1
			[20780]	320080	324891	4	6	0.00576	0.0559	15.3	−0.650	B	ls
			[20694]	320049	324880	2	4	0.00486	0.0624	8.50	−0.904	B	ls
			[20828]	320080	324880	4	4	9.53 × 10^{-4}	0.00620	1.70	−1.606	B	ls
12	4p–5s	^{2}P°–^{2}S (12 uv)	2698.4	408318	445366	6	2	4.09	0.149	7.94	−0.049	B	ca
			2698.70	408322	445366	4	2	2.73	0.149	5.29	−0.225	B	ls
			2697.73	408309	445366	2	2	1.37	0.149	2.65	−0.525	B	ls
13	4d–5p	^{2}D–^{2}P° (13 uv)	2595.14	410336	448859	10	6	0.746	0.0452	3.86	−0.345	B	ca
14	4d–5f	^{2}D–^{2}F° (14 uv)	2524.40	410336	449938	10	14	7.44	0.995	82.7	0.999	B	ca
15	5s–6p	^{2}S–^{2}P° (2)	3936	445366	470763	2	6	0.340	0.237	6.14	−0.325	B	ca
16	5p–6s	^{2}P°–^{2}S (3)	5022.2	448859	468765	6	2	1.40	0.176	17.5	0.024	B	ca
			5023	448861	468765	4	2	0.935	0.177	11.7	−0.150	B	ls
			5021	448854	468765	2	2	0.467	0.176	5.83	−0.453	B	ls
17	5p–6d	^{2}P°–^{2}D (4)	4441.8	448859	471368	6	10	1.05	0.516	45.3	0.491	B	ca
			[4441.8]	448861	471368	4	6	1.05	0.465	27.2	0.270	B	ls
			[4440.4]	448854	471368	2	4	0.874	0.516	15.1	0.014	B	ls
			[4441.8]	448861	471368	4	4	0.175	0.0516	3.02	−0.685	B	ls
18	5d–6p	^{2}D–^{2}P° (5)	4789	449887	470763	10	6	0.341	0.0704	11.1	−0.152	B	ca
19	5d–6f	^{2}D–^{2}F° (6)	4647	449887	471403	10	14	1.85	0.837	128	0.923	B	ca
20	5f–6d	^{2}F°–^{2}D (7)	4665	449938	471368	14	10	0.103	0.0241	5.18	−0.472	B	ca
21	6s–7p	^{2}S–^{2}P° (10)	6592	468765	483931	2	6	0.132	0.258	11.2	−0.288	B	ca
22	6d–8p	^{2}D–^{2}P° (12)	4737	471368	492473	10	6	0.104	0.0210	3.27	−0.678	B	ca

C v

Ground State $1s^2\ ^1S_0$

Ionization Potential $391.986\ eV = 3162450\ cm^{-1}$

Allowed Transitions

The results of extensive non-relativistic variational calculations by Weiss [1] are chosen. Values have been calculated in both the dipole length and dipole velocity approximations and agree to within 1 percent, except for the $3p\ ^1P°-3d\ ^1D$ transition where agreement is not as good. The average of the two approximations is adopted [1].

Reference

[1] Weiss, A. W., private communication (1964).

C v. Allowed Transitions

No.	Transition Array	Multiplet	$\lambda(Å)$	$E_i(cm^{-1})$	$E_k(cm^{-1})$	g_i	g_k	$A_{ki}(10^8\ sec^{-1})$	f_{ik}	$S(at.u.)$	$\log gf$	Accuracy	Source
1	$1s^2-1s2p$	$^1S-^1P°$	[40.270]	0	2483240	1	3	8870	0.647	0.0858	−0.189	A	1
2	$1s^2-1s3p$	$^1S-^1P°$	[34.973]	0	2859350	1	3	2550	0.141	0.0162	−0.852	A	1
3	$1s2s-1s2p$	$^1S-^1P°$	[3540.8]	[2455006]	2483240	1	3	0.165	0.0931	1.09	−1.031	A	1
4	$1s2s-1s3p$	$^1S-^1P°$	[247.31]	[2455006]	2859350	1	3	128	0.351	0.286	−0.455	A	1
5	$1s2p-1s3d$	$^1P°-^1D$	[267.21]	2483240	[2857480]	3	5	396	0.707	1.87	0.327	A	1
6	$1s3d-1s3p$	$^1D-^1P°$	[53460]?	[2857480]	2859350	5	3	3.97×10^{-4}	0.0102	8.98	−1.292	C+	1
7	$1s2s-1s2p$	$^3S-^3P°$	2273.9	2411244	2455207	3	9	0.565	0.132	2.95	−0.404	A	1
8	$1s2s-1s3p$	$^3S-^3P°$	[227.37]	2411244	[2851060]	3	9	136	0.316	0.710	−0.023	A	1
9	$1s2p-1s3d$	$^3P°-^3D$	248.71	2455207	2857286	9	15	425	0.657	4.84	0.772	A	1
10	$1s3p-1s3d$	$^3P°-^3D$	[16057]?	[2851060]	2857286	9	15	0.00753	0.0485	23.1	−0.360	A	1

766–655 O–66—5

NITROGEN

N I

Ground State	$1s^2 2s^2 2p^3 \, {}^4S^o_{3/2}$
Ionization Potential	$14.53 \text{ eV} = 117214 \text{ cm}^{-1}$

Allowed Transitions

List of tabulated lines:

Wavelength [Å]	No.	Wavelength [Å]	No.	Wavelength [Å]	No.
1100.7	19	4222.12	29	6622.54	47
1134.17	1	4223.04	29	6626.8	47
1134.42	1	4224.74	29	6636.94	47
1134.98	1	4230.35	29	6644.96	47
1163.87	10	4253.28	28	6646.51	47
1163.88	10	4254.7	28	6653.46	47
1164.31	10	4258.7	28	6656.51	47
1167.45	9	4261.2	28	6926.90	48
1168.42	9	4263.2	28	6945.22	48
1168.54	9	4264.7	28	6951.7	48
1169.69	8	4269.8	28	6960.4	48
1176.4	14	4384.4	43	6973.0	48
1176.6	14	4391.3	43	6979.10	48
1177.7	14	4914.90	31	6981.8	48
1199.55	2	4935.03	31	7423.64	23
1200.22	2	5170.0	18	7442.30	23
1200.71	2	5181.5	18	7468.31	23
1231.7	20	5186.9	18	8184.85	22
1243.17	5	5197.8	49	8188.01	22
1243.30	5	5201.8	49	8200.36	22
1243.31	5	5281.18	17	8210.71	22
1310.54	13	5292.9	17	8216.32	22
1310.97	13	5293.5	17	8223.12	22
1316.29	12	5305.0	17	8242.37	22
1319.04	11	5309.2	17	8567.74	25
1319.72	11	5310.6	17	8590.01	25
1326.63	15	5314.8	17	8629.24	25
1327.96	15	5328.70	16	8655.87	25
1411.94	6	5344.4	16	8680.27	21
1492.62	3	5354.7	16	8683.40	21
1492.67	3	5356.77	16	8686.16	21
1494.67	3	5367.1	16	8703.26	21
1742.72	4	5372.5	16	8711.71	21
1742.73	4	5372.66	16	8718.84	21
1745.25	4	5378.3	16	8728.91	21
1745.26	4	5401.45	32	8747.36	21
4099.95	26	5411.88	32	9028.92	33
4109.96	26	5816.48	50	9045.88	27
4113.97	26	5829.53	50	9049.47	27
4137.63	30	5834.7	50	9049.89	27
4143.42	30	5841.01	50	9060.72	33
4151.46	30	5850.1	50	9386.81	24
4214.73	29	5854.16	50	9392.79	24
4215.92	29	5856.3	50	9460.68	24
4218.87	29	6606.3	47	9776.90	35

Wavelength [Å]	No.	Wavelength [Å]	No.	Wavelength [Å]	No.
9786.79	35	10563.3	39	11628.0	7
9788.30	35	10591.9	44	11656.0	7
9798.57	35	10596	44	11964	42
9810.02	35	10597.0	44	11997.9	42
9814.03	35	10623.2	38	12074.1	42
9822.75	35	10644.0	38	12107.4	42
9834.62	35	10653.0	38	12128.6	46
9863.33	35	10675	38	12186.9	46
9872.16	35	10693.2	37	12203.4	46
10105.1	34	10713.6	38	12232.9	46
10108.9	34	10718.0	38	12280	46
10112.5	34	10730.5	37	12288.0	46
10114.6	34	10757.9	38	12291	40
10128.3	34	10775.0	37	12307	46
10147.3	34	10879.2	36	12330	40
10164.8	34	10884.6	36	12384	40
10166.8	34	11180.1	45	12461.2	41
10200.0	34	11227.1	45	12467.8	41
10500.3	39	11237.6	45	12582.3	41
10507.0	39	11266.2	45		
10513.4	39	11291.7	45		
10520.6	39	11294.2	45		
10533.8	39	11313.9	45		
10539.6	39	11323.3	45		
10549.6	39	11564.8	7		

The numerical values for the $2s^2\,2p^3 - 2s\,2p^4$, $2p^3 - 2p^2\,3s$, and $2p^3 - 2p^2\,3d$ transitions are taken exclusively from measurements with a wall-stabilized high current arc by Labuhn [1], since the available theoretical treatments for these transitions must be considered quite unreliable because of the strong effects of configuration interaction. However, even the experimental data should be considered with caution since they suffer, for example, from uncertainties in the identification of the lines.

The data for most higher excited transitions are taken from a stabilized-arc experiment by Richter [2], the Coulomb approximation, and approximate self-consistent field calculations by Kelly [6]. For about half of the $3p - 3d$ transitions the numbers agree within an impressive 10 percent, and the results have been averaged. For most $3s - 3p$ and $3s - 4p$ transitions, strong cancellations in the calculations render the theoretical results unreliable. In these cases experimental results are exclusively used whenever available. The above material is supplemented by a few numbers obtained from a shock tube investigation by Doherty [5], a wall-stabilized arc study by Shumaker and Yokley [4], and work with a less refined arc source by Motschmann [3]. Motschmann's absolute values appear to be shifted by a constant factor due to a demixing effect in the arc and have been renormalized by applying a factor of 1.5, which has given the best fit with Richter's data.

References

[1] Labuhn, F., to be published in Z. Naturforsch.
[2] Richter, J., Z. Astrophys. **51**, 177–186 (1961).
[3] Motschmann, H., Z. Physik **143**, 77–92 (1955).
[4] Shumaker, Jr., J. P., and Yokley, C. R., Applied Optics **3**, 83–87 (1964).
[5] Doherty, L. R., Thesis Michigan (1961).
[6] Kelly, P. S., J. Quant. Spectrosc. Radiat. Transfer **4**, 117–148 (1964).

N I. Allowed Transitions

No.	Transition Array	Multiplet	λ(Å)	E_i(cm⁻¹)	E_k(cm⁻¹)	g_i	g_k	A_{ki}(10⁸ sec⁻¹)	f_{ik}	S(at.u.)	log gf	Accuracy	Source
1	$2s^22p^3 -$ $2s2p^4$	$^4S° - {}^4P$ (2 uv)	*1134.6*	0.0	*88135*	4	12	2.3	0.13	2.0	−0.27	D −	1
			1134.98	0.0	88110	4	6	2.2	0.064	0.95	−0.59	D −	1
			1134.42	0.0	88153	4	4	2.5	0.048	0.72	−0.71	D −	1, *ls*
			1134.17	0.0	88173	4	2	2.5	0.024	0.36	−1.02	D −	1, *ls*
2	$2p^3 -$ $2p^2(^3P)3s$	$^4S° - {}^4P$ (1 uv)	*1199.9*	0.0	*83336*	4	12	5.4	0.35	5.5	0.15	D −	1
			1199.55	0.0	83366	4	6	5.5	0.18	2.8	−0.15	D −	1
			1200.22	0.0	83319	4	4	5.3	0.11	1.8	−0.34	D −	1
			1200.71	0.0	83286	4	2	5.5	0.059	0.94	−0.62	D −	1
3		$^2D° - {}^2P$ (4 uv)	*1493.3*	19228	*86193*	10	6	5.5	0.11	5.4	0.04	D	1
			1492.62	19224	86221	6	4	5.3	0.12	3.5	−0.15	D	1, *ls*
			1494.67	19233	86138	4	2	5.0	0.084	1.6	−0.48	D	1
			1492.67	19233	86221	4	4	0.58	0.019	0.38	−1.11	D	1, *ls*
4		$^2P° - {}^2P$ (9 uv)	*1743.6*	28840	*86193*	6	6	2.0	0.091	3.1	−0.26	D	1
			1742.73	28840	86221	4	4	1.8	0.082	1.9	−0.48	D	1, *ls*
			1745.25	28840	86138	2	2	1.3	0.059	0.68	−0.93	D	1, *ls*
			1745.26	28840	86138	4	2	0.65	0.015	0.34	−1.23	D	1, *ls*
			1742.72	28840	86221	2	4	0.35	0.032	0.37	−1.20	D	1, *ls*
5	$2p^3 -$ $2p^2(^1D)3s'$	$^2D° - {}^2D$ (5 uv)	*1243.3*	19228	*99663*	10	10	4.6	0.11	4.4	0.03	D	1
			1243.17	19224	99663	6	6	4.3	0.10	2.4	−0.22	D	*ls*
			1243.30	19233	99663	4	4	4.3	0.10	1.6	−0.40	D	*ls*
			1243.17	19224	99663	6	4	0.45	0.0070	0.17	−1.38	D	*ls*
			1243.31	19233	99663	4	6	0.30	0.010	0.17	−1.38	D	*ls*
6		$^2P° - {}^2D$ (10 uv)	1411.94	28840	99663	6	10	0.52	0.026	0.72	−0.81	D	1
7	$2s2p^4 -$ $2s^22p^2(^3P)3p$	$^4P - {}^4S°$ (12)	*11602*	*88135*	96752	12	4	0.0405	0.0273	12.5	−0.485	C	2
			11564.8	88110	96752	6	4	0.0210	0.0280	6.4	−0.77	C	2, *ls*
			11628.0	88153	96752	4	4	0.0130	0.0264	4.04	−0.98	C	2, *ls*
			11656.0	88173	96752	2	4	0.0066	0.0267	2.05	−1.272	C	2, *ls*
8	$2p^3 -$ $2p^2(^3P)3d$	$^2D° - {}^4F$											
			1169.69	19224	104718	6	8	0.030	8.2×10^{-4}	0.019	−2.31	D	1
9		$^2D° - {}^2F$ (6 uv)	*1167.9*	19228	*104852*	10	14	1.2	0.034	1.3	−0.46	D	1
			1167.45	19224	104883	6	8	1.1	0.030	0.69	−0.75	D	1
			1168.54	19233	104811	4	6	1.3	0.040	0.61	−0.80	D	1, *ls*
			1168.42	19224	104811	6	6	0.095	0.0019	0.045	−1.93	D	1, *ls*
10		$^2D° - {}^2D$ (7 uv)	*1164.0*	19228	*105135*	10	10	0.47	0.0095	0.37	−1.02	D	1
			1163.88	19224	105144	6	6	0.43	0.0087	0.20	−1.28	D	*ls*
			1164.31	19233	105121	4	4	0.43	0.0087	0.13	−1.46	D	*ls*
			1164.31	19224	105121	6	4	0.048	6.5×10^{-4}	0.015	−2.41	D	*ls*
			1163.87	19233	105144	4	6	0.032	9.7×10^{-4}	0.015	−2.41	D	*ls*
11		$^2P° - {}^2P$ (12 uv)	*1319.5*	28840	*104628*	6	6	1.3	0.034	0.88	−0.69	D	1
			1319.72	28840	104615	4	4	1.1	0.029	0.50	−0.94	D	1, *ls*
			1319.04	28840	104655	2	2	0.85	0.022	0.19	−1.35	D	1, *ls*
			1319.04	28840	104655	4	2	0.42	0.0055	0.095	−1.66	D	1, *ls*
			1319.72	28840	104615	2	4	0.22	0.011	0.10	−1.64	D	1, *ls*

No.	Transition Array	Multiplet	λ(Å)	E_i(cm^{-1})	E_k(cm^{-1})	g_i	g_k	A_{ki}(10^8 sec^{-1})	f_{ik}	S(at.u.)	log gf	Accuracy	Source
12		^{2}P$^\circ$ — ^{2}F	1316.29	28840	104811	4	6	0.025	9.6×10^{-4}	0.017	-2.42	D	1
13		^{2}P$^\circ$ — ^{2}D (13 uv)	1310.7	28840	105135	6	10	1.3	0.056	1.4	-0.48	D	1
			1310.54	28840	105144	4	6	1.3	0.050	0.87	-0.70	D	ls
			1310.97	28840	105121	2	4	1.1	0.057	0.49	-0.95	D	ls
			1310.97	28840	105121	4	4	0.23	0.0059	0.10	-1.63	D	ls
14	$2p^3$ — $2p^2(^3$P$)4s$	^{2}D$^\circ$ — ^{2}P	1176.9	19228	104199	10	6	1.1	0.014	0.53	-0.86	D	1
			[1176.4]	19224	104227	6	4	0.95	0.013	0.31	-1.10	D	1, ls
			[1177.7]	19233	104142	4	2	1.3	0.014	0.21	-1.27	D	1
			[1176.6]	19233	104227	4	4	0.11	0.0023	0.035	-2.04	D	1, ls
15		^{2}P$^\circ$ — ^{2}P (11 uv)	1327.0	28840	104199	6	6	0.20	0.0053	0.14	-1.50	D	1
			1326.63	28840	104227	4	4	0.15	0.0040	0.069	-1.80	D	1, ls
			1327.96	28840	104142	2	2	0.17	0.0045	0.039	-2.05	D	1, ls
			1327.96	28840	104142	4	2	0.085	0.0011	0.020	-2.35	D	1, ls
			1326.63	28840	104227	2	4	0.030	0.0016	0.014	-2.50	D	1, ls
16	$2s2p^4$ — $2s^22p^2(^3$P$)4p$	^{4}P — ^{4}D$^\circ$ (13)	5349.0	88135	106825	12	20	0.00252	0.00180	0.380	-1.67	C	2
			5328.70	88110	106871	6	8	0.00254	0.00144	0.152	-2.062	C	3n, ls
			5356.77	88153	106816	4	6	0.00189	0.00122	0.086	-2.312	C	3n, ls
			5372.66	88173	106780	2	4	0.00107	9.3×10^{-4}	0.0328	-2.73	C	3n, ls
			[5344.4]	88110	106816	6	6	6.2×10^{-4}	2.64×10^{-4}	0.0279	-2.80	C	3n, ls
			[5367.1]	88153	106780	4	4	0.00118	5.1×10^{-4}	0.0361	-2.69	C	3n, ls
			[5378.3]	88173	106761	2	2	0.00210	9.1×10^{-4}	0.0323	-2.74	C	3n, ls
			[5354.7]	88110	106780	6	4	1.35×10^{-4}	3.88×10^{-5}	0.00410	-3.63	C	3n, ls
			[5372.5]	88153	106761	4	2	4.31×10^{-4}	9.3×10^{-5}	0.0066	-3.428	C	3n, ls
17		^{4}P — ^{4}P$^\circ$ (14)	5294.9	88135	107016	12	12	0.00373	0.00157	0.328	-1.73	C	2
			5281.18	88110	107039	6	6	0.00282	0.00118	0.123	-2.150	C	3n, ls
			[5305.0]	88153	106998	4	4	5.3×10^{-4}	2.23×10^{-4}	0.0156	-3.049	C	3n, ls
			[5314.8]	88173	106983	2	2	6.9×10^{-4}	2.91×10^{-4}	0.0102	-3.234	C	3n, ls
			[5292.9]	88110	106998	6	4	0.00167	4.68×10^{-4}	0.0489	-2.55	C	3n, ls
			[5309.2]	88153	106983	4	2	0.00273	5.8×10^{-4}	0.0403	-2.64	C	3n, ls
			[5293.5]	88153	107039	4	6	0.00113	7.1×10^{-4}	0.0495	-2.55	C	3n, ls
			[5310.6]	88173	106998	2	4	0.00137	0.00116	0.0404	-2.64	C	3n, ls
18		^{4}P — ^{4}S$^\circ$	5176.7	88135	107447	12	4	0.00427	5.7×10^{-4}	0.117	-2.163	C	2
			[5170.0]	88110	107447	6	4	0.00209	5.6×10^{-4}	0.057	-2.475	C	3n, ls
			[5181.5]	88153	107447	4	4	0.00144	5.8×10^{-4}	0.0395	-2.64	C	3n, ls
			[5186.9]	88173	107447	2	4	7.3×10^{-4}	5.9×10^{-4}	0.0201	-2.93	C	3n, ls
19	$2p^3$ — $2p^2(^3$P$)5s$	^{2}D$^\circ$ — ^{2}P	1100.7	19228	110082	10	6	0.33	0.0036	0.13	-1.44	D$-$	1
20		^{2}P$^\circ$ — ^{2}P	[1231.7]	28840	110029	2	2	0.022	5.0×10^{-4}	0.0041	-2.99	D	1, ls
			[1231.7]	28840	110029	4	2	0.011	1.3×10^{-4}	0.0020	-3.30	D	1, ls
21	$2p^23s$ — $2p^2(^3$P$)3p$	^{4}P — ^{4}D$^\circ$ (1)	8691.6	83337	94839	12	20	0.190	0.358	123	0.63	C	2
			8680.27	83366	94883	6	8	0.191	0.287	49.2	0.236	C	2, ls
			8683.40	83319	94832	4	6	0.133	0.226	25.8	-0.045	C	2, ls
			8686.16	83286	94795	2	4	0.079	0.178	10.2	-0.448	C	2, ls
			8718.84	83366	94832	6	6	0.054	0.062	10.6	-0.433	C	2, ls
			8711.71	83319	94795	4	4	0.101	0.115	13.2	-0.337	C	2, ls
			8703.26	83286	94772	2	2	0.171	0.194	11.1	-0.412	C	2, ls
			8747.36	83366	94795	6	4	0.0079	0.0061	1.05	-1.438	C	2, ls
			8728.91	83319	94772	4	2	0.0300	0.0171	1.97	-1.164	C	2, ls

No.	Transition Array	Multiplet	λ(Å)	E_i(cm⁻¹)	E_k(cm⁻¹)	g_i	g_k	A_{ki}(10⁸ sec⁻¹)	f_{ik}	S(at.u.)	log gf	Accuracy	Source
22		⁴P — ⁴P° (2)	*8211.8*	*83337*	*95511*	12	12	0.228	0.231	75	0.443	C	2, 5
			8216.32	83366	95533	6	6	0.160	0.162	26.3	−0.012	C	2n, ls
			8210.71	83319	95495	4	4	0.0363	0.0367	3.97	−0.83	C	2n, ls
			8200.36	83286	95477	2	2	0.0364	0.0367	1.98	−1.135	C	2n, ls
			8242.37	83366	95495	6	4	0.102	0.069	11.3	−0.381	C	2n, ls
			8223.12	83319	95477	4	2	0.202	0.103	11.1	−0.387	C	2n, ls
			8184.85	83319	95533	4	6	0.063	0.096	10.3	−0.418	C	2n, ls
			8188.01	83286	95495	2	4	0.092	0.185	10.0	−0.431	C	2n, ls
23		⁴P — ⁴S° (3)	*7452.2*	*83337*	*96752*	12	4	0.318	0.088	26.0	0.025	C	2, 5
			7468.31	83366	96752	6	4	0.161	0.089	13.2	−0.270	C	2n, ls
			7442.30	83319	96752	4	4	0.106	0.088	8.6	−0.454	C	2n, ls
			7423.64	83286	96752	2	4	0.052	0.086	4.21	−0.76	C	2n, ls
24		²P — ²D° (7)	*9395.3*	*86193*	*96834*	6	10	0.217	0.478	89	0.458	C	2
			9392.79	86221	96864	4	6	0.218	0.432	53	0.237	C	2, ls
			9386.81	86138	96788	2	4	0.183	0.482	29.8	−0.016	C	2, ls
			9460.68	86221	96788	4	4	0.0334	0.0449	5.6	−0.75	C	2, ls
25		²P — ²P° (8)	*8617.5*	*86193*	*97794*	6	6	0.286	0.318	54	0.281	C	2
			8629.24	86221	97806	4	4	0.238	0.266	30.2	0.027	C	2, ls
			8590.01	86138	97770	2	2	0.190	0.210	11.9	−0.376	C	2, ls
			8655.87	86221	97770	4	2	0.099	0.056	6.3	−0.65	C	2, ls
			8567.74	86138	97806	2	4	0.0458	0.101	5.7	−0.70	C	2, ls
26	2p²(³P)3s — 2p(¹D)3p′	²P — ²D° (10)	*4106.8*	*86193*	*110536*	6	10	0.041	0.017	1.4	−0.98	D	3n
			4109.96	86221	110546	4	6	0.040	0.015	0.83	−1.21	D	ls
			4099.95	86138	110522	2	4	0.034	0.017	0.46	−1.47	D	ls
			4113.97	86221	110522	4	4	0.0068	0.0017	0.093	−2.16	D	ls
27	2p²3s′ — 2p²(¹D)3p′	²D — ²F°	*9047.6*	*99663*	*110713*	10	14	0.272	0.467	139	0.669	B	2, 6, ca
			9045.88	99663	110715	6	8	0.269	0.439	78.5	0.421	B	2n, ls
			9049.89	99663	110711	4	6	0.258	0.475	56.6	0.279	B	2n, ls
			9049.47	99663	110711	6	6	0.0180	0.0222	3.96	−0.876	B	2n, ls
28	2p²3s — 2p²(³P)4p	⁴P — ⁴D° (4)	*4256.3*	*83337*	*106825*	12	20	0.020	0.0089	1.5	−0.97	E	6
			4253.28	83366	106871	6	8	0.020	0.0071	0.60	−1.37	E	ls
			4254.7	83319	106816	4	6	0.014	0.0057	0.32	−1.64	E	ls
			4254.7	83286	106780	2	4	0.0079	0.0043	0.12	−2.07	E	ls
			[4263.2]	83366	106816	6	6	0.0061	0.0017	0.14	−2.00	E	ls
			[4261.2]	83319	106780	4	4	0.010	0.0029	0.16	−1.94	E	ls
			[4258.7]	83286	106761	2	2	0.016	0.0043	0.12	−2.07	E	ls
			[4269.8]	83366	106780	6	4	9.8 × 10⁻⁴	1.8 × 10⁻⁴	0.015	−2.97	E	ls
			[4264.7]	83319	106761	4	2	0.0033	4.5 × 10⁻⁴	0.025	−2.75	E	ls
29		⁴P — ⁴P° (5)	*4222.0*	*83337*	*107016*	12	12	0.073	0.020	3.3	−0.63	D	3n
			4223.04	83366	107039	6	6	0.051	0.014	1.1	−1.09	D	ls
			4222.12	83319	106998	4	4	0.0098	0.0026	0.15	−1.98	D	ls
			4218.87	83286	106983	2	2	0.012	0.0033	0.091	−2.18	D	ls
			4230.35	83366	106998	6	4	0.033	0.0059	0.49	−1.45	D	ls
			4224.74	83319	106983	4	2	0.061	0.0082	0.45	−1.49	D	ls
			4214.73	83319	107039	4	6	0.022	0.0088	0.49	−1.45	D	ls
			4215.92	83286	106998	2	4	0.031	0.016	0.45	−1.49	D	ls
30		⁴P — ⁴S° (6)	*4146.3*	*83337*	*107447*	12	4	0.025	0.0021	0.35	−1.59	D	3n
			4151.46	83366	107447	6	4	0.013	0.0023	0.19	−1.87	D	3n, ls
			4143.42	83319	107447	4	4	0.0078	0.0020	0.11	−2.09	D	3n, ls
			4137.63	83286	107447	2	4	0.0039	0.0020	0.055	−2.40	D	3n, ls

No.	Transition Array	Multiplet	λ(Å)	E_i(cm⁻¹)	E_k(cm⁻¹)	g_i	g_k	A_{ki}(10⁸ sec⁻¹)	f_{ik}	S(at.u.)	log gf	Accuracy	Source
31		²P – ²S° (9)	*4928.2*	*86193*	*106479*	6	2	0.0234	0.00285	0.277	−1.768	B	2, 4
			4935.03	86221	106479	4	2	0.0158	0.00289	0.188	−1.937	B	4n, ls
			4914.90	86138	106479	2	2	0.00759	0.00275	0.0889	−2.260	B	4n, ls
32	2p²(³P)3p – 2p²(¹S)3s″	²P° – ²S	*5408.4*	*97794*	*116279*	6	2	0.0111	0.00162	0.173	−2.013	C	2
			5411.88	97806	116279	4	2	0.0075	0.00164	0.117	−2.183	C	2, ls
			5401.45	97770	116279	2	2	0.00369	0.00161	0.057	−2.491	C	2, ls
33	2p²3p – 2p²(³P)3d	²S° – ²P (15)	*9050.4*	*93582*	*104628*	2	6	0.256	0.945	56.3	0.276	B	2, 6, ca
			9060.72	93582	104615	2	4	0.257	0.634	37.8	0.103	B	2n, ls
			9028.92	93582	104655	2	2	0.255	0.311	18.5	−0.206	B	2n, ls
34		⁴D° – ⁴F (18)	*10117*	*94839*	*104721*	20	28	0.373	0.802	534	1.205	B	2, 6, ca
			10114.6	94883	104767	8	10	0.374	0.717	191	0.759	B	ls
			10112.5	94832	104718	6	8	0.321	0.656	131	0.595	B	ls
			10108.9	94795	104684	4	6	0.281	0.646	86.0	0.412	B	ls
			10105.1	94772	104665	2	4	0.262	0.803	53.4	0.206	B	ls
			10164.8	94883	104718	8	8	0.0523	0.0811	21.7	−0.188	B	ls
			10147.3	94832	104684	6	6	0.0898	0.139	27.8	−0.080	B	ls
			10128.3	94795	104665	4	4	0.104	0.160	21.4	−0.193	B	ls
			10200.0	94883	104684	8	6	0.00353	0.00413	1.11	−1.481	B	ls
			10166.8	94832	104665	6	4	0.00737	0.00762	1.53	−1.340	B	ls
35		⁴D° – ⁴D (19)	*9829.2*	*94839*	*105010*	20	20	0.0992	0.144	93.0	0.458	B	2, 6, ca
			9863.33	94883	105020	8	8	0.101	0.147	38.1	0.069	B	2n, ls
			9822.75	94832	105011	6	6	0.0542	0.0783	15.2	−0.328	B	2n
			9798.57	94795	104998	4	4	0.0346	0.0498	6.42	−0.701	B	2n
			9788.30	94772	104987	2	2	0.0310	0.0445	2.87	−1.050	B	2n, ls
			9872.16	94883	105011	8	6	0.0222	0.0243	6.33	−0.711	B	2n, ls
			9834.62	94832	104998	6	4	0.0461	0.0445	8.65	−0.573	B	2n
			9810.02	94795	104987	4	2	0.0415	0.0300	3.87	−0.921	B	2n, ls
			9814.03	94832	105020	6	8	0.0118	0.0227	4.41	−0.865	B	2n, ls
			9786.79	94795	105011	4	6	0.0144	0.0311	4.01	−0.905	B	2n, ls
			9776.90	94772	104998	2	4	0.0177	0.0506	3.26	−0.995	B	2n
36		⁴P° – ⁴F										C	
			10884.6	95533	104718	6	8	0.00141	0.00335	0.72	−1.70	C	2
			10879.2	95495	104684	4	6	0.00160	0.00426	0.61	−1.77	C	2
37		⁴P° – ²F											
			10693.2	95533	104883	6	8	0.00402	0.0092	1.94	−1.259	C	2
			10730.5	95495	104811	4	6	0.0170	0.0440	6.2	−0.75	C	2
			10775.0	95533	104811	6	6	0.00421	0.0073	1.56	−1.357	C	2
38		⁴P° – ⁴P	*10708*	*95511*	*104847*	12	12	0.126	0.216	91.5	0.414	B	2, 6, ca
			10757.9	95533	104825	6	6	0.0868	0.151	32.0	−0.044	B	ls
			[10675]	95495	104860	4	4	0.0169	0.0289	4.06	−0.937	B	ls
			10623.2	95477	104886	2	2	0.0215	0.0363	2.54	−1.139	B	ls
			10718.0	95533	104860	6	4	0.0564	0.0647	13.7	−0.411	B	ls
			10644.0	95495	104886	4	2	0.107	0.0906	12.7	−0.441	B	ls
			10713.6	95495	104825	4	6	0.0376	0.0971	13.7	−0.411	B	ls
			10653.0	95477	104860	2	4	0.0532	0.181	12.7	−0.441	B	ls
39		⁴P° – ⁴D (28)	*10525*	*95511*	*105010*	12	20	0.248	0.688	286	0.917	B	2, 6, ca
			10539.6	95533	105020	6	8	0.242	0.538	112	0.509	B	2n, ls
			10507.0	95495	105011	4	6	0.132	0.327	45.2	0.116	B	2n
			10500.3	95477	104998	2	4	0.0652	0.216	14.9	−0.366	B	2n
			10549.6	95533	105011	6	6	0.126	0.210	43.8	0.101	B	2n

No.	Transition Array	Multiplet	λ(Å)	E_i(cm^{-1})	E_k(cm^{-1})	g_i	g_k	A_{ki}(10^8 sec^{-1})	f_{ik}	S(at.u.)	log gf	Accuracy	Source
39	(con.)		10520.6	95495	104998	4	4	0.162	0.269	37.2	0.031	B	2n
			10513.4	95477	104987	2	2	0.174	0.289	20.0	−0.238	B	2n
			10563.3	95533	104998	6	4	0.0369	0.0411	8.58	−0.608	B	2n
			10533.8	95495	104987	4	2	0.0405	0.0337	4.67	−0.871	B	2n, ls
40		$^4S°-^4P$ (34)	12350	96752	104847	4	12	0.124	0.85	138	0.53	C	6, ca
			[12384]	96752	104825	4	6	0.123	0.423	69	0.229	C	ls
			[12330]	96752	104860	4	4	0.124	0.283	46.0	0.054	C	ls
			[12291]	96752	104886	4	2	0.125	0.142	23.0	−0.245	C	ls
41		$^2D°-^2F$ (36)	12469	96834	104852	10	14	0.216	0.71	290	0.85	C	6, ca
			12467.8	96864	104883	6	8	0.217	0.67	166	0.61	C	ls
			12461.2	96788	104811	4	6	0.202	0.71	116	0.451	C	ls
			12582.3	96864	104811	6	6	0.0141	0.0334	8.3	−0.70	C	ls
42		$^2D°-^2D$ (37)	12043	96834	105135	10	10	0.060	0.130	52	0.114	C	6, ca
			12074.1	96864	105144	6	6	0.055	0.121	28.8	−0.140	C	ls
			11997.9	96788	105121	4	4	0.054	0.117	18.5	−0.329	C	ls
			12107.4	96864	105121	6	4	0.0059	0.0086	2.06	−1.287	C	ls
			[11964]	96788	105144	4	6	0.00406	0.0131	2.06	−1.282	C	ls
43	2p^2(^{3}P)3p − 2p^2(^{1}D)3d′	$^2P°-^2S$	4389.1	97794	120572	6	2	0.0153	0.00148	0.128	−2.053	C	2
			[4391.3]	97806	120572	4	2	0.0102	0.00147	0.085	−2.231	C	2, ls
			[4384.4]	97770	120572	2	2	0.0052	0.00151	0.0435	−2.52	C	2, ls
44	2p^{2}3p′ − 2p^2(^{1}D)3d′	$^2F°-^2G$	10595	110713	120149	14	18	0.338	0.731	357	1.010	B	2, 6, ca
			10597.0	110715	120149	8	10	0.337	0.709	198	0.754	B	ls
			10591.9	110711	120150	6	8	0.326	0.731	153	0.642	B	ls
			[10596]	110715	120150	8	8	0.0121	0.0204	5.68	−0.788	B	ls
45	2p^{2}3p − 2p^2(^{3}P)4s	$^4D°-^4P$ (17)	11290	94839	103694	20	12	0.147	0.168	125	0.527	C+	2, 6, ca
			11291.7	94883	103737	8	6	0.117	0.168	50.0	0.129	C+	ls
			11313.9	94832	103668	6	4	0.0920	0.118	26.3	−0.151	C+	ls
			11323.2	94795	103618	4	2	0.0726	0.0697	10.4	−0.554	C+	ls
			11227.1	94832	103737	6	6	0.0270	0.0510	11.3	−0.515	C+	ls
			11266.2	94795	103668	4	4	0.475	0.0903	13.4	−0.442	C+	ls
			11294.2	94772	103618	2	2	0.0731	0.140	10.4	−0.553	C+	ls
			11180.1	94795	103737	4	6	0.00302	0.00849	1.25	−1.469	C+	ls
			11237.6	94772	103668	2	4	0.00746	0.0282	2.09	−1.248	C+	ls
46		$^4P°-^4P$ (27)	12217	95511	103694	12	12	0.076	0.171	83	0.312	C	6, ca
			12186.9	95533	103737	6	6	0.054	0.119	28.7	−0.146	C	ls
			12232.9	95495	103668	4	4	0.0101	0.0226	3.64	−1.044	C	ls
			[12280]	95477	103618	2	2	0.0125	0.0282	2.28	−1.249	C	ls
			12288.0	95533	103668	6	4	0.0336	0.051	12.3	−0.52	C	ls
			[12307]	95495	103618	4	2	0.062	0.070	11.4	−0.55	C	ls
			12128.6	95495	103737	4	6	0.0233	0.077	12.3	−0.51	C	ls
			12203.4	95477	103668	2	4	0.0318	0.142	11.4	−0.55	C	ls
47	2p^{2}3p − 2p^2(^{3}P)5s	$^4D°-^4P$ (20)	6644.0	94839	109886	20	12	0.0389	0.0154	6.8	−0.51	C	6, ca
			6644.96	94883	109928	8	6	0.0311	0.0154	2.70	−0.91	C	ls
			6653.46	94832	109858	6	4	0.0244	0.0108	1.42	−1.188	C	ls
			6656.51	94795	109814	4	2	0.0193	0.0064	0.56	−1.59	C	ls
			6622.54	94832	109928	6	6	0.0071	0.00465	0.61	−1.55	C	ls
			6636.94	94795	109858	4	4	0.0125	0.0083	0.72	−1.481	C	ls
			6646.51	94772	109814	2	2	0.0194	0.0128	0.56	−1.59	C	ls
			[6606.3]	94795	109928	4	6	7.9 × 10^{-4}	7.8 × 10^{-4}	0.068	−2.51	C	ls
			[6626.8]	94772	109858	2	4	0.00197	0.00259	0.113	−2.286	C	ls

No.	Transition Array	Multiplet	λ(Å)	E_i(cm⁻¹)	E_k(cm⁻¹)	g_i	g_k	A_{ki}(10⁸ sec⁻¹)	f_{ik}	S(at.u.)	log gf	Accuracy	Source
48		⁴P°—⁴P (29)	6954.6	95511	109886	12	12	0.0212	0.0154	4.22	−0.73	C	6, ca
			6945.22	95533	109928	6	6	0.0149	0.0108	1.48	−1.189	C	ls
			[6960.4]	95495	109858	4	4	0.00281	0.00204	0.187	−2.088	C	ls
			[6973.0]	95477	109814	2	2	0.00350	0.00255	0.117	−2.293	C	ls
			6979.10	95533	109858	6	4	0.0094	0.00459	0.63	−1.56	C	ls
			[6981.8]	95495	109814	4	2	0.0174	0.0064	0.59	−1.59	C	ls
			6926.90	95495	109928	4	6	0.0064	0.0069	0.63	−1.56	C	ls
			[6951.7]	95477	109858	2	4	0.0088	0.0128	0.59	−1.59	C	ls
49	2p²3p — 2p²(³P)5d	²S°—²P	5200.5	93582	112806	2	6	0.023	0.028	0.96	−1.25	D	3n
			[5201.8]	93582	112801	2	4	0.023	0.019	0.64	−1.43	D	ls
			[5197.8]	93582	112816	2	2	0.023	0.0094	0.32	−1.73	D	ls
50	2p²3p — 2p²(³P)6s	⁴P°—⁴P (32)	5836.4	95511	112640	12	12	0.0092	0.00468	1.08	−1.250	C	6, ca
			5829.53	95533	112683	6	6	0.0064	0.00328	0.378	−1.71	C	ls
			5841.01	95495	112611	4	4	0.00122	6.2×10⁻⁴	0.0480	−2.60	C	ls
			[5850.1]	95477	112566	2	2	0.00152	7.8×10⁻⁴	0.0300	−2.81	C	ls
			5854.16	95511	112611	6	4	0.00409	0.00140	0.162	−2.075	C	ls
			[5856.3]	95495	112566	4	2	0.0076	0.00195	0.150	−2.109	C	ls
			5816.48	95495	112683	4	6	0.00278	0.00212	0.162	−2.073	C	ls
			[5834.7]	95477	112611	2	4	0.00383	0.00390	0.150	−2.107	C	ls

Forbidden Transitions

For this ion we have performed the numerical calculations by utilizing Ufford and Gilmour's [1] values for the parameters ζ and η and empirical term intervals, and by employing the general expressions of Shortley, Aller, Baker, and Menzel [2] for the line strengths in the p^3 configuration (see also general introduction). For the electric quadrupole lines we have employed Garstang's [3] estimate of the quadrupole integral s_q. For the ²D°—²D° transition a difference between the transition probability quoted by Garstang [4] and the tabulated value will be noticed. This is due to a revised experimental value for the term interval as given by Bowen [5].

References

[1] Ufford, C. W., and Gilmour, R. M., Astrophys. J. **111**, 580–581 (1950).
[2] Shortley, G. H., Aller, L. H., Baker, J. G., and Menzel, D. H., Astrophys. J. **93**, 178–184 (1941).
[3] Garstang, R. H., Astrophys. J. **115**, 506–508 (1952).
[4] Garstang, R. H., "The Airglow and the Aurora," p. 324 (ed. Armstrong and Dalgarno, Pergamon Press, New York, 1956).
[5] Bowen, I. S., Astrophys. J. **121**, 306 (1955).

N I. Forbidden Transitions

No.	Transition Array	Multiplet	λ(Å)	E_i(cm⁻¹)	E_k(cm⁻¹)	g_i	g_k	Type of Transition	A_{ki}(sec⁻¹)	S(at.u.)	Accuracy	Source
1	2p³ — 2p³	⁴S°—²D° (1 F)										
			5200.7	0	19223.9	4	6	m	7.4×10⁻⁷	2.32×10⁻⁸	C	1
			5200.7	0	19223.9	4	6	e	6.2×10⁻⁶	8.4×10⁻⁵	D	1, 2
			5198.5	0	19233.1	4	4	m	1.23×10⁻⁵	2.55×10⁻⁷	C	1
			5198.5	0	19233.1	4	4	e	4.0×10⁻⁶	3.6×10⁻⁵	D	1, 2
2		⁴S°—²P° (2 F)										
			3466.4	0	28840	4	4	m	0.0062	3.82×10⁻⁵	C	1
			3466.4	0	28840	4	4	e	3.4×10⁻⁸	4.1×10⁻⁸	D	1, 2
			3466.4	0	28840	4	2	m	0.00247	7.6×10⁻⁶	C	1
			3466.4	0	28840	4	2	e	1.1×10⁻⁷	6.4×10⁻⁸	D	1, 2

No.	Transition Array	Multiplet	λ(Å)	E_i(cm⁻¹)	E_k(cm⁻¹)	g_i	g_k	Type of Transition	A_{ki}(sec⁻¹)	S(at.u.)	Accuracy	Source
3		$^2D° — ^2D°$	[10.9 × 10⁶]	19223.9	19233.1	6	4	m	1.25 × 10⁻⁸	2.40	B	1
			[10.9 × 10⁶]	19223.9	19233.1	6	4	e	2.4 × 10⁻²²	8.9 × 10⁻⁵	D	1, 2
4		$^2D° — ^2P°$ (3 F)										
			10395.4	19223.9	28840	6	4	m	9.3 × 10⁻⁴	1.55 × 10⁻⁴	C	1
			10395.4	19223.9	28840	6	4	e	0.054	15.6	C	1, 2
			10395.4	19223.9	28840	6	2	e	0.0308	4.45	C	1, 2
			10404.1	19233.1	28840	4	4	m	0.00165	2.75 × 10⁻⁴	C	1
			10404.1	19233.1	28840	4	4	e	0.0230	6.7	C	1, 2
			10404.1	19233.1	28840	4	2	m	0.00103	8.6 × 10⁻⁵	C	1
			10404.1	19233.1	28840	4	2	e	0.0460	6.7	C	1, 2

N II

Ground State$\qquad\qquad\qquad\qquad\qquad\qquad\qquad\qquad\qquad\qquad$ $1s^2\,2s^2\,2p^2\,{}^3P_0$

Ionization Potential$\qquad\qquad\qquad\qquad\qquad\qquad\qquad$ 29.593 eV = 238751.1 cm⁻¹

Allowed Transitions

List of tabulated lines:

Wavelength [Å]	No.	Wavelength [Å]	No.	Wavelength [Å]	No.
529.343	10	745.836	6	2493.94	47
529.405	10	746.976	8	2496.88	47
529.481	10	775.957	4	2520.27	46
529.627	10	915.603	2	2520.85	46
529.713	10	915.955	2	2522.27	46
529.860	10	916.004	2	2522.46	46
533.504	9	916.700	2	2524.49	46
533.51	9	1083.98	1	2526.17	46
533.577	9	1084.57	1	2709.82	49
533.644	9	1085.5	1	2799.20	48
533.726	9	1085.54	1	3006.86	38
533.809	9	1085.70	1	3023.80	50
572.07	13	1886.82	24	3311.4	39
574.650	12	2206.10	44	3318.14	39
582.150	11	2316.46	45	3324.58	39
635.180	14	2316.65	45	3328.79	39
644.621	3	2317.01	45	3330.30	39
644.825	3	2319.94	45	3331.32	39
645.167	3	2321.65	45	3437.16	20
660.280	5	2325.16	45	3593.60	40
671.014	7	2461.30	51	3609.09	40
671.391	7	2488.12	47	3615.88	40
671.629	7	2488.75	47	3829.80	41
671.770	7	2490.37	47	3838.39	41
671.999	7	2493.16	47	3842.20	41

Wavelength [Å]	No.	Wavelength [Å]	No.	Wavelength [Å]	No.
3847.38	41	5012.03	22	5941.67	31
3855.08	41	5016.39	27	5952.39	31
3856.07	41	5023.11	22	5954.28	60
3919.01	26	5025.67	27	5960.93	31
3995.00	19	5040.76	27	6114.6	52
4026.08	62	5045.10	16	6136.89	52
4040.9	61	5104.45	43	6150.76	52
4124.08	23	5168.24	37	6167.82	52
4133.67	23	5170.08	37	6170.16	52
4145.76	23	5171.30	37	6173.40	52
4176.16	63	5171.46	37	6242.52	59
4227.75	42	5172.32	35	6284.30	34
4239.4	64	5173.37	35	6318.80	55
4417.9	65	5174.46	37	6328.39	55
4427.97	65	5175.89	35	6340.57	55
4431.82	65	5176.56	37	6346.86	55
4432.74	65	5177.06	35	6356.55	55
4433.48	65	5179.50	35	6357.57	55
4441.99	65	5179.50	37	6482.07	18
4447.03	25	5180.34	35	6491.79	54
4459.96	29	5183.21	37	6504.61	54
4465.54	29	5184.96	35	6522.39	54
4475.8	29	5186.17	37	6532.55	54
4477.74	29	5190.42	35	6544.16	54
4488.15	29	5191.97	35	6545.53	54
4507.56	29	5199.50	35	6554.47	54
4530.40	67	5313.43	36	6610.58	33
4552.54	66	5320.96	36	6629.80	53
4601.48	17	5327.45	36	6809.99	58
4607.16	17	5338.66	36	6834.09	58
4613.87	17	5340.20	36	6847.24	58
4621.39	17	5351.21	36	6941.75	57
4630.54	17	5452.12	32	6966.81	57
4643.09	17	5454.26	32	6975.64	57
4677.93	68	5462.62	32	7003.0	57
4774.22	28	5478.13	32	7013.98	57
4779.71	28	5480.10	32	7014.73	57
4781.17	28	5495.70	32	7138.87	56
4788.13	28	5526.26	21	7188.20	56
4793.66	28	5530.27	21	7214.6	56
4803.27	28	5535.39	21	7215.06	56
4810.29	28	5540.16	21	7241.8	56
4987.38	30	5543.49	21	7256.53	56
4991.22	22	5551.95	21		
4994.36	22	5552.54	21		
4994.36	30	5565.30	21		
4997.23	22	5666.64	15		
5001.13	27	5676.02	15		
5001.47	27	5679.56	15		
5002.69	16	5686.21	15		
5005.14	22	5710.76	15		
5005.14	27	5730.67	15		
5007.32	30	5927.82	31		
5010.62	16	5931.79	31		
5011.24	22	5940.25	31		

Data for the vacuum ultraviolet region of the spectrum are available from calculations of Bolotin et al. [1] and Kelly [2]. Bolotin et al. employ a "double configuration" approximation, i.e., they include to a first approximation the effects of configuration interaction which are expected to be drastic for these transitions. Kelly's calculations, in which these effects are neglected, are only used for some vacuum uv transitions for which configuration interaction is expected to be less pronounced. Nevertheless, his results may be quite uncertain. For higher excited lines, mainly in the visible, experimental work with a high current stabilized arc by Mastrup and Wiese [3] compares very well with approximate self-consistent field calculations by Kelly [4] and the Coulomb approximation. All these methods have been equally weighted in arriving at averaged values. However, the Coulomb approximation shows strong cancellation effects for $3s-4p$ and $3p-4d$ transitions and is not used there. Kelly's calculations, which seem to be less affected as judged from his fairly high ratios between the positive and negative contributions to the transition integrals, are exclusively used in these cases. For some multiplets with high azimuthal quantum numbers in the $3d-4f$ array (D-F and F-G) only multiplet values and no line values are listed, since intensity measurements by Eriksson [5] indicate considerable deviations from LS coupling and a transition to pair coupling.

References

[1] Bolotin, A. B., Levinson, I. B., and Levin, L. I., Soviet Phys.—JETP **2**, 391–395 (1956).
[2] Kelly, P. S., Astrophys. J. **140**, 1247–1268 (1964).
[3] Mastrup, F., and Wiese, W., Z. Astrophys. **44**, 259–279 (1958).
[4] Kelly, P. S., J. Quant. Spectrosc. Radiat. Transfer **4**, 117–148 (1964).
[5] Eriksson, K. B. S., Arkiv Fysik **13**, 303–329 (1958).

N II. Allowed Transitions

No.	Transition Array	Multiplet	λ(Å)	E_i(cm⁻¹)	E_k(cm⁻¹)	g_i	g_k	A_{ki}(10⁸ sec⁻¹)	f_{ik}	S(at.u.)	log gf	Accuracy	Source
1	$2s^2 2p^2 - 2s 2p^3$	³P − ³D° (1uv)	1085.1	89.3	92245	9	15	5.7	0.17	5.4	0.18	E	1
			1085.70	131.3	92238	5	7	5.7	0.14	2.5	−0.15	E	ls
			1084.57	49.1	92251	3	5	4.3	0.13	1.4	−0.42	E	ls
			1083.98	0.0	92253	1	3	3.2	0.17	0.60	−0.77	E	ls
			1085.54	131.3	92251	5	5	1.4	0.025	0.45	−0.90	E	ls
			1084.57	49.1	92253	3	3	2.4	0.042	0.45	−0.90	E	ls
			[1085.5]	131.3	92253	5	3	0.16	0.0017	0.030	−2.07	E	ls
2		³P − ³P° (2uv)	916.34	89.3	109219	9	9	18	0.22	6.0	0.30	E	1
			916.700	131.3	109218	5	5	13	0.17	2.5	−0.08	E	ls
			916.004	49.1	109218	3	3	4.4	0.055	0.50	−0.78	E	ls
			916.700	131.3	109218	5	3	7.3	0.055	0.84	−0.56	E	ls
			915.955	49.1	109225	3	1	18	0.074	0.67	−0.65	E	ls
			916.004	49.1	109218	3	5	4.4	0.093	0.84	−0.56	E	ls
			915.603	0.0	109218	1	3	5.9	0.22	0.67	−0.65	E	ls
3		³P − ³S° (4uv)	644.99	89.3	155130	9	3	110	0.23	4.4	0.32	E	1
			645.167	131.3	155130	5	3	62	0.23	2.4	0.06	E	ls
			644.825	49.1	155130	3	3	37	0.23	1.5	−0.16	E	ls
			644.621	0.0	155130	1	3	12	0.23	0.49	−0.64	E	ls
4		¹D − ¹D° (7uv)	775.957	15316	144189	5	5	49	0.45	5.7	0.35	E	1
5		¹D − ¹P° (9uv)	660.280	15316	166766	5	3	77	0.30	3.3	0.18	E	1
6		¹S − ¹P° (12uv)	745.836	32687	166766	1	3	16	0.40	0.98	−0.40	E	1

No.	Transition Array	Multiplet	$\lambda(\text{Å})$	$E_i(\text{cm}^{-1})$	$E_k(\text{cm}^{-1})$	g_i	g_k	$A_{ki}(10^8\,\text{sec}^{-1})$	f_{ik}	$S(\text{at.u.})$	$\log gf$	Accuracy	Source
7	$2p^2 -$ $2p(^2P°)3s$	$^3P - ^3P°$ (3uv)	*671.48*	*89.3*	*149013*	9	9	13	0.089	1.8	-0.10	E	2
			671.391	131.3	149077	5	5	9.9	0.067	0.74	-0.48	E	*ls*
			671.629	49.1	148941	3	3	3.3	0.022	0.15	-1.18	E	*ls*
			671.999	131.3	148941	5	3	5.5	0.022	0.25	-0.95	E	*ls*
			671.770	49.1	148909	3	1	13	0.030	0.20	-1.05	E	*ls*
			671.014	49.1	149077	3	5	3.3	0.037	0.25	-0.95	E	*ls*
			671.391	0.0	148941	1	3	4.4	0.89	0.20	-1.05	E	*ls*
8		$^1D - ^1P°$ (8uv)	746.976	15316	149189	5	3	20	0.10	1.2	-0.30	E	2
9	$2p^2 -$ $2p(^2P°)3d$	$^3P - ^3D°$ (5uv)	*533.67*	*89.3*	*187472*	9	15	36	0.26	4.1	0.37	D$-$	2
			533.726	131.3	187493	5	7	36	0.22	1.9	0.04	D$-$	*ls*
			533.577	49.1	187462	3	5	27	0.19	1.0	-0.23	D$-$	*ls*
			533.504	0.0	187438	1	3	20	0.26	0.45	-0.59	D$-$	*ls*
			533.809	131.3	187462	5	5	9.1	0.039	0.34	-0.71	D$-$	*ls*
			533.644	49.1	187438	3	3	15	0.065	0.34	-0.71	D$-$	*ls*
			[533.51]	0.0	187438	5	3	1.0	0.0026	0.023	-1.89	D$-$	*ls*
10		$^3P - ^3P°$ (6uv)	*529.68*	*89.3*	*188884*	9	9	20	0.082	1.3	-0.13	D$-$	2
			529.860	131.3	188858	5	5	15	0.062	0.54	-0.51	D$-$	*ls*
			529.481	49.1	188910	3	3	4.9	0.020	0.11	-1.21	D$-$	*ls*
			529.713	131.3	188910	5	3	8.1	0.021	0.18	-0.99	D$-$	*ls*
			529.405	49.1	188938	3	1	20	0.027	0.14	-1.09	D$-$	*ls*
			529.627	49.1	188858	3	5	4.9	0.034	0.18	-0.99	D$-$	*ls*
			529.343	0.0	188910	1	3	6.5	0.082	0.14	-1.09	D$-$	*ls*
11		$^1D - ^1D°$ (10uv)	582.150	15316	187092	5	5	13	0.064	0.61	-0.50	D$-$	2
12		$^1D - ^1F°$ (11uv)	574.650	15316	189336	5	7	35	0.24	2.3	0.08	D$-$	2
13		$^1D - ^1P°$	[572.07]	15316	190121	5	3	0.97	0.0029	0.0270	-1.84	D$-$	2
14		$^1S - ^1P°$ (13uv)	635.180	32687	190121	1	3	18	0.32	0.68	-0.49	D$-$	2
15	$2p3s -$ $2p(^2P°)3p$	$^3P° - ^3D$ (3)	*5679.4*	*149013*	*166616*	9	15	0.56	0.452	76	0.61	C	3, 4, *ca*
			5679.56	149077	166679	5	7	0.56	0.380	35.5	0.278	C	*ls*
			5666.64	148941	166583	3	5	0.423	0.339	19.0	0.008	C	*ls*
			5676.02	148909	166522	1	3	0.310	0.450	8.4	-0.347	C	*ls*
			5710.76	149077	166583	5	5	0.137	0.067	6.3	-0.475	C	*ls*
			5686.21	148941	166522	3	3	0.231	0.112	6.3	-0.473	C	*ls*
			5730.67	149077	166522	5	3	0.0152	0.00448	0.423	-1.65	C	*ls*
16		$^3P° - ^3S$ (4)	*5028.8*	*149013*	*168893*	9	3	0.76	0.097	14.4	-0.061	C	3, 4, *ca*
			5045.10	149077	168893	5	3	0.410	0.094	7.8	-0.328	C	*3n*
			5010.62	148941	168893	3	3	0.268	0.101	5.0	-0.52	C	*3n*
			5002.69	148909	168893	1	3	0.085	0.095	1.57	-1.021	C	*3n*
17		$^3P° - ^3P$ (5)	*4623.2*	*149013*	*170637*	9	9	1.05	0.337	46.1	0.481	C	3, 4, *ca*
			4630.54	149077	170667	5	5	0.84	0.269	20.5	0.129	C	*3n*
			4613.87	148941	170609	3	3	0.196	0.063	2.85	-0.73	C	*3n*
			4643.09	149077	170609	5	3	0.466	0.090	6.9	-0.345	C	*3n*
			4621.39	148941	170573	3	1	0.90	0.096	4.37	-0.54	C	*3n*
			4601.48	148941	170667	3	5	0.270	0.143	6.5	-0.368	C	*3n*
			4607.16	148909	170609	1	3	0.340	0.325	4.93	-0.488	C	*3n*

No.	Transition Array	Multiplet	$\lambda(\text{Å})$	$E_i(\text{cm}^{-1})$	$E_k(\text{cm}^{-1})$	g_i	g_k	$A_{ki}(10^8 \text{ sec}^{-1})$	f_{ik}	$S(\text{at.u.})$	$\log gf$	Accuracy	Source
18		$^1P° - {}^1P$ (8)	6482.07	149189	164612	3	3	0.365	0.230	14.7	−0.162	C	4, *ca*
19		$^1P° - {}^1D$ (12)	3995.00	149189	174213	3	5	1.58	0.63	24.8	0.276	C	4, *ca*
20		$^1P° - {}^1S$ (13)	3437.16	149189	178274	3	1	2.40	0.142	4.82	−0.371	C	4, *ca*
21	$2s2p^23s - 2s2p^2(^4P)3p$	$^5P - {}^5D°$ (63)	*5537.4*	*205677*	*223731*	*15*	*25*	0.56	0.432	118	0.81	C	*ca*
			5535.39	205726	223787	7	9	0.56	0.334	42.6	0.368	C	*ls*
			5530.27	205656	223733	5	7	0.377	0.242	22.0	0.083	C	*ls*
			5526.26	205600	223690	3	5	0.198	0.151	8.3	−0.343	C	*ls*
			5551.95	205726	223733	7	7	0.187	0.086	11.0	−0.219	C	*ls*
			5543.49	205656	223690	5	5	0.327	0.151	13.8	−0.123	C	*ls*
			5535.39	205600	223660	3	3	0.422	0.194	10.6	−0.235	C	*ls*
			5565.30	205726	223690	7	5	0.0370	0.0123	1.57	−1.066	C	*ls*
			5552.54	205656	223660	5	3	0.140	0.0387	3.54	−0.71	C	*ls*
			5540.16	205600	223645	3	1	0.56	0.086	4.71	−0.59	C	*ls*
22		$^5P - {}^5P°$ (64)	*5006.9*	*205677*	*225644*	*15*	*15*	0.77	0.291	72	0.64	C	*ca*
			5012.03	205726	225673	7	7	0.51	0.194	22.4	0.132	C	*ls*
			5005.14	205656	225629	5	5	0.064	0.0242	2.00	−0.92	C	*ls*
			4997.23	205600	225605	3	3	0.194	0.073	3.59	−0.66	C	*ls*
			5023.11	205726	225629	7	5	0.358	0.097	11.2	−0.170	C	*ls*
			5011.24	205656	225605	5	3	0.58	0.131	10.8	−0.185	C	*ls*
			4994.36	205656	225673	5	7	0.260	0.136	11.2	−0.170	C	*ls*
			4991.22	205600	225629	3	5	0.351	0.218	10.8	−0.184	C	*ls*
23		$^5P - {}^5S°$ (65)	*4137.4*	*205677*	*229840*	*15*	*5*	1.37	0.117	24.0	0.244	C	*ca*
			4145.76	205726	229840	7	5	0.64	0.117	11.2	−0.087	C	*ls*
			4133.67	205656	229840	5	5	0.458	0.117	8.0	−0.232	C	*ls*
			4124.08	205600	229840	3	5	0.276	0.117	4.78	−0.453	C	*ls*
24	$2p3s - 2p(^2P°)4p$	$^1P° - {}^1P$ (14uv)	1886.82	149189	202170	3	3	0.52	0.028	0.52	−1.08	D	4
25	$2p3p - 2p(^2P°)3d$	$^1P - {}^1D°$ (15)	4447.03	164612	187092	3	5	1.30	0.642	28.2	0.285	C+	3, 4, *ca*
26		$^1P - {}^1P°$ (17)	3919.01	164612	190121	3	3	1.00	0.231	8.93	−0.160	C+	3, 4, *ca*
27		$^3D - {}^3F°$ (19)	*5004.5*	*166616*	*186593*	*15*	*21*	1.22	0.639	158	0.982	C+	3, 4, *ca*
			5005.14	166679	186653	7	9	1.22	0.588	67.8	0.614	C+	*ls*
			5001.47	166583	186572	5	7	1.08	0.568	46.8	0.454	C+	*ls*
			5001.13	166522	186512	3	5	1.02	0.640	31.6	0.283	C+	*ls*
			5025.67	166679	186572	7	7	0.134	0.0506	5.86	−0.451	C+	*ls*
			5016.39	166583	186512	5	5	0.188	0.0710	5.86	−0.450	C+	*ls*
			5040.76	166679	186512	7	5	0.00525	0.00143	0.166	−1.999	C+	*ls*
28		$^3D - {}^3D°$ (20)	*4793.5*	*166616*	*187472*	*15*	*15*	0.356	0.123	29.0	0.264	C+	3, 4, *ca*
			4803.27	166679	187493	7	7	0.313	0.108	12.0	−0.120	C+	*ls*
			4788.13	166583	187462	5	5	0.248	0.0854	6.73	−0.370	C+	*ls*
			4779.71	166522	187438	3	3	0.269	0.0921	4.35	−0.558	C+	*ls*
			4810.29	166679	187462	7	5	0.0550	0.0136	1.51	−1.021	C+	*ls*
			4793.66	166583	187438	5	3	0.0889	0.0184	1.45	−1.037	C+	*ls*
			4781.17	166583	187493	5	7	0.0400	0.0192	1.51	−1.018	C+	*ls*
			4774.22	166522	187462	3	5	0.0540	0.0308	1.45	−1.035	C+	*ls*

No.	Transition Array	Multiplet	λ(Å)	E_i(cm⁻¹)	E_k(cm⁻¹)	g_i	g_k	A_{ki}(10⁸ sec⁻¹)	f_{ik}	S(at.u.)	log gf	Accuracy	Source
29		³D — ³P° (21)	4489.4	166616	188884	15	9	0.0460	0.0083	1.85	−0.90	C	4, ca
			4507.56	166679	188858	7	5	0.0381	0.0083	0.86	−1.237	C	ls
			4477.74	166583	188910	5	3	0.0348	0.0063	0.463	−1.50	C	ls
			4459.96	166522	188938	3	1	0.0468	0.00465	0.205	−1.86	C	ls
			4488.15	166583	188858	5	5	0.0069	0.00208	0.154	−1.98	C	ls
			4465.54	166522	188910	3	3	0.0117	0.00349	0.154	−1.98	C	ls
			[4475.8]	166522	188858	3	5	4.65 × 10⁻⁴	2.33 × 10⁻⁴	0.0103	−3.156	C	ls
30		³S — ³P° (24)	5000.8	168893	188884	3	9	0.75	0.84	41.4	0.401	C	3, 4, ca
			5007.32	168893	188858	3	5	0.77	0.483	23.9	0.161	C	3n
			4994.36	168893	188910	3	3	0.74	0.276	13.6	−0.082	C	3n
			4987.38	168893	188938	3	1	0.63	0.078	3.83	−0.63	C	3n
31		³P — ³D° (28)	5938.5	170637	187472	9	15	0.565	0.498	87.6	0.651	C+	3, 4, ca
			5941.67	170667	187493	5	7	0.564	0.418	40.9	0.320	C+	ls
			5931.79	170609	187462	3	5	0.425	0.374	21.9	0.050	C+	ls
			5927.82	170573	187438	1	3	0.315	0.498	9.72	−0.303	C+	ls
			5952.39	170667	187462	5	5	0.140	0.0745	7.30	−0.429	C+	ls
			5940.25	170609	187438	3	3	0.235	0.124	7.30	−0.428	C+	ls
			5960.93	170667	187438	5	3	0.0155	0.00496	0.487	−1.605	C+	ls
32		³P — ³P° (29)	5478.8	170637	188884	9	9	0.400	0.180	29.2	0.209	C	4, ca
			5495.70	170667	188858	5	5	0.298	0.135	12.2	−0.171	C	ls
			5462.62	170609	188910	3	3	0.101	0.0450	2.43	−0.87	C	ls
			5480.10	170667	188910	5	3	0.167	0.0450	4.06	−0.65	C	ls
			5454.26	170609	188938	3	1	0.405	0.060	3.24	−0.74	C	ls
			5478.13	170609	188858	3	3	0.100	0.075	4.06	−0.65	C	ls
			5452.12	170573	188910	1	3	0.135	0.181	3.24	−0.74	C	ls
33		¹D — ¹F° (31)	6610.58	174213	189336	5	7	0.59	0.54	59	0.433	C	4, ca
34		¹D — ¹P° (32)	6284.30	174213	190121	5	3	0.0188	0.0067	0.69	−1.477	C	4, ca
35	2s2p²3p — 2s2p²(⁴P)3d	⁵D° — ⁵F (66)	5177.8	223731	243039	25	35	1.02	0.57	244	1.154	C	ca
			5179.50	223787	243088	9	11	1.02	0.50	70	0.65	C	ls
			5175.89	223733	243048	7	9	0.85	0.440	52	0.488	C	ls
			5173.37	223690	243014	5	7	0.70	0.394	33.5	0.294	C	ls
			5172.32	223660	242989	3	5	0.57	0.382	19.5	0.060	C	ls
			5172.32	223645	242973	1	3	0.476	0.57	9.8	−0.242	C	ls
			5190.42	223787	243048	9	9	0.169	0.068	10.5	−0.211	C	ls
			5184.96	223733	243014	7	7	0.305	0.123	14.7	−0.066	C	ls
			5180.34	223690	242989	5	5	0.407	0.164	14.0	−0.087	C	ls
			5177.06	223660	242973	3	3	0.475	0.191	9.8	−0.242	C	ls
			5199.50	223787	243014	9	7	0.0144	0.00454	7.0	−1.388	C	ls
			5191.97	223733	242989	7	5	0.0405	0.0117	1.40	−1.088	C	ls
			5184.96	223690	242973	5	3	0.068	0.0163	1.40	−1.088	C	ls
36		⁵P° — ⁵P (69)	5335.8	225644	244380	15	15	0.417	0.178	46.8	0.427	C	ca
			5351.21	225673	244355	7	7	0.275	0.118	14.6	−0.082	C	ls
			5327.45	225629	244393	5	5	0.0349	0.0148	1.30	−1.129	C	ls
			5313.43	225605	244419	3	3	0.106	0.0447	2.34	−0.87	C	ls
			5340.20	225673	244393	7	5	0.194	0.059	7.3	−0.382	C	ls
			5320.96	225629	244419	5	3	0.315	0.080	7.0	−0.396	C	ls
			5338.66	225629	244355	5	7	0.139	0.083	7.3	−0.383	C	ls
			5320.96	225605	244393	3	5	0.189	0.134	7.0	−0.397	C	ls

No.	Transition Array	Multiplet	λ(Å)	E_i(cm^{-1})	E_k(cm^{-1})	g_i	g_k	A_{ki}(10^8 sec^{-1})	f_{ik}	S(at.u.)	log gf	Accuracy	Source
37		^{5}P°—^{5}D (70)	*5175.9*	*225644*	*244959*	15	25	0.83	0.56	142	0.92	C	*ca*
			5179.50	225673	244974	7	9	0.83	0.429	51	0.478	C	*ls*
			5171.46	225629	244960	5	7	0.56	0.312	26.5	0.193	C	*ls*
			5168.24	225605	244949	3	5	0.292	0.195	9.9	−0.233	C	*ls*
			5183.21	225673	244960	7	7	0.276	0.111	13.3	−0.109	C	*ls*
			5174.46	225629	244949	5	5	0.485	0.195	16.6	−0.012	C	*ls*
			5170.08	225605	244941	3	3	0.62	0.250	12.8	−0.124	C	*ls*
			5186.17	225673	244949	7	5	0.055	0.0159	1.90	−0.95	C	*ls*
			5176.56	225629	244941	5	3	0.208	0.050	4.26	−0.60	C	*ls*
			5171.30	225605	244937	3	1	0.83	0.111	5.7	−0.477	C	*ls*
38	2p3p — 2p(^{2}P°)4s	^{1}P—^{1}P° (18)	3006.86	164612	197859	3	3	0.54	0.073	2.17	−0.66	C	*ca*
39		^{3}D—^{3}P° (22)	*3328.3*	*166616*	*196653*	15	9	1.11	0.111	18.2	0.220	C	*ca*
			3328.79	166679	196712	7	5	0.93	0.111	8.5	−0.110	C	*ls*
			3331.32	166583	196593	5	3	0.83	0.083	4.55	−0.382	C	*ls*
			3330.30	166522	196541	3	1	1.11	0.061	2.02	−0.73	C	*ls*
			3318.14	166583	196712	5	5	0.169	0.0278	1.52	−0.86	C	*ls*
			3324.58	166522	196593	3	3	0.279	0.0463	1.52	−0.86	C	*ls*
			[3311.4]	166522	196712	3	5	0.0113	0.00309	0.101	−2.033	C	*ls*
40		^{3}S—^{3}P° (26)	*3601.3*	*168893*	*196653*	3	9	0.230	0.134	4.77	−0.395	C	*ca*
			3593.60	168893	196712	3	5	0.231	0.075	2.65	−0.65	C	*ls*
			3609.09	168893	196593	3	3	0.228	0.0446	1.59	−0.87	C	*ls*
			3615.88	168893	196541	3	1	0.227	0.0148	0.53	−1.351	C	*ls*
41		^{3}P—^{3}P° (30)	*3842.7*	*170637*	*196653*	9	9	0.69	0.153	17.4	0.138	C	*ca*
			3838.39	170667	196712	5	5	0.52	0.116	7.3	−0.238	C	*ls*
			3847.38	170609	196593	3	3	0.172	0.0382	1.45	−0.94	C	*ls*
			3856.07	170667	196593	5	3	0.285	0.0381	2.42	−0.72	C	*ls*
			3855.08	170609	196541	3	1	0.68	0.051	1.93	−0.82	C	*ls*
			3829.80	170609	196712	3	5	0.175	0.064	2.42	−0.72	C	*ls*
			3842.20	170573	196593	1	3	0.230	0.153	1.93	−0.82	C	*ls*
42		^{1}D—^{1}P° (33)	4227.75	174213	197859	5	3	1.06	0.171	11.9	−0.068	C	*ca*
43		^{1}S—^{1}P° (34)	5104.45	178274	197859	1	3	0.189	0.222	3.73	−0.65	C	*ca*
44	2p3p — 2p(^{2}P°)4d	^{1}P—^{1}D° (15uv)	2206.10	164612	209927	3	5	0.49	0.060	1.3	−0.75	D−	4
45		^{3}D—^{3}F° (16uv)	*2317.1*	*166616*	*209761*	15	21	0.56	0.063	7.2	−0.03	D−	4
			2317.01	166679	209825	7	9	0.56	0.058	3.1	−0.39	D−	*ls*
			2316.46	166583	209740	5	7	0.49	0.055	2.1	−0.56	D−	*ls*
			2316.65	166522	209675	3	5	0.46	0.061	1.4	−0.74	D−	*ls*
			2321.65	166679	209740	7	7	0.062	0.0050	0.27	−1.45	D−	*ls*
			2319.94	166583	209675	5	5	0.088	0.0071	0.27	−1.45	D−	*ls*
			2325.16	166679	209675	7	5	0.0024	1.4 × 10^{-4}	0.0076	−3.00	D−	*ls*
46		^{3}P—^{3}D° (19uv)	*2521.9*	*170637*	*210278*	9	15	0.33	0.052	3.9	−0.33	D−	4
			2522.27	170667	210302	5	7	0.32	0.043	1.8	−0.66	D−	*ls*
			2520.85	170609	210266	3	5	0.25	0.039	0.97	−0.93	D−	*ls*
			2520.27	170573	210240	1	3	0.18	0.052	0.43	−1.29	D−	*ls*
			2524.49	170667	210266	5	5	0.081	0.0077	0.32	−1.41	D−	*ls*
			2522.46	170609	210240	3	3	0.13	0.013	0.32	−1.41	D−	*ls*
			2526.17	170667	210240	5	3	0.0092	5.3 × 10^{-4}	0.022	−2.58	D−	*ls*

No.	Transition Array	Multiplet	$\lambda(\text{Å})$	$E_i(\text{cm}^{-1})$	$E_k(\text{cm}^{-1})$	g_i	g_k	$A_{ki}(10^8 \text{ sec}^{-1})$	f_{ik}	S(at.u.)	log gf	Accuracy	Source
47		$^3P-^3P°$ (20uv)	2493.5	170637	210729	9	9	0.19	0.018	1.3	-0.80	D$-$	4
			2496.88	170667	210705	5	5	0.14	0.013	0.54	-1.18	D$-$	*ls*
			2490.37	170609	210752	3	3	0.048	0.0045	0.11	-1.87	D$-$	*ls*
			2493.94	170667	210752	5	3	0.078	0.0044	0.18	-1.66	D$-$	*ls*
			2488.75	170609	210777	3	1	0.18	0.0057	0.14	-1.77	D$-$	*ls*
			2493.16	170609	210705	3	5	0.047	0.0073	0.18	-1.66	D$-$	*ls*
			2488.12	170573	210752	1	3	0.061	0.017	0.14	-1.77	D$-$	*ls*
48		$^1D-^1D°$ (21uv)	2799.20	174213	209927	5	5	0.079	0.0093	0.43	-1.33	D$-$	4
49		$^1D-^1F°$ (22uv)	2709.82	174213	211031	5	7	0.35	0.054	2.4	-0.57	D$-$	4
50		$^1S-^1P°$ (35)	3023.80	178274	211336	1	3	0.14	0.057	0.57	-1.24	D$-$	4
51	$2p3p-$ $2p(^2P°)5s$	$^1D-^1P°$ (23uv)	2461.30	174213	214828	5	3	0.353	0.0193	0.78	-1.017	C	4, *ca*
52	$2p3d-$ $2p(^2P°)4p$	$^3F°-^3D$ (36)	6168.1	186593	202801	21	15	0.363	0.148	63	0.492	C	4, *ca*
			6167.82	186653	202862	9	7	0.333	0.148	27.0	0.124	C	*ls*
			6173.40	186572	202766	7	5	0.320	0.131	18.6	-0.039	C	*ls*
			6170.16	186512	202715	5	3	0.362	0.124	12.6	-0.207	C	*ls*
			6136.89	186572	202862	7	7	0.0293	0.0165	2.34	-0.94	C	*ls*
			6150.76	186512	202766	5	5	0.0407	0.0231	2.34	-0.94	C	*ls*
			6114.6	186512	202862	5	7	8.4×10^{-4}	6.6×10^{-4}	0.066	-2.48	C	*ls*
53		$^1D°-^1P$ (41)	6629.80	187092	202170	5	3	0.283	0.112	12.2	-0.253	C	4, *ca*
54		$^3D°-^3D$ (45)	6521.8	187472	202801	15	15	0.058	0.0373	12.0	-0.253	C	4, *ca*
			6504.61	187493	202862	7	7	0.052	0.0332	4.98	-0.63	C	*ls*
			6532.55	187462	202766	5	5	0.0404	0.0259	2.78	-0.89	C	*ls*
			6544.16	187438	202715	3	3	0.0434	0.0278	1.80	-1.078	C	*ls*
			6545.53	187493	202766	7	5	0.0090	0.00411	0.62	-1.54	C	*ls*
			6554.47	187462	202715	5	3	0.0144	0.0056	0.60	-1.56	C	*ls*
			6491.79	187462	202862	5	7	0.0066	0.0058	0.62	-1.54	C	*ls*
			6522.39	187438	202766	3	5	0.0088	0.0093	0.60	-1.55	C	*ls*
55		$^3D°-^3P$ (46)	6345.8	187472	203226	15	9	0.306	0.111	34.7	0.220	C	4, *ca*
			6340.57	187493	203260	7	5	0.258	0.111	16.2	-0.110	*C*	*ls*
			6356.55	187462	203189	5	3	0.229	0.083	8.7	-0.381	C	*ls*
			6357.57	187438	203165	3	1	0.304	0.061	3.85	-0.74	C	*ls*
			6328.39	187462	203260	5	5	0.0462	0.0277	2.89	-0.86	C	*ls*
			6346.86	187438	203189	3	3	0.076	0.0461	2.89	-0.86	C	*ls*
			6318.80	187438	203260	3	5	0.00310	0.00310	0.193	-2.033	C	*ls*
56		$^3P°-^3D$ (52)	7183.5	188884	202801	9	15	0.00324	0.00418	0.89	-1.424	C	4, *ca*
			7138.87	188858	202862	5	7	0.00332	0.00355	0.417	-1.75	C	*ls*
			7215.06	188910	202766	3	5	0.00242	0.00314	0.224	-2.026	C	*ls*
			7256.53	188938	202715	1	3	0.00175	0.00414	0.099	-2.383	C	*ls*
			7188.20	188858	202766	5	5	8.1×10^{-4}	6.3×10^{-4}	0.074	-2.50	C	*ls*
			[7241.8]	188910	202715	3	3	0.00132	0.00103	0.074	-2.51	C	*ls*
			[7214.6]	188858	202715	5	3	8.9×10^{-5}	4.18×10^{-5}	0.00497	-3.68	C	*ls*
57		$^3P°-^3P$ (53)	6970.6	188884	203226	9	9	0.086	0.062	12.9	-0.250	C	4, *ca*
			6941.75	188858	203260	5	5	0.065	0.0473	5.4	-0.63	C	*ls*
			7003.0	188910	203189	3	3	0.0224	0.0165	1.14	-1.306	C	*ls*
			6975.64	188858	203189	5	3	0.0356	0.0156	1.79	-1.108	C	*ls*

766-655 O-66-6

No.	Transition Array	Multiplet	λ(Å)	E_i(cm^{-1})	E_k(cm^{-1})	g_i	g_k	A_{ki}(10^8 sec^{-1})	f_{ik}	S(at.u.)	log gf	Accuracy	Source
			7013.98	188910	203165	3	1	0.084	0.0206	1.43	−1.208	C	*ls*
			6966.81	188910	203260	3	5	0.0215	0.0260	1.79	−1.108	C	*ls*
			7014.73	188938	203189	1	3	0.0280	0.062	1.43	−1.208	C	*ls*
58		^{3}P°—^{3}S (54)	*6824.5*	*188884*	203533	9	3	0.355	0.083	16.7	−0.129	C	4, *ca*
			6809.99	188858	203533	5	3	0.199	0.083	9.3	−0.382	C	*ls*
			6834.09	188910	203533	3	3	0.118	0.083	5.6	−0.60	C	*ls*
			6847.24	188938	203533	1	3	0.0389	0.082	1.85	−1.086	C	*ls*
59		^{1}F°—^{1}D (57)	6242.52	189336	205351	7	5	0.341	0.142	20.5	−0.001	C	4, *ca*
60		^{1}P°—^{1}S (60)	5954.28	190121	206911	3	1	0.421	0.075	4.39	−0.65	C−	4, *ca*
61	2p3d — 2p(^{2}P°)4f	^{3}F°—^{3}G (39)	*4040.9*	*186593*	*211332*	21	27	2.64	0.83	232	1.243	C	4, *ca*
62		^{3}F°—^{1}G (40)											
			4026.08	186572	211403	7	9	0.90	0.280	26.0	0.293	C	3
63		^{1}D°—^{1}F (42)	4176.16	187092	211031	5	7	2.19	0.80	55	0.60	C	4, *ca*
64		^{3}D°—^{3}F (48)	*4239.4*	*187472*	*211053*	15	21	2.14	0.81	169	1.083	C	4, *ca*
65		^{3}P°—^{3}D (55)	*4434.6*	*188884*	*211428*	9	15	1.84	0.91	119	0.91	C	4, *ca*
			4432.74	188858	211411	5	7	1.86	0.77	56	0.58	C	*ls*
			4441.99	188910	211416	3	5	1.38	0.68	29.8	0.309	C	*ls*
			4433.48	188938	211487	1	3	1.02	0.90	13.2	−0.044	C	*ls*
			4431.82	188858	211416	5	5	0.461	0.136	9.9	−0.168	C	*ls*
			4427.97	188910	211487	3	3	0.77	0.226	9.9	−0.168	C	*ls*
			[4417.9]	188858	211487	5	3	0.052	0.0091	0.66	−1.343	C	*ls*
66		^{1}F°—^{3}G (58)											
			4552.54	189336	211296	7	9	0.76	0.305	32.0	0.329	C	3
67		^{1}F°—^{1}G (59)	4530.40	189336	211403	7	9	1.69	0.67	70	0.67	C	3
68		^{1}P°—^{1}D (62)	4677.93	190121	211491	3	5	1.65	0.90	41.8	0.434	C	4, *ca*

Forbidden Transitions

The adopted values represent, as in the case of CI, the work of Garstang [1], Naqvi [2], and Yamanouchi and Horie [3], who have independently done essentially the same calculations and arrived at very similar results. For the selection of values, the same considerations as for CI are applied.

References

[1] Garstang, R. H., Monthly Notices Roy. Astron. Soc. **111**, 115–124 (1951).
[2] Naqvi, A. M., Thesis Harvard (1951).
[3] Yamanouchi, T., and Horie, H., J. Phys. Soc. Japan **7**, 52–56 (1952).

N II. Forbidden Transitions

No.	Transition Array	Multiplet	λ(Å)	E_i(cm^{-1})	E_k(cm^{-1})	g_i	g_k	Type of Transition	A_{ki}(sec^{-1})	S(at.u.)	Accuracy	Source
1	$2p^2 - 2p^2$	$^3P - {}^3P$										
			[20.36 × 10⁵]	0.0	49.1	1	3	m	2.13×10^{-6}	2.00	B	1, 2, 3
			[76.14 × 10⁴]	0.0	131.3	1	5	e	1.30×10^{-12}	0.99	C	1
			[12.16 × 10⁵]	49.1	131.3	3	5	m	7.48×10^{-6}	2.50	B	1, 2, 3
			[12.16 × 10⁵]	49.1	131.3	3	5	e	2.90×10^{-13}	2.30	C	1
2		$^3P - {}^1D$ (1 F)										
			6527.4	0.0	15315.7	1	5	e	4.2×10^{-7}	1.5×10^{-5}	D	1
			6548.1	49.1	15315.7	3	5	m	0.00103	5.4×10^{-5}	C	1, 2, 3
			6548.1	49.1	15315.7	3	5	e	1.4×10^{-6}	5.0×10^{-5}	D	1
			6583.6	131.3	15315.7	5	5	m	0.00303	1.60×10^{-4}	C	1, 2, 3
			6583.6	131.3	15315.7	5	5	e	9.4×10^{-6}	3.5×10^{-4}	D	1
3		$^3P - {}^1S$ (2 F)										
			3063.0	49.1	32687.1	3	1	m	0.0340	3.62×10^{-5}	C	1, 3
			3070.8	131.3	32687.1	5	1	e	1.6×10^{-4}	2.6×10^{-5}	D	1
4		$^1D - {}^1S$ (3 F)										
			5754.8	15315.7	32687.1	5	1	e	1.08	4.06	C	1

N III

Ground State	$1s^2\, 2s^2\, 2p\, {}^2P^\circ_{1/2}$
Ionization Potential	47.426 eV = 382625.5 cm^{-1}

Allowed Transitions

List of tabulated lines:

Wavelength [Å]	No.	Wavelength [Å]	No.	Wavelength [Å]	No.
374.204	11	772.93	6	1804.3	24
374.44	11	772.975	6	1805.5	24
374.441	11	979.77	5	1885.25	27
451.869	10	979.842	5	1908.11	28
452.226	10	979.919	5	1917.7	29
684.996	3	980.01	5	1918.7	29
685.513	3	989.790	1	1919.5	29
685.816	3	991.514	1	1919.7	29
686.335	3	991.579	1	1920.0	29
763.340	2	1006.0	7	1920.86	29
764.357	2	1183.03	9	1921.49	29
771.544	4	1184.54	9	2063.50	30
771.901	4	1747.86	8	2063.99	30
772.385	4	1751.24	8	2068.25	30
772.891	6	1751.75	8	2247.7	25

Wavelength [Å]	No.	Wavelength [Å]	No.	Wavelength [Å]	No.
2247.92	25	3771.08	14	4527.86	22
2248.88	25	3934.41	18	4530.84	13
2453.85	26	3938.52	18	4534.57	13
2459.2	26	3942.78	18	4535.11	22
2462.56	26	3998.69	31	4546.36	22
2462.9	26	4003.6	31	4547.34	13
2466.3	26	4003.64	31	4858.74	20
2468.36	26	4097.31	12	4858.88	20
2469.1	26	4103.37	12	4861.33	20
2471.2	26	4195.70	16	4867.18	20
2972.60	19	4200.02	16	4873.58	20
2977.3	19	4215.69	16	4881.81	20
2978.8	19	4321.37	21	4884.14	20
2983.58	19	4323.93	21	4896.71	20
3342.77	17	4328.15	21	6445.05	23
3353.78	15	4330.14	21	6450.78	23
3354.29	15	4330.44	21	6453.95	23
3355.47	17	4335.53	21	6463.03	23
3358.72	15	4339.52	21	6466.86	23
3361.90	15	4348.36	21	6468.77	23
3365.79	15	4353.66	21	6478.69	23
3367.36	15	4510.92	13	6487.55	23
3374.06	15	4514.89	13		
3745.83	14	4518.18	13		
3754.62	14	4523.60	13		

As in the case of analogous configurations, the data for the lower excited transitions, which are obtained from the calculations by Bolotin and Yutsis [1] and Kelly [2], are quite uncertain because of the strong effects of configuration interaction. The latter are either crudely taken into account (Bolotin and Yutsis) or entirely neglected (Kelly). For some higher excited transitions self-consistent field calculations by Kelly [3] including exchange affects are available and are averaged with the results of the Coulomb approximation. For other prominent transitions the Coulomb approximation is applied whenever it is expected to give reliable results.

References

[1] Bolotin, A. B., and Yutsis, A. P., Zhur. Eksptl. i Teoret. Fiz. **24**, 537–543 (1953) (Translated in "Optical Transition Probabilities", Office of Technical Services, U.S. Department of Commerce, Washington, D.C.).
[2] Kelly, P. S., Astrophys. J. **140**, 1247–1268 (1964).
[3] Kelly, P. S., J. Quant. Spectrosc. Radiat. Transfer 4, 117–148 (1964).

N III. Allowed Transitions

No.	Transition Array	Multiplet	λ(Å)	E_i(cm⁻¹)	E_k(cm⁻¹)	g_i	g_k	A_{ki}(10⁸ sec⁻¹)	f_{ik}	S(at.u.)	log gf	Accu-racy	Source
1	$2s^2 2p - 2s2p^2$	$^2P° - ^2D$ (1 uv)	990.98	116.3	101027	6	10	7.3	0.18	3.5	0.03	E	1
			991.579	174.5	101024	4	6	7.3	0.16	2.1	−0.19	E	ls
			989.790	0.0	101032	2	4	6.3	0.18	1.2	−0.43	E	ls
			991.514	174.5	101032	4	4	1.2	0.018	0.23	−1.15	E	ls
2		$^2P° - ^2S$ (2 uv)	764.01	116.3	131004	6	2	39	0.11	1.7	−0.17	E	1
			764.357	174.5	131004	4	2	25	0.11	1.1	−0.36	E	ls
			763.340	0.0	131004	2	2	13	0.11	0.57	−0.64	E	ls
3		$^2P° - ^2P$ (3 uv)	685.71	116.3	145950	6	6	64	0.45	6.1	0.43	E	1
			685.816	174.5	145987	4	4	53	0.38	3.4	0.18	E	ls
			685.513	0.0	145876	2	2	44	0.31	1.4	−0.21	E	ls
			686.335	174.5	145876	4	2	21	0.075	0.68	−0.52	E	ls
			684.996	0.0	145987	2	4	11	0.15	0.68	−0.52	E	ls
4	$2s2p^2 - 2p^3$	$^4P - ^4S°$ (8 uv)	772.09	57283	186802	12	4	56	0.17	5.1	0.30	E	2
			772.385	57333	186802	6	4	29	0.17	2.6	0.01	E	ls
			771.901	57252	186802	4	4	19	0.17	1.7	−0.17	E	ls
			771.544	57192	186802	2	4	9.4	0.17	0.85	−0.48	E	ls
5		$^2D - ^2D°$ (12 uv)	979.89	101027	203079	10	10	14	0.20	6.6	0.31	E	2
			979.919	101024	203072	6	6	13	0.19	3.7	0.06	E	ls
			979.842	101032	203089	4	4	13	0.19	2.4	−0.13	E	ls
			[979.77]	101024	203089	6	4	1.4	0.013	0.26	−1.09	E	ls
			[980.01]	101032	203072	4	6	0.93	0.020	0.26	−1.09	E	ls
6		$^2D - ^2P°$ (13 uv)	772.91	101027	230408	10	6	16	0.086	2.2	−0.06	E	2
			772.891	101024	230409	6	4	14	0.085	1.3	−0.29	E	ls
			772.975	101032	230405	4	2	16	0.072	0.73	−0.54	E	ls
			[772.93]	101032	230409	4	4	1.6	0.015	0.15	−1.23	E	ls
7		$^2S - ^2P°$ (17 uv)	1006.0	131004	230408	2	6	6.0	0.27	1.8	−0.26	E	2
8		$^2P - ^2D°$ (19 uv)	1750.4	145950	203079	6	10	2.6	0.20	6.9	0.08	E	2
			1751.75	145987	203072	4	6	2.6	0.18	4.1	−0.15	E	ls
			1747.86	145876	203089	2	4	2.2	0.20	2.3	−0.40	E	ls
			1751.24	145987	203089	4	4	0.43	0.020	0.46	−1.10	E	ls
9		$^2P - ^2P°$ (20 uv)	1184.0	145950	230408	6	6	8.5	0.18	4.2	0.03	E	2
			1184.54	145987	230409	4	4	7.0	0.15	2.3	−0.23	E	ls
			1183.03	145876	230405	2	2	5.7	0.12	0.93	−0.62	E	ls
			1184.54	145987	230405	4	2	2.9	0.030	0.47	−0.92	E	ls
			1183.03	145876	230409	2	4	1.4	0.060	0.47	−0.92	E	ls
10	$2p - (^1S)3s$	$^2P° - ^2S$ (4 uv)	452.11	116.3	221302	6	2	45	0.046	0.41	−0.56	E	2
			452.226	174.5	221302	4	2	30	0.045	0.27	−0.74	E	ls
			451.869	0.0	221302	2	2	15	0.047	0.14	−1.03	E	ls
11	$2p - (^1S)3d$	$^2P° - ^2D$ (5 uv)	374.36	116.3	267242	6	10	110	0.39	2.9	0.37	D−	2
			374.441	174.5	267244	4	6	110	0.34	1.7	0.14	D−	ls
			374.204	0.0	267239	2	4	94	0.39	0.97	−0.10	D−	ls
			[374.44]	174.5	267239	4	4	18	0.039	0.19	−0.81	D−	ls
12	$3s - (^1S)3p$	$^2S - ^2P°$ (1)	4099.2	221302	245690	2	6	0.97	0.73	19.7	0.164	C	3, ca
			4097.31	221302	245702	2	4	0.96	0.486	13.1	−0.013	C	ls
			4103.37	221302	245666	2	2	0.97	0.244	6.6	−0.311	C	ls

No.	Transition Array	Multiplet	λ(Å)	E_i(cm^{-1})	E_k(cm^{-1})	g_i	g_k	A_{ki}(10^8 sec^{-1})	f_{ik}	S(at.u.)	log gf	Accuracy	Source
13	2s2p3s — 2s2p(^{3}P°)3p	^{4}P° — ^{4}D (3)	*4517.3*	*287646*	*309777*	12	20	0.70	0.357	64	0.63	C	*ca*
			4514.89	287714	309857	6	8	0.70	0.286	25.5	0.235	C	*ls*
			4510.92	287598	309761	4	6	0.492	0.225	13.4	−0.046	C	*ls*
			4510.92	287536	309698	2	4	0.293	0.179	5.3	−0.446	C	*ls*
			4534.57	287714	309761	6	6	0.208	0.064	5.7	−0.416	C	*ls*
			4523.60	287598	309698	4	4	0.372	0.114	6.8	−0.341	C	*ls*
			4518.18	287536	309663	2	2	0.58	0.178	5.3	−0.449	C	*ls*
			4547.34	287714	309698	6	4	0.0344	0.0071	0.64	−1.371	C	*ls*
			4530.84	287598	309663	4	2	0.116	0.0178	1.06	−1.148	C	*ls*
14		^{4}P° — ^{4}S (4)	*3761.4*	*287646*	*314224*	12	4	1.24	0.088	13.1	0.024	C	*ca*
			3771.08	287714	314224	6	4	0.61	0.087	6.5	−0.282	C	*ls*
			3754.62	287598	314224	4	4	0.416	0.088	4.35	−0.454	C	*ls*
			3745.83	287536	314224	2	4	0.209	0.088	2.17	−0.75	C	*ls*
15		^{4}P° — ^{4}P (5)	*3363.9*	*287646*	*317365*	12	12	1.74	0.296	39.3	0.55	C	*ca*
			3367.36	287714	317402	6	6	1.22	0.207	13.8	0.094	C	*ls*
			3361.90	287598	317343	4	4	0.233	0.0395	1.75	−0.80	C	*ls*
			3358.72	287536	317300	2	2	0.292	0.0494	1.09	−1.005	C	*ls*
			3374.06	287714	317343	6	4	0.78	0.089	5.9	−0.273	C	*ls*
			3365.79	287598	317300	4	2	1.45	0.123	5.5	−0.308	C	*ls*
			3354.29	287598	317402	4	6	0.53	0.134	5.9	−0.271	C	*ls*
			3353.78	287536	317343	2	4	0.73	0.247	5.5	−0.306	C	*ls*
16		^{2}P° — ^{2}D (6)	*4199.6*	*297225*	*321030*	6	10	1.00	0.442	36.7	0.424	C	*ca*
			4200.02	297263	321066	4	6	1.00	0.398	22.0	0.202	C	*ls*
			4195.70	297150	320977	2	4	0.84	0.442	12.2	−0.054	C	*ls*
			4215.69	297263	320977	4	4	0.165	0.0440	2.44	−0.75	C	*ls*
17		^{2}P° — ^{2}S (7)	*3351.1*	*297225*	*327057*	6	2	2.00	0.112	7.4	−0.173	C	*ca*
			3355.47	297263	327057	4	2	1.33	0.112	4.95	−0.349	C	*ls*
			3342.77	297150	327057	2	2	0.67	0.113	2.49	−0.65	C	*ls*
18	2s2p3p — 2s2p(^{3}P°)3d	^{2}P — ^{2}D° (8)	*3937.4*	*309168*	*334558*	6	10	0.96	0.372	28.9	0.349	C	*ca*
			3938.52	309186	334569	4	6	0.96	0.335	17.4	0.127	C	*ls*
			3934.41	309133	334542	2	4	0.80	0.372	9.6	−0.128	C	*ls*
			3942.78	309186	334542	4	4	0.160	0.0372	1.93	−0.83	C	*ls*
19		^{2}P — ^{2}P° (25 uv)	*2979.9*	*309168*	*342717*	6	6	1.38	0.184	10.8	0.043	C	*ca*
			2983.58	309186	342693	4	4	1.14	0.153	6.0	−0.214	C	*ls*
			2972.60	309133	342764	2	2	0.93	0.123	2.40	−0.61	C	*ls*
			[2977.3]	309186	342764	4	2	0.461	0.0307	1.20	−0.91	C	*ls*
			[2978.8]	309133	342693	2	4	0.230	0.061	1.20	−0.91	C	*ls*
20		^{4}D — ^{4}F° (9)	*4864.8*	*309777*	*330327*	20	28	0.63	0.312	100	0.80	C	*ca*
			4867.18	309857	330397	8	10	0.63	0.279	35.8	0.349	C	*ls*
			4861.33	309761	330325	6	8	0.54	0.255	24.5	0.185	C	*ls*
			4858.88	309698	330274	4	6	0.471	0.250	16.0	0.000	C	*ls*
			4858.74	309663	330238	2	4	0.441	0.312	10.0	−0.205	C	*ls*
			4884.14	309857	330325	8	8	0.089	0.0318	4.09	−0.59	C	*ls*
			4873.58	309761	330274	6	6	0.152	0.054	5.2	−0.490	C	*ls*
			4867.18	309698	330238	4	4	0.175	0.062	3.97	−0.61	C	*ls*
			4896.71	309857	330274	8	6	0.0059	0.00158	0.204	−1.90	C	*ls*
			4881.81	309761	330238	6	4	0.0124	0.00296	0.285	−1.75	C	*ls*

No.	Transition Array	Multiplet	$\lambda(\text{Å})$	$E_i(\text{cm}^{-1})$	$E_k(\text{cm}^{-1})$	g_i	g_k	$A_{ki}(10^8\ \text{sec}^{-1})$	f_{ik}	$S(\text{at.u.})$	$\log gf$	Accu-racy	Source
21		$^4D - {}^4D^\circ$ (10)	4335.7	309777	332835	20	20	0.234	0.066	18.8	0.121	C	*ca*
			4348.36	309857	332860	8	8	0.198	0.056	6.4	−0.349	C	*ls*
			4335.53	309761	332832	6	6	0.134	0.0378	3.24	−0.64	C	*ls*
			4328.15	309698	332810	4	4	0.094	0.0263	1.50	−0.98	C	*ls*
			4323.93	309663	332797	2	2	0.117	0.0329	0.94	−1.182	C	*ls*
			4353.66	309857	332832	8	6	0.0436	0.0093	1.07	−1.128	C	*ls*
			4339.52	309761	332810	6	4	0.081	0.0153	1.31	−1.037	C	*ls*
			4330.44	309698	332797	4	2	0.117	0.0164	0.94	−1.183	C	*ls*
			4330.14	309761	332860	6	8	0.0334	0.0125	1.07	−1.125	C	*ls*
			4323.93	309698	332832	4	6	0.056	0.0236	1.34	−1.025	C	*ls*
			4321.37	309663	332810	2	4	0.059	0.0329	0.94	−1.182	C	*ls*
22		$^4S - {}^4P^\circ$ (13)	4539.6	314224	336246	4	12	0.99	0.91	54	0.56	C	*ca*
			4546.36	314224	336213	4	6	0.99	0.456	27.2	0.261	C	*ls*
			4535.11	314224	336268	4	4	0.99	0.304	18.2	0.085	C	*ls*
			4527.86	314224	336303	4	2	0.99	0.152	9.1	−0.216	C	*ls*
23		$^4P - {}^4D^\circ$ (14)	6462.3	317365	332835	12	20	0.432	0.451	115	0.73	C	*ca*
			6466.86	317402	332860	6	8	0.432	0.361	46.1	0.336	C	*ls*
			6453.95	317343	332832	4	6	0.304	0.285	24.2	0.057	C	*ls*
			6445.05	317300	332810	2	4	0.181	0.226	9.6	−0.345	C	*ls*
			6478.69	317402	332832	6	6	0.129	0.081	10.4	−0.313	C	*ls*
			6463.03	317343	332810	4	4	0.232	0.145	12.3	−0.237	C	*ls*
			6450.78	317300	332797	2	2	0.362	0.226	9.6	−0.345	C	*ls*
			6487.55	317402	332810	6	4	0.0214	0.0090	1.15	−1.268	C	*ls*
			6468.77	317343	332797	4	2	0.072	0.0226	1.93	−1.044	C	*ls*
24	$3p - ({}^1S)4s$	$^2P^\circ - {}^2S$ (22 uv)	1805.1	245690	301088	6	2	6.8	0.110	3.93	−0.180	C	3, *ca*
			1805.5	245702	301088	4	2	4.51	0.110	2.62	−0.356	C	*ls*
			1804.3	245666	301088	2	2	2.26	0.110	1.31	−0.66	C	*ls*
25	$3d - ({}^1S)4p$	$^2D - {}^2P^\circ$ (23 uv)	2248.2	267242	311708	10	6	1.6	0.074	5.5	−0.13	D	3, *ca*
			2247.92	267244	311716	6	4	1.5	0.074	3.3	−0.35	D	*ls*
			2248.88	267239	311691	4	2	1.6	0.062	1.8	−0.61	D	*ls*
			[2247.7]	267239	311716	4	4	0.16	0.012	0.37	−1.30	D	*ls*
26	$2s2p3d -$ $2s2p({}^3P^\circ)4p$	$^4P^\circ - {}^4D$ (28 uv)	2460.4	336246	376877	12	20	0.014	0.0022	0.21	−1.59	D	*ca*
			2453.85	336213	376953	6	8	0.015	0.0018	0.085	−1.98	D	*ls*
			2462.56	336268	376864	4	6	0.010	0.0014	0.046	−2.25	D	*ls*
			2468.36	336303	376803	2	4	0.0062	0.0011	0.018	−2.65	D	*ls*
			[2459.2]	336213	376864	6	6	0.0044	4.0×10^{-4}	0.019	−2.62	D	*ls*
			[2466.3]	336268	376803	4	4	0.0079	7.2×10^{-4}	0.023	−2.54	D	*ls*
			[2471.2]	336303	376757	2	2	0.012	0.0011	0.018	−2.64	D	*ls*
			[2462.9]	336213	376803	6	4	7.4×10^{-4}	4.5×10^{-5}	0.0022	−3.57	D	*ls*
			[2469.1]	336268	376757	4	2	0.0025	1.1×10^{-4}	0.0037	−3.34	D	*ls*
27	$3d - ({}^1S)4f$	$^2D - {}^2F^\circ$ (24 uv)	1885.25	267242	320285	10	14	11.9	0.89	55	0.95	C	3, *ca*
28	$2s2p3d -$ $2s2p({}^3P^\circ)4f$	$^2D^\circ - {}^2F$ (27 uv)	1908.11	334558	386965	10	14	11.0	0.84	53	0.92	C	*ca*

No.	Transition Array	Multiplet	λ(Å)	E_i(cm⁻¹)	E_k(cm⁻¹)	g_i	g_k	A_{ki}(10⁸ sec⁻¹)	f_{ik}	S(at.u.)	log gf	Accuracy	Source
29		⁴P°—⁴D (29 uv)	*1920.6*	*336246*	*388313*	12	20	10.3	0.95	72	1.057	C	*ca*
			1920.86	336213	388273	6	8	10.3	0.76	28.7	0.66	C	*ls*
			1921.49	336268	388311	4	6	7.2	0.60	15.1	0.38	C	*ls*
			1920.86	336303	388359	2	4	4.27	0.472	6.0˙	−0.025	C	*ls*
			[1919.5]	336213	388311	6	6	3.08	0.170	6.4	0.009	C	*ls*
			[1919.7]	336268	388359	4	4	5.5	0.302	7.6	0.082	C	*ls*
			[1920.0]	336303	388387	2	2	8.5	0.471	6.0	−0.026	C	*ls*
			[1917.7]	336213	388359	6	4	0.51	0.0188	0.71	−0.95	C	*ls*
			[1918.7]	336268	388387	4	2	1.71	0.0471	1.19	−0.72	C	*ls*
30		²F°—²G (30 uv)	*2063.8*	*339808*	*388246*	14	18	11.3	0.93	88	1.115	C	*ca*
			2063.99	339856	388290	8	10	11.3	0.90	48.9	0.86	C	*ls*
			2063.50	339744	388190	6	8	10.9	0.93	37.9	0.75	C	*ls*
			2068.25	339856	388190	8	8	0.402	0.0258	1.41	−0.69	C	*ls*
31	4d−(¹S)5f	²D—²F° (16)	*4001.8*	*317770*	*342752*	10	14	2.11	0.709	93.4	0.851	C+	*ca*
			4003.64	317782	342752	6	8	2.10	0.674	53.3	0.609	C+	*ls*
			3998.69	317751	342752	4	6	1.98	0.710	37.4	0.454	C+	*ls*
			[4003.6]	317782	342752	6	6	0.140	0.0338	2.67	−0.693	C+	*ls*

Forbidden Transitions

Naqvi's calculation [1] of the one possible transition in the ground state configuration $2p$ is the only available source.   The line strength should be quite accurate, since it does not sensitively depend on the choice of the interaction parameters.

Reference

[1] Naqvi, A. M., Thesis Harvard (1951).

N III.   Forbidden Transitions

No.	Transition Array	Multiplet	λ(Å)	E_i(cm⁻¹)	E_k(cm⁻¹)	g_i	g_k	Type of Transition	A_{ki}(sec⁻¹)	S(at.u.)	Accuracy	Source
1	2p−2p	²P°—²P°	[57.29 × 10⁴]	0	174.5	2	4	m	4.77 × 10⁻⁵	1.33	B	1

N IV

Ground State $1s^2\,2s^2\,{}^1S_0$

Ionization Potential $77.450\ \mathrm{eV} = 624851\ \mathrm{cm}^{-1}$

Allowed Transitions

List of tabulated lines:

Wavelength [Å]	No.	Wavelength [Å]	No.	Wavelength [Å]	No.
225.025	10	923.211	3	4685.4	20
225.098	10	923.669	3	4723	20
225.13	10	924.274	3	4733	20
225.136	10	955.335	5	4740	20
225.20	10	1718.52	4	4752	20
247.205	2	3443	15	4762	20
283.420	8	3445	15	5073	21
283.47	8	3454	15	5236	13
283.470	8	3461.34	15	5245	13
283.579	8	3463.36	15	5280.9	13
283.59	8	3474.56	15	5281	13
322.503	6	3478.69	11	5303.9	13
322.570	6	3482.98	11	5349.8	13
322.724	6	3484.90	11	5734	19
335.050	9	3747.66	16	6383	12
387.353	7	4057.80	17	7103.28	18
765.140	1	4479	14	7109.48	18
921.982	3	4495	14	7111.28	18
922.507	3	4528	14	7123.10	18
923.045	3	4678.6	20	7127.21	18
				7129	18

Values for the $2s^2 - 2s2p$ and $2s2p - 2p^2$ transition arrays are taken from the self-consistent field calculations of Weiss [1]. These calculations do not include the important effects of configuration interaction; hence large uncertainties must be expected. The average of the dipole length and velocity approximations is adopted [1]. Accuracies within 50% are indicated by the following comparison: Weiss [1] has undertaken refined calculations, including configuration interaction, for the same transitions in Be I—the first member of this isoelectronic sequence—in addition to calculations of the type done for this ion. In all cases the agreement with the average of the dipole length and velocity approximations is close.

For the remaining low-lying transitions Kelly's approximate Hartree-Fock calculations [2] are adopted, while for the moderately excited transitions Kelly's values are averaged with the Coulomb approximation, with which they agree quite well.

References

[1] Weiss, A. W., private communication (1964).
[2] Kelly, P. S., J. Quant. Spectrosc. Radiat. Transfer 4, 117–148 (1964).

No.	Transition Array	Multiplet	$\lambda(\text{Å})$	$E_i(\text{cm}^{-1})$	$E_k(\text{cm}^{-1})$	g_i	g_k	$A_{ki}(10^8\text{sec}^{-1})$	f_{ik}	$S(\text{at.u.})$	$\log gf$	Accuracy	Source
1	$2s^2 -$ $2s(^2S)2p$	$^1S - {}^1P°$ (1 uv)	765.140	0	130695	1	3	24	0.64	1.6	-0.19	D	1
2	$2s^2 -$ $2s(^2S)3p$	$^1S - {}^1P°$ (2 uv)	247.205	0	404521	1	3	200	0.55	0.45	-0.26	D	2
3	$2s2p -$ $2p^2$	$^3P° - {}^3P$ (3 uv)	923.15	[67273]	[175598]	9	9	17	0.21	5.8	0.28	D	1
			923.211	[67344]	[175662]	5	5	13	0.16	2.4	-0.10	D	ls
			923.045	[67200]	[175537]	3	3	4.2	0.053	0.49	-0.80	D	ls
			924.274	[67344]	[175537]	5	3	6.9	0.053	0.81	-0.58	D	ls
			923.669	[67200]	[175464]	3	1	17	0.071	0.65	-0.67	D	ls
			921.982	[67200]	[175662]	3	5	4.2	0.089	0.81	-0.57	D	ls
			922.507	[67136]	[175537]	1	3	5.6	0.21	0.65	-0.67	D	ls
4		$^1P° - {}^1D$ (7 uv)	1718.52	130695	188885	3	5	5.1	0.38	6.4	0.05	D	1
5		$^1P° - {}^1S$ (8 uv)	955.335	130695	235370	3	1	16	0.074	0.70	-0.66	D	1
6	$2s2p -$ $2s(^2S)3s$	$^3P° - {}^3S$ (4 uv)	322.65	[67273]	[377206]	9	3	113	0.059	0.56	-0.278	C	2
			322.724	[67344]	[377206]	5	3	62	0.059	0.311	-0.53	C	ls
			322.570	[67200]	[377206]	3	3	37.6	0.059	0.187	-0.75	C	ls
			322.503	[67136]	[377206]	1	3	12.5	0.058	0.062	-1.234	C	ls
7		$^1P° - {}^1S$ (9 uv)	387.353	130695	388858	3	1	65	0.0489	0.187	-0.83	C	2
8	$2s2p -$ $2s(^2S)3d$	$^3P° - {}^3D$ (5 uv)	283.53	[67273]	[419974]	9	15	314	0.63	5.3	0.75	C	2
			283.579	[67344]	[419979]	5	7	311	0.52	2.45	0.419	C	ls
			283.470	[67200]	[419971]	3	5	235	0.471	1.32	0.151	C	ls
			283.420	[67136]	[419968]	1	3	172	0.62	0.58	-0.207	C	ls
			[283.59]	[67344]	[419971]	5	5	78	0.094	0.438	-0.329	C	ls
			[283.47]	[67200]	[419968]	3	3	130	0.156	0.438	-0.329	C	ls
			[283.59]	[67344]	[419968]	5	3	8.6	0.0063	0.0292	-1.50	C	ls
9		$^1P° - {}^1D$ (10 uv)	335.050	130695	429158	3	5	189	0.53	1.75	0.200	C	2
10	$2s2p -$ $2s(^2S)4d$	$^3P° - {}^3D$ (6 uv)	225.17	[67273]	[511382]	9	15	92	0.117	0.78	0.022	C	2
			225.025	[67344]	[511384]	5	7	92	0.098	0.364	-0.309	C	ls
			225.136	[67200]	[511376]	3	5	69	0.088	0.195	-0.58	C	ls
			225.098	[67136]	[511387]	1	3	52	0.117	0.087	-0.93	C	ls
			[225.20]	[67344]	[511376]	5	5	23.1	0.0175	0.065	-1.057	C	ls
			[225.13]	[67200]	[511387]	3	3	38.5	0.0292	0.065	-1.057	C	ls
			[225.20]	[67344]	[511387]	5	3	2.56	0.00117	0.00433	-2.234	C	ls
11	$2s3s -$ $2s(^2S)3p$	$^3S - {}^3P°$ (1)	3480.8	[377206]	[405927]	3	9	1.16	0.634	21.8	0.279	C+	2, ca
			3478.69	[377206]	[405944]	3	5	1.16	0.352	12.1	0.024	C+	ls
			3482.98	[377206]	[405909]	3	3	1.16	0.211	7.27	-0.198	C+	ls
			3484.90	[377206]	[405893]	3	1	1.16	0.0703	2.42	-0.676	C+	ls
12		$^1S - {}^1P°$ (2)	6383	388858	404521	1	3	0.193	0.353	7.42	-0.452	C+	2, ca
13	$2p3s -$ $2p(^2P°)3p$	$^3P° - {}^3D$ (5)	5255.1	[465382]	[484406]	9	15	0.343	0.237	36.9	0.329	C	ca
			5245	[465463]	[484525]	5	7	0.345	0.199	17.2	-0.002	C	ls
			5236	[465301]	[484394]	3	5	0.261	0.178	9.2	-0.271	C	ls
			5281	[465223]	[484150]	1	3	0.188	0.236	4.10	-0.63	C	ls
			[5280.9]	[465463]	[484394]	5	5	0.085	0.0354	3.08	-0.75	C	ls
			[5303.9]	[465301]	[484150]	3	3	0.139	0.059	3.08	-0.75	C	ls
			[5349.8]	[465463	[484150]	5	3	0.0090	0.00233	0.205	-1.93	C	ls

No.	Transition Array	Multiplet	λ(Å)	E_i(cm⁻¹)	E_k(cm⁻¹)	g_i	g_k	A_{ki}(10⁸sec⁻¹)	f_{ik}	S(at.u.)	log gf	Accuracy	Source
14		³P°—³S (6)	*4511.4*	*[465382]*	*[487542]*	9	3	0.56	0.056	7.5	−0.295	C	*ca*
			4528	[465463]	[487542]	5	3	0.305	0.056	4.19	−0.55	C	*ls*
			4495	[465301]	[487542]	3	3	0.189	0.057	2.54	−0.77	C	*ls*
			4479	[465223]	[487542]	1	3	0.063	0.057	0.84	−1.245	C	*ls*
15		³P°—³P (7)	*3456.7*	*[465382]*	*[494303]*	9	9	1.27	0.227	23.2	0.310	C	*ca*
			3463.36	[465463]	[494338]	5	5	0.94	0.170	9.7	−0.072	C	*ls*
			3454	[465301]	[494240]	3	3	0.316	0.057	1.93	−0.77	C	*ls*
			3474.56	[465301]	[494338]	3	5	0.311	0.094	3.22	−0.55	C	*ls*
			3461.34	[465223]	[494240]	1	3	0.420	0.226	2.58	−0.65	C	*ls*
			3443	[465463]	[494240]	5	3	0.53	0.057	3.22	−0.55	C	*ls*
			3445	[465301]	[494320]	3	1	1.28	0.076	2.58	−0.64	C	*ls*
16		¹P°—¹D (8)	3747.66	473032	499708	3	5	1.06	0.371	13.7	0.047	C	*ca*
17	2s3p — 2s(²S)3d	¹P°—¹D (3)	4057.80	388858	429158	3	5	0.758	0.312	12.5	−0.029	C+	2, *ca*
18		³P°—³D (4)	*7117.0*	*[405927]*	*[419974]*	9	15	0.132	0.167	35.3	0.178	C+	2, *ca*
			7123.10	[405944]	[419979]	5	7	0.132	0.141	16.5	−0.153	C+	*ls*
			7109.48	[405909]	[419971]	3	5	0.0995	0.126	8.82	−0.424	C+	*ls*
			7103.28	[405893]	[419968]	1	3	0.0739	0.168	3.92	−0.776	C+	*ls*
			7127.21	[405944]	[419971]	5	5	0.0329	0.0251	2.94	−0.902	C+	*ls*
			7111.28	[405909]	[419968]	3	3	0.0552	0.0419	2.94	−0.901	C+	*ls*
			7129	[405944]	[419968]	5	3	0.00365	0.00167	0.196	−2.078	C+	*ls*
19	2p3p — 2p(²P°)3d	¹P—¹D° (9)	5734	480880	498315	3	5	0.178	0.146	8.3	−0.359	C	*ca*
20		³D—³D° (11)	*4732.2*	*[484406]*	*[505532]*	15	15	0.116	0.0389	9.1	−0.234	C	*ca*
			4752	[484525]	[505561]	7	7	0.102	0.0344	3.77	−0.62	C	*ls*
			4733	[484394]	[505518]	5	5	0.081	0.0271	2.11	−0.87	C	*ls*
			[4685.4]	[484150]	[505487]	3	3	0.089	0.0294	1.36	−1.055	C	*ls*
			4762	[484525]	[505518]	7	5	0.0177	0.00431	0.473	−1.52	C	*ls*
			4740	[484394]	[505487]	5	3	0.0289	0.0058	0.455	−1.54	C	*ls*
			4723	[484394]	[505561]	5	7	0.0130	0.0061	0.473	−1.52	C	*ls*
			[4678.6]	[484150]	[505518]	3	5	0.0180	0.0098	0.455	−1.53	C	*ls*
21		¹D—¹P° (17)	5073	499708	519414	5	3	0.0127	0.00295	0.246	−1.83	C	*ca*

Forbidden Transitions

Naqvi's calculations [1] are the only available source. The results for the ³P°—³P° transitions are essentially independent of the choice of the interaction parameters. For the ³P°—¹P° transitions, Naqvi has used empirical term intervals, i.e., the effects of configuration interaction should be partially included.

Reference

[1] Naqvi, A. M., Thesis Harvard (1951).

N IV. Forbidden Transitions

No.	Transition Array	Multiplet	$\lambda(\text{Å})$	$E_i(\text{cm}^{-1})$	$E_k(\text{cm}^{-1})$	g_i	g_k	Type of Transi-tion	$A_{ki}(\text{sec}^{-1})$	$S(\text{at.u.})$	Accu-racy	Source
1	$2s2p -$ $2s\,(^2S)\,2p$	$^3P° - \,^3P°$	$[15.82 \times 10^5]$	$[67136.4]$	$[67199.6]$	1	3	m	4.56×10^{-6}	2.00	B	1
			$[69.33 \times 10^4]$	$[67199.6]$	$[67343.8]$	3	5	m	4.05×10^{-5}	2.50	B	1
2		$^3P° - \,^1P°$										
			$[1573.4]$	$[67136.4]$	130695	1	3	m	0.0118	5.1×10^{-6}	C	1
			$[1574.9]$	$[67199.6]$	130695	3	3	m	5.5	0.00240	C	1
			$[1578.5]$	$[67343.8]$	130695	5	3	m	0.0146	6.4×10^{-6}	C	1

N v

Ground State $\qquad\qquad\qquad\qquad\qquad\qquad\qquad\qquad\qquad\qquad\qquad$ $1s^2\,2s\,{}^2S_{1/2}$

Ionization Potential $\qquad\qquad\qquad\qquad\qquad\qquad\qquad$ $97.863\ \text{eV} = 789532.9\ \text{cm}^{-1}$

Allowed Transitions

List of tabulated lines:

Wavelength [Å]	No.	Wavelength [Å]	No.	Wavelength [Å]	No.
162.562	3	266.375	4	5067	13
186.070	6	1238.81	1	5273	11
186.153	6	1242.80	1	6719	16
186.16	6	3161	9	7330	17
209.270	2	4335	10	15088	8
209.303	2	4603.83	7	15203	8
247.563	5	4619.9	7	15258	8
247.710	5	4751	12		
247.72	5	4933	14		
266.192	4	4952	15		

The values taken from Weiss' calculations [1] are estimated to be accurate to within 10 percent because of the very close agreement between his dipole length and dipole velocity approximations. The values calculated with the length approximation are adopted. The Coulomb approximation should be quite reliable for the highly excited transitions and is given preference over Kelly's approximate Hartree-Fock calculations [2], with which it sometimes disagrees.

References

[1] Weiss, A. W., Astrophys. J. **138,** 1262–1276 (1963).
[2] Kelly, P. S., J. Quant. Spectrosc. Radiat. Transfer **4,** 117 (1964).

No.	Transition Array	Multiplet	$\lambda(\text{Å})$	$E_i(\text{cm}^{-1})$	$E_k(\text{cm}^{-1})$	g_i	g_k	$A_{ki}(10^8\text{sec}^{-1})$	f_{ik}	$S(\text{at.u.})$	$\log gf$	Accuracy	Source
1	$2s-2p$	$^2S-^2P^\circ$ (1 uv)	1240.1	0.0	80637	2	6	3.38	0.234	1.91	-0.330	A	1
			1238.81	0.0	80723	2	4	3.38	0.156	1.27	-0.507	A	ls
			1242.80	0.0	80465	2	2	3.36	0.0778	0.637	-0.808	A	ls
2	$2s-3p$	$^2S-^2P^\circ$ (2 uv)	209.28	0.0	477826	2	6	120	0.235	0.324	-0.327	B+	1
			209.270	0.0	477851	2	4	119	0.157	0.216	-0.504	B+	ls
			209.303	0.0	477777	2	2	119	0.0784	0.108	-0.805	B+	ls
3	$2s-4p$	$^2S-^2P^\circ$ (3 uv)	162.562	0.0	615150	2	6	56.3	0.0669	0.0716	-0.874	B	ca
4	$2p-3s$	$^2P^\circ-^2S$ (4 uv)	266.31	80637	456134	6	2	90.9	0.0322	0.169	-0.714	B+	1
			266.375	80723	456134	4	2	60.6	0.0322	0.113	-0.890	B+	ls
			266.192	80465	456134	2	2	30.2	0.0321	0.0563	-1.192	B+	ls
5	$2p-3d$	$^2P^\circ-^2D$ (5 uv)	247.66	80637	484417	6	10	429	0.658	3.22	0.596	B+	1
			247.710	80723	484427	4	6	429	0.592	1.93	0.374	B+	ls
			247.563	80465	484403	2	4	357	0.656	1.07	0.118	B+	ls
			[247.72]	80723	484403	4	4	71.6	0.0659	0.215	-0.579	B+	ls
6	$2p-4d$	$^2P^\circ-^2D$ (6 uv)	186.13	80637	617905	6	10	140	0.121	0.445	-0.139	B	ca
			186.153	80723	617905	4	6	140	0.109	0.267	-0.361	B	ls
			186.070	80465	617905	2	4	116	0.121	0.148	-0.617	B	ls
			[186.16]	80723	617905	4	4	23.3	0.0121	0.0297	-1.315	B	ls
7	$3s-3p$	$^2S-^2P^\circ$ (1)	4608.7	456134	477826	2	6	0.413	0.395	12.0	-0.103	B	1
			4603.83	456134	477851	2	4	0.415	0.264	8.00	-0.278	B	ls
			4619.9	456134	477777	2	2	0.411	0.131	4.00	-0.580	B	ls
8	$3p-3d$	$^2P^\circ-^2D$	15168	477826	484417	6	10	0.00946	0.0544	16.3	-0.486	B	1
			[15203]	477851	484427	4	6	0.00940	0.0489	9.78	-0.709	B	ls
			[15088]	477777	484403	2	4	0.00801	0.0547	5.43	-0.961	B	ls
			[15258]	477851	484403	4	4	0.00155	0.00542	1.09	-1.664	B	ls
9	$5p-6s$	$^2P^\circ-^2S$ (2)	3161	678297	[709947]	6	2	3.06	0.153	9.55	-0.037	B	ca
10	$6s-7p$	$^2S-^2P^\circ$ (3)	4335	[709947]	732993	2	6	0.376	0.318	9.08	-0.197	B	ca
11	$6p-7s$	$^2P^\circ-^2S$ (4)	5273	712464	[731432]	6	2	1.41	0.196	20.4	0.070	B	ca
12	$6p-7d$	$^2P^\circ-^2D$ (5)	4751	712464	[733516]	6	10	0.963	0.543	51.0	0.513	B	ca
13	$6d-7p$	$^2D-^2P^\circ$ (6)	5067	713289	732993	10	6	0.423	0.0977	16.3	-0.010	B	ca
14	$6d-7f$	$^2D-^2F^\circ$ (7)	4933	713289	[733547]	10	14	1.62	0.828	134	0.918	B	ca
15	$6f-7d$	$^2F^\circ-^2D$ (8)	4952	[713327]	[733516]	14	10	0.161	0.0423	9.66	-0.227	B	ca
16	$7s-8p$	$^2S-^2P^\circ$ (11)	6719	[731432]	[746311]	2	6	0.171	0.348	15.4	-0.157	B	ca
17	$7p-8d$	$^2P^\circ-^2D$ (12)	7330	732993	[746649]	6	10	0.454	0.610	88.3	0.564	B	ca

N VI

Ground State $1s^2\ ^1S_0$

Ionization Potential $551.925\ eV = 4452800\ cm^{-1}$

Allowed Transitions

The results of extensive non-relativistic variational calculations by Weiss [1] are used. Values have been calculated in both the dipole length and dipole velocity approximations and agree to within 1%, except for the $3p\ ^1P° - 3d\ ^1D$ transition where agreement is not as good. The average of the two approximations is adopted [1].

Reference

[1] Weiss, A. W., private communication (1964).

N VI. Allowed Transitions

No.	Transition Array	Multiplet	$\lambda(\text{Å})$	$E_i(cm^{-1})$	$E_k(cm^{-1})$	g_i	g_k	$A_{ki}(10^8 sec^{-1})$	f_{ik}	$S(\text{at.u.})$	$\log gf$	Accuracy	Source
1	$1s^2 - 1s2p$	$^1S - ^1P°$	[28.787]	0	3473790	1	3	18100	0.674	0.0639	-0.171	A	1
2	$1s^2 - 1s3p$	$^1S - ^1P°$	[24.898]	0	4016390	1	3	5160	0.144	0.0118	-0.842	A	1
3	$1s2s - 1s2p$	$^1S - ^1P°$	[2914.6]	[3439490]	3473790	1	3	0.206	0.0786	0.754	-1.105	A	1
4	$1s2s - 1s3p$	$^1S - ^1P°$	[173.34]	[3439490]	4016390	1	3	269	0.364	0.208	-0.439	A	1
5	$1s2p - 1s3d$	$^1P° - ^1D$	[185.09]	3473790	[4014057]	3	5	825	0.706	1.29	0.326	A	1
6	$1s3d - 1s3p$	$^1D - ^1P°$	[42850]?	[4014057]	4016390	5	3	5.44×10^{-4}	0.00899	6.34	-1.347	C+	1
7	$1s2s - 1s2p$	$^3S - ^3P°$	[1901.5]	[3385890]	[3438480]	3	9	0.678	0.110	2.07	-0.481	A	1
8	$1s2s - 1s3p$	$^3S - ^3P°$	[161.40]	[3385890]	[4005471]	3	9	285	0.334	0.533	0.001	A	1
9	$1s2p - 1s3d$	$^3P° - ^3D$	[173.98]	[3438480]	[4013259]	9	15	876	0.662	3.41	0.775	A	1
10	$1s3p - 1s3d$	$^3P° - ^3D$	[12837]?	[4005471]	[4013259]	9	15	0.0102	0.0419	15.9	-0.424	A	1

OXYGEN

O I

Ground State $1s^2 2s^2 2p^4 {}^3P_2$

Ionization Potential $13.614 \text{ eV} = 109836.7 \text{ cm}^{-1}$

Allowed Transitions

List of tabulated lines:

Wavelength [Å]	No.	Wavelength [Å]	No.	Wavelength [Å]	No.
811.37	9	5435.16	40	7943.15	14
877.804	5	5435.76	40	7947.20	14
877.885	5	5436.83	40	7947.56	14
878.979	5	6046.4	41	7950.83	14
879.027	5	6106.5	34	7952.18	14
879.108	5	6155.99	32	7981.97	27
879.553	5	6156.78	32	7982.3	27
936.011	10	6158.19	32	7982.41	27
988.581	3	6242.5	15	7987.00	27
988.658	3	6259.6	36	7987.34	27
988.777	3	6269.4	35	7995.12	27
990.132	3	6453.64	37	8073.7	19
990.120	3	6454.48	37	8221.84	13
990.799	3	6456.01	37	8227.64	13
999.494	6	6653.78	24	8230.01	13
1025.77	8	7002.1	33	8232.99	13
1027.42	8	7156.80	17	8235.31	13
1028.16	8	7194.6	21	8446.5	12
1152.16	4	7254.4	38	8508.63	22
1217.64	7	7471.36	20	8820.45	16
1302.17	2	7473.23	20	9260.88	28
1304.87	2	7476.45	20	9262.73	28
1306.04	2	7477.21	20	9265.99	28
1355.61	1	7479.06	20	9391.2	18
1358.52	1	7480.66	20	11287	29
3947.29	25	7771.96	11	11295.0	30
4368.30	26	7774.18	11	11297.5	30
5328.98	39	7775.40	11	11302.2	30
5329.59	39	7886.31	23	13164	31
5330.66	39	7939.49	14		

The data for the ultraviolet lines are taken from the theoretical work by Garstang [1] and Kelly [2], with the exception of one multiplet where an experimental value by Prag and Clark [3] is available. Even though the agreement between theory and experiment is quite good in this case, namely within 25%, this may be accidental, since the extensive comparisons between theory and experiment for similar transitions of C I and N I reveal many strong discrepancies. As in the case of the other two atoms, one must again expect that the theoretical values are drastically affected by configuration interaction which is entirely neglected in the calculations. Thus, only the most prominent transitions are listed, with an accuracy rating of "E".

Considerable material is available for the lines in the visible and near infrared region of the spectrum. The tabulated values are taken from Kelly's earlier self-consistent field calculations [4] (which include exchange effects in an approximate way), Vainshtein's semi-empirical calculations [5], the Coulomb approximation by Bates and Damgaard, and experimental work by Jürgens [6], Foster [7], Doherty [8], Buttrey and Gibson [9], Wiese and Shumaker [10], and Solarski and Wiese [11]. In all experiments the emission of thermal plasmas generated in stabilized arcs or shock tubes has been studied. The agreement between the various theoretical and experimental methods is often quite remarkable. This is particularly true for the multiplets at 6157, 6455, 6654, 7157, 7477, 7773, 7886, 8227, and 8446 Å for which the spread between the highest and lowest result is only 25% or less. Based on this good agreement, an accuracy of 10% for the averaged values is indicated. In arriving at best values, theoretical and experimental methods have usually been equally weighted, but among the experimental methods, the recent more advanced work [8, 9, 10, 11] is regarded as superseding the earlier work [6, 7]. For the multiplets of the moderately excited $3s - 3p$ array, the advanced experimental methods are used exclusively, since the theoretical papers do not take into account the existence of weak intercombination lines from the upper levels. The theoretical methods are also not too reliable for two other multiplets at 3947 and 4368 Å, since cancellation in the transition integral occurs. In these cases, the experimental results are chosen. In the case of the strong multiplet $3p\,^3P - 3s'\,^3D°$ at 7989 Å recourse is taken to a calculation by Petrie [12] because the use of approximate, hydrogen-like wave functions in this paper has given reasonable results for $3s - 3p$ transitions, but appears to fail otherwise.

References

[1] Garstang, R. H., Proc. Cambridge Phil. Soc. **57,** 115–120 (1961).

[2] Kelly, P. S., Astrophys. J. **140,** 1247–1268 (1964).

[3] Prag, A. B., and Clark, K. C., Phys. Rev. Letters **12,** 34–35 (1964).

[4] Kelly, P. S., J. Quant. Spectrosc. Radiat. Transfer **4,** 117–148 (1964).

[5] Vainshtein, L. A., Optika i Spektroskopiya **3,** 313–321 (1957).

[6] Jürgens, G., Z. Physik **138,** 613–622 (1954).

[7] Foster, E. W., Proc. Phys. Soc. London A **79,** 94–104 (1962).

[8] Doherty, L. R., Thesis Michigan (1961).

[9] Buttrey, D. E., and Gibson, J. B., Technical Documentary Report No. RTD–TDR–63–3047 (1964).

[10] Wiese, W. L., and Shumaker, Jr., J. B., J. Opt. Soc. Am. **51,** 937–942 (1961).

[11] Solarski, J., and Wiese, W. L., Phys. Rev. **135,** A1236–A1241 (1964).

[12] Petrie, W., J. Geophys. Research **55,** 143–151 (1950).

O I.   Allowed Transitions

No.	Transition Array	Multiplet	λ(Å)	E_i(cm⁻¹)	E_k(cm⁻¹)	g_i	g_k	A_{ki}(10⁸sec⁻¹)	f_{ik}	S(at.u.)	log gf	Accuracy	Source
1	$2p^4 -$ $2p^3(^4S°)3s$	$^3P - ^5S°$ (1 uv)											
			1355.61	0.0	73768	5	5	1.3×10^{-5}	3.6×10^{-7}	8.0×10^{-6}	−5.74	E	1
			1358.52	158.5	73768	3	5	3.8×10^{-6}	1.8×10^{-7}	2.4×10^{-6}	−6.27	E	1
2		$^3P - ^3S°$ (2 uv)	*1303.5*	*78.0*	*76795*	*9*	*3*	*3.8*	*0.031*	*1.2*	*−0.54*	D	1, 2, 3
			1302.17	0.0	76795	5	3	2.1	0.031	0.68	−0.80	D	1n
			1304.87	158.5	76795	3	3	1.3	0.032	0.41	−1.02	D	1n
			1306.04	226.5	76795	1	3	0.41	0.031	0.14	−1.50	D	1n
3	$2p^4 -$ $2p^3(^2D°)3s'$	$^3P - ^3D°$ (5 uv)	*989.46*	*78.0*	*101143*	*9*	*15*	*2.3*	*0.056*	*1.6*	*−0.30*	E	1, 2
			988.777	0.0	101135	5	7	2.3	0.047	0.76	−0.63	E	1n
			990.210	158.5	101147	3	5	1.7	0.042	0.42	−0.90	E	1n
			990.799	226.5	101155	1	3	1.2	0.054	0.18	−1.27	E	1n
			988.658	0.0	101147	5	5	0.58	0.0085	0.14	−1.37	E	1n
			990.132	158.5	101155	3	3	0.95	0.014	0.14	−1.38	E	1n
			988.581	0.0	101155	5	3	0.066	5.8×10^{-5}	0.0094	−2.54	E	1n
4		$^1D - ^1D°$ (6 uv)	1152.16	15868	102662	5	5	4.5	0.090	1.7	−0.35	E	1, 2

No.	Transition Array	Multiplet	$\lambda(\text{Å})$	$E_i(\text{cm}^{-1})$	$E_k(\text{cm}^{-1})$	g_i	g_k	$A_{ki}(10^8\text{sec}^{-1})$	f_{ik}	$S(\text{at.u.})$	$\log gf$	Accuracy	Source
5	$2p^4-$ $2p^3(^2P°)3s''$	$^3P-^3P°$	878.45	78.0	113916	9	9	3.2	0.037	0.96	-0.48	E	1, 2
			877.885	0.0	113910	5	5	2.4	0.027	0.39	-0.87	E	1n
			879.027	158.5	113921	3	3	0.79	0.0091	0.079	-1.56	E	1n
			877.804	0.0	113921	5	3	1.3	0.0092	0.13	-1.34	E	1n
			878.979	158.5	113927	3	1	3.2	0.012	0.11	-1.43	E	1n
			879.108	158.5	113910	3	5	0.83	0.016	0.14	-1.32	E	1n
			879.553	226.5	113921	1	3	1.1	0.038	0.11	-1.42	E	1n
6		$^1D-^1P°$ (7 uv)	999.494	15868	115918	5	3	3.9	0.035	0.57	-0.76	E	1, 2
7		$^1S-^1P°$ (9 uv)	1217.64	33792	115918	1	3	2.0	0.13	0.53	-0.88	E	1, 2
8	$2p^4-$ $2p^3(^4S°)3d$	$^3P-^3D°$ (4 uv)	1026.6	78.0	97488	9	15	0.39	0.010	0.31	-1.04	D$-$	2
			1025.77	0.0	97488	5	7	0.39	0.0086	0.15	-1.36	D$-$	ls
			1027.42	158.5	97488	3	5	0.29	0.0077	0.078	-1.65	D$-$	ls
			1028.16	226.5	97488	1	3	0.20	0.010	0.035	-1.98	D$-$	ls
			1025.77	0.0	97488	5	5	0.097	0.0015	0.026	-2.12	D$-$	ls
			1027.42	158.5	97488	3	3	0.16	0.0026	0.026	-2.12	D$-$	ls
			1025.77	0.0	97488	5	3	0.011	1.0×10^{-4}	0.0017	-3.29	D$-$	ls
9	$2p^4-$ $2p^3(^2D°)3d'$	$^3P-^3P°$	811.37	78.0	123326	9	9	0.78	0.0077	0.18	-1.16	D$-$	2
10		$^1D-^1F°$ (8 uv)	936.011	15868	124326	5	7	0.83	0.015	0.23	-1.12	D$-$	2
11	$2p^33s-$ $2p^3(^4S°)3p$	$^5S°-^5P$ (1)	7773.4	73768	86629	5	15	0.340	0.922	118	0.664	B	4, 5, 8, 11, ca
			7771.96	73768	86631	5	7	0.340	0.431	55.1	0.333	B	ls
			7774.18	73768	86627	5	5	0.340	0.307	39.3	0.186	B	ls
			7775.40	73768	86625	5	3	0.340	0.184	23.6	-0.035	B	ls
12		$^3S°-^3P$ (4)	8446.5	76795	88631	3	9	0.280	0.898	74.9	0.430	B	4, 8, 11, ca
13	$2p^33s'-$ $2p^3(^2D°)3p'$	$^3D°-^3D$ (34)	8226.8	101143	113295	15	15	0.323	0.327	133	0.691	B	4, 6, ca
			8221.84	101135	113294	7	7	0.292	0.296	56.1	0.316	B	ls
			8230.01	101147	113295	5	5	0.211	0.214	29.0	0.029	B	ls
			8232.99	101155	113298	3	3	0.261	0.266	21.6	-0.099	B	ls
			8221.84	101135	113295	7	5	0.0663	0.0480	9.09	-0.474	B	ls
			8227.64	101147	113298	5	3	0.0834	0.0508	6.88	-0.595	B	ls
			8230.01	101147	113294	5	7	0.0261	0.0371	5.03	-0.732	B	ls
			8235.31	101155	113295	3	5	0.0432	0.0732	5.95	-0.659	B	ls
14		$^3D°-^3F$ (35)	7949.3	101143	113719	15	21	0.373	0.495	194	0.87	C	4, 6, ca
			7947.56	101135	113714	7	9	0.373	0.454	83	0.50	C	ls
			7950.83	101147	113721	5	7	0.331	0.439	58	0.342	C	ls
			7952.18	101155	113727	3	5	0.313	0.495	38.8	0.171	C	ls
			7943.15	101135	113721	7	7	0.0417	0.0394	7.2	-0.56	C	ls
			7947.20	101147	113727	5	5	0.058	0.055	7.2	-0.56	C	ls
			7939.49	101135	113727	7	5	0.00165	0.00111	0.203	-2.109	C	ls
15		$^3D°-^3P$	[6242.5]?	101143	[117158]?	15	9	0.73	0.257	79	0.59	C	4
16		$^1D°-^1F$ (37)	8820.45	102662	113996	5	7	0.261	0.426	62	0.328	C	4, ca
17		$^1D°-^1D$ (38)	7156.80	102662	116631	5	5	0.473	0.363	42.8	0.259	B	4, 11, ca
18		$^1D°-^1P$	[9391.2]?	102662	[113307]?	5	3	0.215	0.171	26.4	-0.069	C	4

No.	Transition Array	Multiplet	$\lambda(\text{Å})$	$E_i(\text{cm}^{-1})$	$E_k(\text{cm}^{-1})$	g_i	g_k	$A_{ki}(10^8\text{sec}^{-1})$	f_{ik}	$S(\text{at.u.})$	$\log gf$	Accuracy	Source
19		$^3P° - {}^3S$	[8073.7]?	113916	[126298]?	9	3	0.339	0.110	26.4	−0.003	C	4
20	$2p^33s'' - 2p^3(^2P°)3p''$	$^3P° - {}^3D$ (55)	7477.3	113916	127286	9	15	0.408	0.570	126	0.710	B	4, 6, *ca*
			7476.45	113910	127282	5	7	0.408	0.479	58.9	0.379	B	*ls*
			7479.06	113921	127288	3	5	0.306	0.428	31.6	0.108	B	*ls*
			7480.66	113927	127291	1	3	0.226	0.570	14.0	−0.244	B	*ls*
			7473.23	113910	127288	5	5	0.102	0.0856	10.5	−0.369	B	*ls*
			7477.21	113921	127291	3	3	0.170	0.143	10.5	−0.369	B	*ls*
			7471.36	113910	127291	5	3	0.0114	0.00571	0.702	−1.545	B	*ls*
21		$^3P° - {}^3P$	[7194.6]?	113916	[127811]?	9	9	0.478	0.371	79	0.52	C	4
22		$^1P° - {}^1P$	8508.63	115918	127668	3	3	0.289	0.314	26.4	−0.026	C	4
23		$^1P° - {}^1D$ (64)	7886.31	115918	128595	3	5	0.370	0.575	44.8	0.236	B	4, 6, *ca*
24		$^1P° - {}^1S$ (65)	6653.78	115918	130943	3	1	0.600	0.133	8.72	−0.400	B	4, 11, *ca*
25	$2p^33s - 2p^3(^4S°)4p$	$^5S° - {}^5P$ (3)	3947.29	73768	99095	5	15	0.00326	0.00229	0.149	−1.94	C	4, 7
26		$^3S° - {}^3P$ (5)	4368.30	76795	99680	3	9	0.0066	0.0056	0.242	−1.77	C	9, 11
27	$2p^3(^4S°)3p - 2p^3(^2D°)3s'$	$^3P - {}^3D°$ (19)	7989.9	88631	101143	9	15	0.29	0.46	110	0.61	D	12
			7995.12	88631	101135	5	7	0.29	0.38	50	0.28	D	*ls*
			7987.00	88630	101147	3	5	0.21	0.34	27	0.01	D	*ls*
			7982.41	88631	101155	1	3	0.16	0.46	12	−0.34	D	*ls*
			7987.34	88631	101147	5	5	0.072	0.068	9.0	−0.47	D	*ls*
			7981.97	88631	101155	3	3	0.12	0.11	9.0	−0.47	D	*ls*
			[7982.3]	88631	101155	5	3	0.0080	0.0046	0.60	−1.64	D	*ls*
28	$2p^33p - 2p^3(^4S°)3d$	$^5P - {}^5D°$ (8)	9263.9	86629	97420	15	25	0.419	0.90	412	1.130	C	4, *ca*
			9265.99	86631	97420	7	9	0.419	0.69	148	0.69	C	*ls*
			9262.73	86627	97420	5	7	0.280	0.50	77	0.401	C	*ls*
			9260.88	86625	97420	3	5	0.147	0.315	28.8	−0.025	C	*ls*
			9265.99	86631	97420	7	7	0.180	0.140	38.4	0.100	C	*ls*
			9262.73	86627	97420	5	5	0.245	0.315	48.0	0.197	C	*ls*
			9260.88	86625	97421	3	3	0.315	0.405	37.0	0.085	C	*ls*
			9265.99	86631	97420	7	5	0.0279	0.0257	5.5	−0.75	C	*ls*
			9262.73	86627	97421	5	3	0.105	0.081	12.4	−0.393	C	*ls*
			9260.88	86625	97421	3	1	0.420	0.0180	16.5	−0.268	C	*ls*
29		$^3P - {}^3D°$	11287	88631	97488	9	15	0.235	0.75	250	0.83	C	4
30	$2p^33p - 2p^3(^4S°)4s$	$^5P - {}^5S°$ (7)	11299	86629	95476	15	5	0.272	0.173	97	0.415	C	4, *ca*
			11302.2	86631	95476	7	5	0.127	0.173	45.1	0.084	C	*ls*
			11297.5	86627	95476	5	5	0.091	0.173	32.2	−0.062	C	*ls*
			11295.0	86625	95476	3	5	0.054	0.173	19.3	−0.284	C	*ls*
31		$^3P - {}^3S°$	13164	88631	96226	9	3	0.188	0.163	63	0.165	C	4, *ca*

No.	Transition Array	Multiplet	$\lambda(\text{Å})$	$E_i(\text{cm}^{-1})$	$E_k(\text{cm}^{-1})$	g_i	g_k	$A_{ki}(10^8\text{sec}^{-1})$	f_{ik}	S(at.u.)	$\log gf$	Accuracy	Source
32	$2p^33p -$ $2p^3(^4S°)4d$	$^5P - ^5D°$ (10)	6157.3	86629	102865	15	25	0.0701	0.0664	20.2	−0.001	B	4, 11, ca
			6158.19	86631	102865	7	9	0.0701	0.0512	7.27	−0.445	B	ls
			6156.78	86627	102865	5	7	0.0468	0.0372	3.77	−0.731	B	ls
			6155.99	86625	102865	3	5	0.0245	0.0232	1.41	−1.158	B	ls
			6158.19	86631	102865	7	7	0.0234	0.0133	1.89	−1.031	B	ls
			6156.78	86627	102865	5	5	0.0410	0.0233	2.36	−0.934	B	ls
			6155.99	86625	102865	3	3	0.0527	0.0299	1.82	−1.047	B	ls
			6158.19	86631	102865	7	5	0.00467	0.00190	0.269	−1.877	B	ls
			6156.78	86627	102865	5	3	0.0175	0.00598	0.606	−1.524	B	ls
			6155.99	86625	102865	3	1	0.0702	0.0133	0.808	−1.399	B	ls
33		$^3P - ^3D°$ (21)	7002.1	88631	102908	9	15	0.0325	0.0398	8.3	−0.446	C	4, 6, ca
34	$2p^33p' -$ $2p^3(^2D°)4d'$	$^3D - ^3F°$ (43)	[6106.5]	113295	[129667]	15	21	0.0460	0.0360	10.9	−0.268	C	4, 6, ca
35		$^3F - ^3F°$ (48)	[6269.4]	113719	[129667]	21	21	0.0198	0.0117	5.1	−0.61	C	4, 6, ca
36		$^3F - ^3G°$ (50)	6259.6	113719	129690	21	27	0.063	0.0475	20.6	−0.001	C	4, 6, ca
37	$2p^33p -$ $2p^3(^4S°)5s$	$^5P - ^5S°$ (9)	6455.0	86629	102116	15	5	0.0710	0.0148	4.71	−0.654	B	4, 11, ca
			6456.01	86631	102116	7	5	0.0331	0.0148	2.20	−0.985	B	ls
			6454.48	86627	102116	5	5	0.0237	0.0148	1.57	−1.131	B	ls
			6453.64	86625	102116	3	5	0.0142	0.0148	0.942	−1.353	B	ls
38		$^3P - ^3S°$ (20)	7254.4	88631	102412	9	3	0.062	0.0162	3.48	−0.84	C	4, 6, ca
39	$2p^33p -$ $2p^3(^4S°)5d$	$^5P - ^5D°$ (12)	5330.0	86629	105385	15	25	0.0197	0.0140	3.68	−0.68	C	4, 6, 7, ca
			5330.66	86631	105385	7	9	0.0196	0.0107	1.32	−1.124	C	ls
			5329.59	86627	105385	5	7	0.0131	0.0078	0.69	−1.407	C	ls
			5328.98	86625	105385	3	5	0.0069	0.00490	0.258	−1.83	C	ls
			5330.66	86631	105385	7	7	0.0066	0.00279	0.343	−1.71	C	ls
			5329.59	86627	105385	5	5	0.0115	0.00489	0.429	−1.61	C	ls
			5328.98	86625	105385	3	3	0.0148	0.0063	0.331	−1.72	C	ls
			5330.66	86631	105385	7	5	0.00131	4.00×10^{-4}	0.0491	−2.55	C	ls
			5329.59	86627	105385	5	3	0.00491	0.00125	0.110	−2.203	C	ls
			5328.98	86625	105385	3	1	0.0197	0.00279	0.147	−2.077	C	ls
40	$2p^33p -$ $2p^3(^4S°)6s$	$^5P - ^5S°$ (11)	5436.1	86629	105019	15	5	0.0305	0.00450	1.21	−1.170	C	4, 5, 6, 7, ca
			5436.83	86631	105019	7	5	0.0142	0.00451	0.57	−1.50	C	ls
			5435.76	86627	105019	5	5	0.0102	0.00450	0.403	−1.65	C	ls
			5435.16	86625	105019	3	5	0.0061	0.00451	0.242	−1.87	C	ls
41		$^3P - ^3S°$ (22)	6046.4	88631	105165	9	3	0.0234	0.00427	0.77	−1.415	C	4, 6, ca

Forbidden Transitions

The list of forbidden lines for O I is a very interesting one since it contains some of the very few cases of experimental determinations of forbidden line strengths. This fortunate circumstance is due to the appearance of strong forbidden lines in the aurora, so that the latter could be used as a "light source." Extensive measurements by Omholt [1] have given, for the 5577 Å line, a transition probability of 1.43 sec^{-1} ± 14%, whereas Garstang [2] with a refined calculation has obtained 1.25 sec^{-1}. For another case, namely the lifetime for the ^{1}D state, the averaged experimental result [3, 4] is approximately 160 sec, whereas the theory [5, 7] gives 135 sec. In both instances the mean value is adopted. Attempts have also been made in the laboratory to obtain experimental results, but they are all subject to some doubt and are therefore omitted in this compilation.

Aside from applications in atmospheric physics, the importance of the above lines lies in the circumstance that the experimental determinations give a reliable indication of the uncertainties in the theory of forbidden line strengths which in itself does not allow error estimates.

A number of other transitions in the p^4 configuration have been investigated by several authors. All electric quadrupole line strengths are taken from Garstang [6], since his estimate of the quadrupole integral s_q is the most advanced one available. Naqvi [5], and Yamanouchi and Horie [7], in their calculations of magnetic dipole line strengths, retain the spin-spin and spin-other-orbit parameter in the transformation coefficients, while Garstang neglects it. Thus, their values are used for the ^{3}P − ^{1}D and ^{3}P − ^{1}S transitions, where this gives an improvement of about 15%. For the latter line, however, only Yamanouchi and Horie's [7] data are employed, since Naqvi's treatment of configuration interaction effects, which are important for this line, appears to be inadequate (see also general introduction).

References

[1] Omholt, A., Geofys. Publikasjoner Norske Videnskaps. Akad. Oslo **21**, 1–38 (1959).
[2] Garstang, R. H., The Airglow and the Aurorae, 324–327 (ed. Armstrong and Dalgarno, Pergamon Press, New York, 1956).
[3] Stoffregen, W., and Derblom, H., Nature **185**, 28–29 (1960).
[4] Omholt, A., Planetary and Space Science **2**, 246–248 (1960).
[5] Naqvi, A. M., Thesis Harvard (1951).
[6] Garstang, R. H., Monthly Notices Roy. Astron. Soc. **111**, 115–124 (1951).
[7] Yamanouchi, T., and Horie, H., J. Phys. Soc. Japan **7**, 52–56 (1952).

O I.   Forbidden Transitions

No.	Transition Array	Multiplet	λ(Å)	E_i(cm^{-1})	E_k(cm^{-1})	g_i	g_k	Type of Transition	A_{ki}(sec^{-1})	S(at.u.)	Accuracy	Source
1	$2p^4 - 2p^4$	^{3}P − ^{3}P										
			[63.07 × 10^4]	0.0	158.5	5	3	e	1.30 × 10^{-11}	2.32	C	6
			[63.07 × 10^4]	0.0	158.5	5	3	m	8.95 × 10^{-5}	2.50	B	5, 6, 7
			[44.14 × 10^4]	0.0	226.5	5	1	e	1.00 × 10^{-10}	1.03	C	6
			[14.70 × 10^5]	158.5	226.5	3	1	m	1.70 × 10^{-5}	2.00	B	5, 6, 7
2		^{3}P − ^{1}D (1 F)										
			6300.23	0.0	15867.7	5	5	e	2.4 × 10^{-5}	7.1 × 10^{-4}	D	6
			6300.23	0.0	15867.7	5	5	m	5.1 × 10^{-3}	2.37 × 10^{-4}	C	3, 4, 5, 7
			6363.88	158.5	15867.7	3	5	e	3.2 × 10^{-6}	9.9 × 10^{-5}	D	6
			6363.88	158.5	15867.7	3	5	m	1.64 × 10^{-3}	7.9 × 10^{-5}	C	3, 4, 5, 7
			[6391.6]	226.5	15867.7	1	5	e	1.1 × 10^{-6}	3.5 × 10^{-5}	D	6
3		^{3}P − ^{1}S (2 F)										
			[2958.4]	0.0	33792.4	5	1	e	3.7 × 10^{-4}	5.0 × 10^{-5}	D	6
			2972.3	158.5	33792.4	3	1	m	0.067	6.5 × 10^{-5}	C	7
4		^{1}D − ^{1}S (3 F)	5577.35	15867.7	33792.4	5	1	e	1.34	4.31	C+	1, 2

O II

Ground State $1s^2\,2s^2\,2p^3\,{}^4S^{\circ}_{3/2}$

Ionization Potential $35.108\ \mathrm{eV} = 283244\ \mathrm{cm}^{-1}$

Allowed Transitions

List of tabulated lines:

Wavelength [Å]	No.	Wavelength [Å]	No.	Wavelength [Å]	No.
424.66	22	3007.4	84	3488.18	36
429.918	10	3007.74	85	3496.27	36
430.041	10	3008.28	85	3712.75	25
430.177	10	3008.8	84	3727.33	25
440.58	18	3009.7	85	3729.34	73
442.03	17	3009.81	85	3735.9	73
445.62	16	3010.0	85	3735.94	73
464.78	21	3010.5	85	3739.92	69
468.77	20	3012.8	85	3749.49	25
470.41	19	3013.0	85	3762.63	69
481.66	13	3013.37	84	3777.60	69
483.752	12	3014.0	84	3794.48	70
483.796	12	3019.8	84	3803.14	70
484.03	12	3032.08	86	3821.68	70
485.086	11	3032.50	86	3830.45	70
485.47	11	3047.5	86	3833.10	43
485.515	11	3113.71	66	3842.82	42
515.498	15	3122.62	66	3843.58	43
515.640	15	3124.02	66	3847.89	42
517.937	14	3129.44	66	3850.81	42
518.242	14	3134.32	66	3851.04	42
539.086	5	3134.82	66	3851.47	43
539.547	5	3138.44	66	3856.16	42
539.853	5	3139.77	66	3857.18	43
555.056	8	3270.9	71	3863.50	42
555.121	8	3270.98	71	3864.13	41
600.585	9	3273.52	71	3864.45	42
616.291	6	3277.69	67	3864.68	42
616.363	6	3282.0	39	3872.45	41
617.051	6	3287.59	67	3874.10	41
644.148	4	3290.13	67	3875.82	43
672.948	7	3295.13	67	3882.20	42
673.768	7	3301.56	67	3882.45	41
718.484	2	3305.15	67	3883.15	42
718.562	2	3306.60	67	3893.53	41
796.661	3	3377.20	38	3896.30	41
832.754	1	3390.25	38	3907.45	41
833.326	1	3407.38	72	3911.96	33
834.462	1	3409.84	72	3912.09	33
2733.34	65	3447.98	68	3919.29	33
2747.46	65	3460.6	26	3926.58	41
3000.1	84	3470.42	68	3945.05	30
3002.2	84	3470.81	68	3954.37	30
3006.0	84	3474.94	37	3967.44	47
3007.08	85	3479.7	26	3973.26	30

Wavelength [Å]	No.	Wavelength [Å]	No.	Wavelength [Å]	No.
3982.72	30	4272.3	34	4596.17	31
3985.46	47	4275.52	78	4598.2	50
4060.8	82	4276.71	77	4602.11	81
4069.64	40	4276.71	78		
4069.90	40			4609.42	81
		4277.40	78	4613.11	81
4072.16	40	4277.90	78	4638.85	23
4075.87	40	4281.40	77	4641.81	23
4078.86	40	4282.82	77	4649.14	23
4084.66	46	4282.96	78		
4085.12	40			4650.84	23
		4283.13	78	4661.64	23
4087.16	76	4283.75	78	4673.75	23
4089.30	76	4284.0	78	4676.23	23
4092.94	40	4284.4	78	4690.97	62
4094.18	40	4288.8	77		
4095.63	76			4691.47	62
		4288.83	77	4696.36	23
4096.18	76	4294.82	77	4698.48	60
4096.54	46	4295.5	29	4699.21	49
4097.26	45	4303.82	77	4699.21	60
4097.26	76	4317.14	24		
4103.02	45			4701.23	62
		4319.63	24	4701.76	62
4104.74	45	4319.93	63	4703.18	60
4105.00	45	4325.77	24	4705.36	49
4106.03	40	4328.62	63	4710.04	48
4108.75	76	4329.0	29		
4109.3	76			4741.71	49
		4336.87	24	4751.34	48
4109.8	59	4340.36	79	4752.70	48
4110.20	59	4342.00	79	4845.0	54
4110.80	45	4345.56	24	4856.49	53
4112.03	46	4347.43	32		
4113.82	59			4856.76	53
		4349.1	32	4861.03	61
4114.4	76	4349.43	24	4864.95	53
4119.22	45	4351.27	32	4871.58	61
4120.28	45	4351.5	32	4872.2	61
4120.55	45	4359.38	51		
4121.48	44			4890.93	52
		4366.90	24	4906.88	52
4126.1	76	4369.28	51	4924.60	52
4129.34	44	4371.3	79	4941.12	56
4132.81	44	4395.95	51	4943.06	56
4140.74	44	4406.02	51		
4141.96	64			4955.78	56
		4414.91	28	5160.02	55
4142.08	64	4416.98	28	5176.00	55
4142.24	64	4443.05	57	5190.56	55
4143.4	64	4443.7	57	5206.73	55
4143.52	64	4447.7	57		
4143.77	64			6627.62	75
		4448.21	57	6640.90	27
4145.6	64	4452.38	28	6666.94	75
4145.90	64	4465.40	35	6678.19	75
4146.09	64	4466.6	80	6718.1	75
4153.30	44	4467.88	35		
4156.54	44			6721.35	27
		4469.32	35	6810.6	74
4169.23	44	4489.48	80	6844.1	74
4185.46	58	4491.25	80	6846.97	74
4189.6	58	4539.6	50	6869.74	74
4189.79	58	4563.2	50		
4253.9	83			6885.07	74
		4590.97	31	6895.29	74
4263.2	77	4596.0	31	6906.54	74
				6908.11	74
				6910.75	74

Most data on the vacuum ultraviolet lines are taken from the self-consistent field calculations by Kelly [1] in which exchange effects have been considered. The data for the strong $2s^2 2p^3 - 2s2p^4$ and $2p^3 - 2p^2 3s$ transitions are probably quite uncertain since these are sensitively affected by configuration interaction which has not been taken into account. Two transitions of the $2s^2 2p^3 - 2s2p^4$ array could be taken, however, from the calculations of Levinson et al. [2] in which the effects of configuration interaction have been approximately included.

For the multiplets in the visible four data sources have been selected: simplified self-consistent field calculations by Kelly [3] (with exchange effects approximately taken into account), the Coulomb approximation by Bates and Damgaard, emission measurements by Mastrup and Wiese [4], and intermediate coupling calculations by Garstang [5]. The absolute multiplet values have been obtained by averaging the results of the first three methods mentioned. The agreement is quite remarkable, often within 30%. For the breakdown of the multiplets into lines the intermediate coupling calculations by Garstang [5] and, whenever available, the experimental results by Mastrup and Wiese [4] are employed, both normalized to the absolute total multiplet values. The two sets of data agree very well, while LS-coupling values show large deviations for some multiplets of the $3p - 3d$ array.

The absolute values of the intercombination lines are obtained by normalizing Garstang's coupling calculations [5] to the Coulomb approximation, as he has proposed in his paper.

References

[1] Kelly, P. S., Astrophys. J. **140**, 1247–1268 (1964).
[2] Levinson, I. B., Bolotin, A. B., and Levin, L. I., Trudy Vil'nyusskogo Univ. **5**, 49–55 (1956).
[3] Kelly, P. S., J. Quant. Spectrosc. Radiat. Transfer **4**, 117–148 (1964).
[4] Mastrup, F., and Wiese, W. L., Z. Astrophys. **44**, 259–279 (1958).
[5] Garstang, R. H., Monthly Notices Roy. Astron. Soc. **114**, 118–133 (1954).

O II. Allowed Transitions

No.	Transition Array	Multiplet	$\lambda(\text{Å})$	$E_i(\text{cm}^{-1})$	$E_k(\text{cm}^{-1})$	g_i	g_k	$A_{ki}(10^8\ \text{sec}^{-1})$	f_{ik}	$S(\text{at.u.})$	$\log gf$	Accuracy	Source
1	$2s^2 2p^3 - 2s2p^4$	$^4S^\circ - {}^4P$ (1 uv)	833.80	0.0	119933	4	12	14	0.43	4.7	0.23	E	1
			834.462	0.0	119838	4	6	13	0.21	2.3	−0.08	E	ls
			833.326	0.0	120001	4	4	14	0.15	1.6	−0.23	E	ls
			832.754	0.0	120084	4	2	14	0.07	0.77	−0.55	E	ls
2		$^2D^\circ - {}^2D$ (4 uv)	718.54	26817	165991	10	10	32	0.25	5.9	0.40	E	1
			718.484	26808	165988	6	6	30	0.23	3.3	0.14	E	ls
			718.562	26829	165996	4	4	29	0.22	2.1	−0.05	E	ls
			718.484	26808	165996	6	4	3.1	0.016	0.23	−1.01	E	ls
			718.562	26829	165988	4	6	2.1	0.024	0.23	−1.01	E	ls
3		$^2P^\circ - {}^2D$ (11 uv)	796.661	40467	165991	6	10	4.4	0.070	1.1	−0.38	E	2
4		$^2P^\circ - {}^2S$ (13 uv)	644.148	40467	195710	6	2	72	0.15	1.9	−0.05	E	2
5	$2p^3 - 2p^2(^3P)3s$	$^4S^\circ - {}^4P$ (2 uv)	539.37	0.0	185402	4	12	8.6	0.11	0.80	−0.35	E	1
			539.086	0.0	185499	4	6	8.6	0.056	0.40	−0.65	E	ls
			539.547	0.0	185341	4	4	8.6	0.037	0.27	−0.82	E	ls
			539.853	0.0	185235	4	2	8.6	0.019	0.13	−1.13	E	ls
6		$^2D^\circ - {}^2P$ (5 uv)	616.56	26817	189008	10	6	18	0.061	1.2	−0.21	E	1
			616.291	26808	189068	6	4	16	0.061	0.74	−0.44	E	ls
			617.051	26829	188888	4	2	18	0.051	0.41	−0.69	E	ls
			616.363	26829	189068	4	4	1.8	0.010	0.083	−1.39	E	ls

No.	Transition Array	Multiplet	λ(Å)	E_i(cm^{-1})	E_k(cm^{-1})	g_i	g_k	A_{ki}(10^8 sec^{-1})	f_{ik}	S(at.u.)	log gf	Accuracy	Source
7		^{2}P°—^{2}P (12 uv)	673.22	40467	189008	6	6	9.2	0.063	0.84	−0.42	E	1
			672.948	40467	189068	4	4	7.7	0.052	0.46	−0.68	E	ls
			673.768	40468	188888	2	2	6.2	0.042	0.19	−1.08	E	ls
			673.768	40467	188888	4	2	3.1	0.010	0.093	−1.38	E	ls
			672.948	40468	189068	2	4	1.5	0.021	0.093	−1.38	E	ls
8	$2p^3$ — $2p^2(^1D)3s'$	^{2}D°—^{2}D (6 uv)	555.08	26817	206972	10	10	15	0.067	1.2	−0.17	E	1
			555.056	26808	206971	6	6	14	0.063	0.69	−0.42	E	ls
			555.121	26829	206972	4	4	13	0.061	0.44	−0.62	E	ls
			555.056	26808	206972	6	4	1.5	0.0045	0.049	−1.57	E	ls
			555.121	26829	206971	4	6	0.97	0.0067	0.049	−1.57	E	ls
9		^{2}P°—^{2}D (14 uv)	600.585	40467	206972	6	10	4.3	0.039	0.46	−0.63	E	1
10	$2p^3$ — $2p^2(^3P)3d$	^{4}S°—^{4}P (3 uv)	430.09	0.0	232511	4	12	39	0.32	1.8	0.11	D−	1
			430.177	0.0	232463	4	6	39	0.16	0.91	−0.19	D−	ls
			430.041	0.0	232536	4	4	39	0.11	0.61	−0.37	D−	ls
			429.918	0.0	232603	4	2	39	0.054	0.31	−0.67	D−	ls
11		^{2}D°—^{2}F (8 uv)	485.27	26817	232889	10	14	25	0.12	1.9	0.08	D−	1
			485.086	26808	232959	6	8	25	0.12	1.1	−0.16	D−	ls
			485.515	26829	232796	4	6	23	0.12	0.78	−0.31	D−	ls
			[485.47]	26808	232796	6	6	1.6	0.0058	0.056	−1.46	D−	ls
12		^{2}D°—^{2}P (9 uv)	483.91	26817	233468	10	6	0.84	0.0018	0.028	−1.75	D−	1
			483.976	26808	233430	6	4	0.76	0.0018	0.017	−1.97	D−	ls
			483.752	26829	233544	4	2	0.84	0.0015	0.0094	−2.23	D−	ls
			[484.03]	26829	233430	4	4	0.084	3.0×10^{-4}	0.0019	−2.93	D−	ls
13		^{2}D°—^{2}D (10 uv)	481.66	26817	234434	10	10	5.4	0.019	0.30	−0.73	D−	1
14		^{2}P°—^{2}P (16 uv)	518.13	40467	233468	6	6	11	0.045	0.46	−0.57	D−	1
			518.242	40467	233430	4	4	9.4	0.038	0.26	−0.82	D−	ls
			517.937	40468	233544	2	2	7.5	0.030	0.10	−1.22	D−	ls
			517.937	40467	233544	4	2	3.7	0.0075	0.051	−1.52	D−	ls
			518.242	40468	233430	2	4	1.9	0.015	0.051	−1.52	D−	ls
15		^{2}P°—^{2}D (17 uv)	515.55	40467	234434	6	10	15	0.097	0.98	−0.24	D−	1
			515.498	40467	234454	4	6	15	0.087	0.59	−0.46	D−	ls
			515.640	40468	234402	2	4	12	0.097	0.33	−0.71	D−	ls
			515.640	40467	234402	4	4	2.4	0.0097	0.066	−1.41	D−	ls
16	$2p^3$ — $2p^2(^1D)3d'$	^{2}D°—^{2}F	445.62	26817	251222	10	14	26	0.11	1.6	0.04	D−	1
17		^{2}D°—^{2}D	442.03	26817	253048	10	10	21	0.063	0.91	−0.20	D−	1
18		^{2}D°—^{2}P	440.58	26817	253791	10	6	7.7	0.013	0.20	−0.87	D−	1
19		^{2}P°—^{2}D	470.41	40467	253048	6	10	6.5	0.036	0.33	−0.67	D−	1
20		^{2}P°—^{2}P	468.77	40467	253791	6	6	12	0.039	0.36	−0.64	D−	1
21		^{2}P°—^{2}S	464.78	40467	255622	6	2	16	0.017	0.16	−0.99	D−	1
22	$2p^3$ — $2p^2(^1S)3d''$	^{2}P°—^{2}D	[424.66]	40467	[275951]	6	10	19	0.086	0.72	−0.29	D−	1

No.	Transition Array	Multiplet	$\lambda(\text{Å})$	$E_i(\text{cm}^{-1})$	$E_k(\text{cm}^{-1})$	g_i	g_k	$A_{ki}(10^8 \text{ sec}^{-1})$	f_{ik}	$S(\text{at.u.})$	$\log gf$	Accuracy	Source
23	$2p^23s -$ $2p^2(^3P)3p$	$^4P - {^4D}°$ (1)	4651.5	185402	206895	12	20	1.02	0.55	101	0.82	C	3, 4, ca
			4649.14	185499	207003	6	8	1.04	0.448	41.1	0.429	C	4n, 5n
			4641.81	185341	206878	4	6	0.79	0.381	23.3	0.183	C	4n, 5n
			4638.85	185235	206786	2	4	0.422	0.272	8.3	−0.264	C	4n, 5n
			4676.23	185499	206878	6	6	0.257	0.084	7.8	−0.296	C	4n, 5n
			4661.64	185341	206786	4	4	0.52	0.169	10.4	−0.169	C	4n, 5n
			4650.84	185235	206731	2	2	0.82	0.265	8.1	−0.277	C	4n, 5n
			4696.36	185499	206786	6	4	0.0372	0.0082	0.76	−1.308	C	4n, 5n
			4673.75	185341	206731	4	2	0.131	0.0214	1.32	−1.067	C	4n, 5n
24		$^4P - {^4P}°$ (2)	4341.3	185402	208431	12	12	1.05	0.297	51	0.55	C	3, 4, ca
			4349.43	185499	208484	6	6	0.74	0.211	18.1	0.102	C	4n, 5n
			4336.87	185341	208392	4	4	0.164	0.0462	2.64	−0.73	C	4n, 5n
			4325.77	185235	208346	2	2	0.155	0.0435	1.24	−1.060	C	4n, 5n
			4366.90	185499	208392	6	4	0.50	0.096	8.3	−0.239	C	4n, 5n
			4345.56	185341	208346	4	2	0.89	0.125	7.2	−0.300	C	4n, 5n
			4319.63	185341	208484	4	6	0.284	0.119	6.8	−0.321	C	4n, 5n
			4317.14	185235	208392	2	4	0.424	0.237	6.7	−0.325	C	4n, 5n
25		$^4P - {^4S}°$ (3)	3735.9	185402	212162	12	4	1.77	0.123	18.2	0.170	C	3, 4, ca
			3749.49	185499	212162	6	4	0.90	0.127	9.4	−0.119	C	4n, 5n
			3727.33	185341	212162	4	4	0.59	0.122	6.0	−0.312	C	4n, 5n
			3712.75	185235	212162	2	4	0.280	0.116	2.83	−0.64	C	4n, 5n
26		$^4P - {^2P}°$	[3479.7]	185499	214229	6	4	0.00101	1.22×10^{-4}	0.0084	−3.135	C	5
			[3460.6]	185341	214229	4	4	0.00154	2.76×10^{-4}	0.0126	−2.96	C	5
27		$^2P - {^2S}°$ (4)	6694.4	189008	203942	6	2	0.287	0.064	8.5	−0.414	C	3, ca
			6721.35	189068	203942	4	2	0.189	0.064	5.7	−0.59	C	ls
			6640.90	188888	203942	2	2	0.098	0.065	2.83	−0.89	C	ls
28		$^2P - {^2D}°$ (5)	4418.1	189008	211636	6	10	1.13	0.55	48.1	0.52	C	3, 4, ca
			4414.91	189068	211713	4	6	1.15	0.50	29.3	0.305	C	4n, 5n
			4416.98	188888	211522	2	4	0.95	0.55	16.1	0.044	C	4n, 5n
			4452.38	189068	211522	4	4	0.154	0.0457	2.68	−0.74	C	4n, 5n
29		$^2P - {^4S}°$	[4329.0]	189068	212162	4	4	0.00157	4.42×10^{-4}	0.0252	−2.75	C	5
			[4295.5]	188888	212162	2	4	0.268×10^{-3}	1.48×10^{-4}	0.00420	−3.53	C	5
30		$^2P - {^2P}°$ (6)	3966.9	189008	214210	6	6	1.46	0.343	26.9	0.314	C	3, 4, ca
			3973.26	189068	214229	4	4	1.27	0.300	15.7	0.080	C	4n, 5n
			3954.37	188888	214170	2	2	0.95	0.222	5.8	−0.353	C	4n, 5n
			3982.72	189068	214170	4	2	0.447	0.053	2.79	−0.67	C	4n, 5n
			3945.05	188888	214229	2	4	0.217	0.101	2.63	−0.69	C	4n, 5n
31	$2p^23s' -$ $2p^2(^1D)3p'$	$^2D - {^2F}°$ (15)	4593.2	206972	228737	10	14	1.11	0.490	74	0.69	C	3, 4, ca
			4590.97	206971	228747	6	8	1.11	0.466	42.3	0.447	C	5n
			4596.17	206972	228723	4	6	1.03	0.487	29.5	0.290	C	5n
			[4596.0]	206971	228723	6	6	0.079	0.0251	2.28	−0.82	C	5n
32		$^2D - {^2D}°$ (16)	4349.7	206972	229955	10	10	1.04	0.296	42.4	0.471	C	3, 4, ca
			4351.27	206971	229947	6	6	0.97	0.275	23.6	0.217	C	5n
			4347.43	206972	229968	4	4	0.94	0.267	15.3	0.029	C	5n
			[4349.1]	206971	229968	6	4	0.102	0.0192	1.65	−0.94	C	5n
			[4351.5]	206972	229947	4	6	0.075	0.0318	1.82	−0.90	C	5n

No.	Transition Array	Multiplet	$\lambda(\text{Å})$	$E_i(\text{cm}^{-1})$	$E_k(\text{cm}^{-1})$	g_i	g_k	$A_{ki}(10^8\,\text{sec}^{-1})$	f_{ik}	$S(\text{at.u.})$	$\log gf$	Accuracy	Source
33		$^2D - {}^2P°$ (17)	3914.4	206972	232511	10	6	1.40	0.193	24.9	0.286	C	3, 4, ca
			3911.96	206971	232527	6	4	1.27	0.194	15.0	0.066	C	5n
			3919.29	206972	232480	4	2	1.40	0.161	8.3	−0.192	C	5n
			3912.09	206972	232527	4	4	0.137	0.0314	1.62	−0.90	C	5n
34	$2p^23s'' -$ $2p^2(^1S)3p''$	$^2S - {}^2P°$	[4272.3]	[226851]	[250251]	2	6	1.08	0.89	25.0	0.250	C	3, ca
35	$2s2p^33s''' -$ $2s2p^3(^5S°)$ $3p'''$	$^6S° - {}^6P$ (94)	4467.2	[245396]	[267775]	6	18	0.92	0.83	73	0.70	C	ca
			4465.40	[245396]	[267783]	6	8	0.92	0.367	32.4	0.343	C	ls
			4467.88	[245396]	[267771]	6	6	0.92	0.275	24.3	0.218	C	ls
			4469.32	[245396]	[267763]	6	4	0.92	0.184	16.2	0.042	C	ls
36	$2p^23p -$ $2p^2(^3P)3d$	$^2S° - {}^4P$ (7)											
			3496.27	203942	232536	2	4	0.0111	0.00408	0.094	−2.088	C	5
			3488.18	203942	232603	2	2	0.0084	0.00152	0.0350	−2.52	C	5
37		$^2S° - {}^4D$ (8)											
			3474.94	203942	232712	2	2	0.0085	0.00153	0.0351	−2.51	C	5
38		$^2S° - {}^2P$ (9)	3385.9	203942	233468	2	6	1.86	0.96	21.4	0.283	C	3, ca
			3390.25	203942	233430	2	4	1.86	0.64	14.3	0.108	C	ls
			3377.20	203942	233544	2	2	1.88	0.321	7.1	−0.193	C	ls
39		$^2S° - {}^2D$	[3282.0]	203942	234402	2	4	0.0168	0.0054	0.117	−1.97	C	5
40		$^4D° - {}^4F$ (10)	4074.8	206895	231429	20	28	1.98	0.69	185	1.140	C	3, ca
			4075.87	207003	231530	8	10	1.98	0.62	66	0.69	C	ls
			4072.16	206878	231428	6	8	1.70	0.56	45.3	0.53	C	ls
			4069.90	206786	231350	4	6	1.49	0.55	29.7	0.346	C	ls
			4069.64	206731	231296	2	4	1.39	0.69	18.5	0.140	C	ls
			4092.94	207003	231428	8	8	0.278	0.070	7.5	−0.253	C	ls
			4085.12	206878	231350	6	6	0.478	0.120	9.7	−0.144	C	ls
			4078.86	206786	231296	4	4	0.55	0.138	7.4	−0.259	C	ls
			4106.03	207003	231350	8	6	0.0187	0.00354	0.383	−1.55	C	ls
			4094.18	206878	231296	6	4	0.0390	0.0065	0.53	−1.406	C	ls
41		$^4D° - {}^4P$ (11)	3902.7	206895	232511	20	12	0.063	0.0086	2.21	−0.76	C	3, ca
			3926.58	207003	232463	8	6	0.0493	0.0085	0.88	−1.165	C	ls
			3896.30	206878	232536	6	4	0.0397	0.0060	0.464	−1.442	C	ls
			3872.45	206786	232603	4	2	0.0321	0.00361	0.184	−1.84	C	ls
			3907.45	206878	232463	6	6	0.0113	0.00258	0.199	−1.81	C	ls
			3882.45	206786	232536	4	4	0.0204	0.00462	0.236	−1.73	C	ls
			3864.13	206731	232603	2	2	0.0323	0.0072	0.184	−1.84	C	ls
			3893.53	206786	232463	4	6	0.00126	4.31×10^{-4}	0.0221	−2.76	C	ls
			3874.10	206731	232536	2	4	0.00321	0.00144	0.0368	−2.54	C	ls
42		$^4D° - {}^4D$ (12)	3867.2	206895	232746	20	20	0.58	0.130	33.2	0.416	C	3, ca
			3882.20	207003	232754	8	8	0.493	0.111	11.4	−0.050	C	ls
			3864.45	206878	232748	6	6	0.334	0.075	5.7	−0.348	C	ls
			3851.04	206786	232746	4	4	0.236	0.052	2.66	−0.68	C	ls
			3847.89	206731	232712	2	2	0.295	0.066	1.66	−0.88	C	ls
			3883.15	207003	232748	8	6	0.109	0.0185	1.89	−0.83	C	ls
			3864.68	206878	232746	6	4	0.204	0.0304	2.32	−0.74	C	ls
			3856.16	206786	232712	4	2	0.293	0.0327	1.66	−0.88	C	ls
			3863.50	206878	232754	6	8	0.083	0.0248	1.89	−0.83	C	ls
			3850.81	206786	232748	4	6	0.137	0.0458	2.32	−0.74	C	ls
			3842.82	206731	232746	2	4	0.148	0.066	1.66	−0.88	C	ls

No.	Transition Array	Multiplet	$\lambda(\text{Å})$	$E_i(\text{cm}^{-1})$	$E_k(\text{cm}^{-1})$	g_i	g_k	$A_{ki}(10^8\ \text{sec}^{-1})$	f_{ik}	$S(\text{at.u.})$	$\log gf$	Accuracy	Source
43		$^4D° - ^2F$ (13)											
			3851.47	207003	232959	8	8	0.0223	0.0050	0.50	−1.402	C	5
			3857.18	206878	232796	6	6	0.0448	0.0100	0.76	−1.222	C	5
			3875.82	207003	232796	8	6	0.0095	0.00161	0.164	−1.89	C	5
			3833.10	206878	232959	6	8	0.0095	0.00279	0.211	−1.78	C	5
			3843.58	206786	232796	4	6	0.0222	0.0074	0.374	−1.53	C	5
44		$^4P° - ^4P$ (19)	*4151.7*	*208431*	*232511*	12	12	1.01	0.261	42.8	0.496	C	3, 4 *ca*
			4169.28	208484	232463	6	6	0.220	0.057	4.73	−0.463	C	5n
			4140.74	208392	232536	4	4	0.0236	0.0061	0.331	−1.61	C	5n
			4121.48	208346	232603	2	2	0.93	0.237	6.4	−0.324	C	5n
			4156.54	208484	232536	6	4	0.157	0.0270	2.22	−0.79	C	5n
			4129.34	208392	232603	4	2	0.150	0.0191	1.04	−1.116	C	5n
			4153.30	208392	232463	4	6	0.77	0.298	16.3	0.076	C	5n
			4132.81	208346	232536	2	4	0.84	0.430	11.7	−0.066	C	5n
45		$^4P° - ^4D$ (20)	*4111.4*	*208431*	*232746*	12	20	1.49	0.63	102	0.88	C	3, *ca*
			4119.22	208484	232754	6	8	1.48	0.50	40.8	0.478	C	*ls*
			4104.74	208392	232748	4	6	1.04	0.396	21.4	0.200	C	*ls*
			4097.26	208346	232746	2	4	0.63	0.315	8.5	−0.201	C	*ls*
			4120.28	208484	232748	6	6	0.443	0.113	9.2	−0.170	C	*ls*
			4105.00	408392	232746	4	4	0.80	0.202	10.9	−0.093	C	*ls*
			4103.02	208346	232712	2	2	1.25	0.315	8.5	−0.201	C	*ls*
			4120.55	208484	232746	6	4	0.074	0.0125	1.02	−1.124	C	*ls*
			4110.80	208392	232712	4	2	0.248	0.0314	1.70	−0.90	C	*ls*
46		$^4P° - ^2F$ (21)											
			4084.66	208484	232959	6	8	0.065	0.0216	1.74	−0.89	C	5
			4096.54	208392	232796	4	6	0.092	0.0347	1.87	−0.86	C	5
			4112.03	208484	232796	6	6	0.109	0.0275	2.23	−0.78	C	5
47		$^4P° - ^2P$ (22)											
			3967.44	208346	233544	2	2	0.0133	0.00314	0.082	−2.203	C	5
			3985.46	208346	233430	2	4	0.0084	0.00400	0.105	−2.097	C	5
48		$^2D° - ^4D$ (24)											
			4751.34	211713	232754	6	8	0.059	0.0264	2.48	−0.80	C	5
			4710.04	211522	232748	4	6	0.170	0.085	5.3	−0.469	C	5
			4752.70	211713	232748	6	6	0.0088	0.00300	0.281	−1.75	C	5
49		$^2D° - ^2F$ (25)	*4703.9*	*211636*	*232889*	10	14	1.38	0.64	99	0.81	C	3, *ca*
			4705.36	211713	232959	6	8	1.38	0.61	57	0.56	C	*ls*
			4699.21	211522	232796	4	6	1.29	0.64	39.6	0.408	C	*ls*
			4741.71	211713	232796	6	6	0.090	0.0302	2.83	−0.74	C	*ls*
50		$^2D° - ^2P$ (23)	*4579.2*	*211636*	*233468*	10	6	0.0418	0.0079	1.19	−1.103	C	3, *ca*
			[4598.2]	211713	233430	6	4	0.0372	0.0079	0.71	−1.326	C	*ls*
			[4539.6]	211522	233544	4	2	0.0430	0.0066	0.397	−1.58	C	*ls*
			[4563.2]	211522	233430	4	4	0.0423	0.00132	0.079	−2.278	C	*ls*
51		$^2D° - ^2D$ (26)	*4385.3*	*211636*	*234434*	10	10	0.430	0.124	17.9	0.093	C	3, *ca*
			4395.95	211713	234454	6	6	0.398	0.115	10.0	−0.161	C	*ls*
			4369.28	211522	234402	4	4	0.391	0.112	6.4	−0.349	C	*ls*
			4406.02	211713	234402	6	4	0.0424	0.0082	0.72	−1.307	C	*ls*
			4359.38	211522	234454	4	6	0.0292	0.0125	0.72	−1.302	C	*ls*

No.	Transition Array	Multiplet	λ(Å)	E_i(cm⁻¹)	E_k(cm⁻¹)	g_i	g_k	A_{ki}(10⁸ sec⁻¹)	f_{ik}	S(at.u.)	log gf	Accuracy	Source
52		⁴S°—⁴P (28)	4913.0	212162	232511	4	12	0.67	0.73	47.3	0.466	C	3, ca
			4924.60	212162	232463	4	6	0.67	0.365	23.7	0.165	C	ls
			4906.88	212162	232536	4	4	0.68	0.245	15.8	−0.011	C	ls
			4890.93	212162	232603	4	2	0.68	0.122	7.9	−0.310	C	ls
53		⁴S°—⁴D (29)											
			4856.49	212162	232748	4	6	0.094	0.050	3.19	−0.70	C	5
			4856.76	212162	232746	4	4	0.176	0.062	3.97	−0.61	C	5
			4864.95	212162	232712	4	2	0.235	0.0417	2.67	−0.78	C	5
54		⁴S°—²F (30)											
			4845.0	212162	232796	4	6	0.0094	0.0050	0.316	−1.70	C	5
55		²P°—²P (32)	5191.1	214210	233468	6	6	0.53	0.213	21.8	0.106	C	3, 4, ca
			5206.73	214229	233430	4	4	0.391	0.160	10.9	−0.197	C	4n, 5n
			5160.02	214170	233544	2	2	0.350	0.140	4.75	−0.55	C	4n, 5n
			5176.00	214229	233544	4	2	0.171	0.0343	2.34	−0.86	C	4n, 5n
			5190.56	214170	233430	2	4	0.137	0.111	3.78	−0.66	C	4n, 5n
56		²P°—²D (33)	4943.2	214210	234434	6	10	1.07	0.65	64	0.59	C	3, 4, ca
			4943.06	214229	234454	4	6	1.06	0.58	37.9	0.367	C	5n
			4941.12	214170	234402	2	4	0.83	0.61	19.7	0.083	C	5n
			4955.78	214229	234402	4	4	0.256	0.094	6.1	−0.424	C	5n
57	2p²3p′— 2p²(¹D)3d′	²F°—²F (35)	4446.1	228737	251222	14	14	0.59	0.176	36.0	0.391	C	3, 4, ca
			4448.21	228747	251221	8	8	0.57	0.169	19.8	0.131	C	ls
			4443.05	228723	251224	6	6	0.57	0.167	14.7	0.002	C	ls
			[4447.7]	228747	251224	8	6	0.0282	0.0063	0.74	−1.299	C	ls
			[4443.7]	228723	251221	6	8	0.0212	0.0084	0.74	−1.299	C	ls
58		²F°—³G (36)	4187.9	228737	252608	14	18	2.51	0.85	164	1.075	C	3, 4, ca
			4189.79	228747	252608	8	10	2.51	0.83	91	0.82	C	ls
			4185.46	228723	252609	6	8	2.43	0.85	70	0.71	C	ls
			[4189.6]	228747	252609	8	8	0.090	0.0236	2.60	−0.72	C	ls
59		²F°—²D (37)	4112.3	228737	253048	14	10	0.132	0.0239	4.53	−0.476	C	3, ca
			4113.82	228747	253048	8	6	0.126	0.0239	2.59	−0.72	C	ls
			4110.20	228723	253046	6	4	0.132	0.0223	1.81	−0.87	C	ls
			[4109.8]	228723	253048	6	6	0.0063	0.00159	0.129	−2.021	C	ls
60		²D°—²F (40)	4700.8	229955	251222	10	14	0.88	0.410	63	0.61	C	3, ca
			4699.21	229947	251221	6	8	0.88	0.390	36.2	0.369	C	ls
			4703.18	229968	251224	4	6	0.82	0.410	25.4	0.215	C	ls
			4698.48	229947	251224	6	6	0.059	0.0195	1.81	−0.93	C	ls
61		²P°—²D (57)	4868.1	232511	253048	6	10	0.437	0.259	24.9	0.191	C	3, ca
			4871.58	232527	253048	4	6	0.435	0.232	14.9	−0.032	C	ls
			4861.03	232480	253046	2	4	0.366	0.259	8.3	−0.285	C	ls
			[4872.2]	232527	253046	4	4	0.073	0.0259	1.66	−0.99	C	ls
62		²P°—²P (58)	4698.0	232511	253791	6	6	1.05	0.347	33.2	0.319	C	3, ca
			4701.23	232527	253792	4	4	0.87	0.289	17.9	0.063	C	ls
			4691.47	232480	253790	2	2	0.70	0.232	7.2	−0.334	C	ls
			4701.76	232527	253790	4	2	0.349	0.058	3.58	−0.64	C	ls
			4690.97	232480	253792	2	4	0.176	0.116	3.58	−0.64	C	ls

No.	Transition Array	Multiplet	$\lambda(\text{Å})$	$E_i(\text{cm}^{-1})$	$E_k(\text{cm}^{-1})$	g_i	g_k	$A_{ki}(10^8\ \text{sec}^{-1})$	f_{ik}	$S(\text{at.u.})$	log gf	Accuracy	Source
63		²P° − ²S (61)	*4325.7*	*232511*	255622	6	2	1.81	0.170	14.5	**0.008**	C	3, *ca*
			4328.62	232527	255622	4	2	1.21	0.170	9.7	−0.168	C	*ls*
			4319.93	232480	255622	2	2	0.61	0.170	4.83	−0.469	C	*ls*
64	2s2p³3p‴ − 2s2p³(⁵S°) 3d‴	⁶P − ⁶D° (106)	*4144.4*	*[267775]*	*[291897]*	18	30	0.211	0.090	22.2	**0.211**	C	*ca*
			4146.09	[267783]	[291896]	8	10	0.210	0.068	7.4	−0.266	C	*ls*
			4143.77	[267771]	[291897]	6	8	0.135	0.0464	3.80	−0.55	C	*ls*
			4142.24	[267763]	[291898]	4	6	0.066	0.0253	1.38	−0.99	C	*ls*
			4145.90	[267783]	[291897]	8	8	0.075	0.0194	2.12	−0.81	C	*ls*
			4143.52	[267771]	[291898]	6	6	0.129	0.0331	2.71	−0.70	C	*ls*
			4141.96	[267763]	[291899]	4	4	0.148	0.0380	2.07	−0.82	C	*ls*
			[4145.6]	[267783]	[291898]	8	6	0.0167	0.00323	0.353	−1.59	C	*ls*
			[4143.4]	[267771]	[291899]	6	4	0.063	0.0108	0.89	−1.186	C	*ls*
			4142.08	[267763]	[291900]	4	2	0.211	0.0271	1.48	−0.96	C	*ls*
65	2p³3p − 2p²(³P)4s	²S° − ²P (20 uv)	*2738.0*	*203942*	*240454*	2	6	0.36	0.12	2.2	−0.61	D	3, *ca*
			2733.34	203942	240516	2	4	0.37	0.082	1.5	−0.79	D	*ls*
			2747.46	203942	240329	2	2	0.36	0.041	0.74	−1.09	D	*ls*
66		⁴D° − ⁴P (14)	*3133.9*	*206895*	*238795*	20	12	1.53	0.135	27.9	**0.432**	C	3, *ca*
			3134.82	207003	238893	8	6	1.23	0.136	11.2	0.036	C	*ls*
			3138.44	206878	238732	6	4	0.96	0.095	5.9	−0.246	C	*ls*
			3139.77	206786	238626	4	2	0.76	0.056	2.33	−0.65	C	*ls*
			3122.62	206878	238893	6	6	0.278	0.0407	2.51	−0.61	C	*ls*
			3129.44	206786	238732	4	4	0.493	0.072	2.98	−0.54	C	*ls*
			3134.32	206731	238626	2	2	0.77	0.113	2.33	−0.65	C	*ls*
			3113.71	206786	238893	4	6	0.0312	0.0068	0.279	−1.57	C	*ls*
			3124.02	206731	238732	2	4	0.077	0.0226	0.465	−1.345	C	*ls*
67		⁴P° − ⁴P (23)	*3292.4*	*208431*	*238795*	12	12	0.85	0.138	18.0	**0.220**	C	3, *ca*
			3287.59	208484	238893	6	6	0.60	0.097	6.3	−0.235	C	*ls*
			3295.13	208392	238732	4	4	0.113	0.0184	0.80	−1.132	C	*ls*
			3301.56	208346	238626	2	2	0.141	0.0230	0.50	−1.337	C	*ls*
			3305.15	208484	238732	6	4	0.379	0.0414	2.70	−0.61	C	*ls*
			3306.60	208392	238626	4	2	0.70	0.057	2.50	−0.64	C	*ls*
			3277.69	208392	238893	4	6	0.259	0.063	2.70	−0.60	C	*ls*
			3290.13	208346	238732	2	4	0.356	0.115	2.50	−0.64	C	*ls*
68		²D° − ²P (27)	*3469.1*	*211636*	*240454*	10	6	1.25	0.135	15.4	**0.130**	C	3, *ca*
			3470.81	211713	240516	6	4	1.12	0.135	9.2	−0.092	C	*ls*
			3470.42	211522	240329	4	2	1.24	0.112	5.1	−0.348	C	*ls*
			3447.98	211522	240516	4	4	0.127	0.0227	1.03	−1.042	C	*ls*
69		⁴S° − ⁴P (31)	*3753.7*	*212162*	*238795*	4	12	0.265	0.168	8.3	**−0.173**	C	3, 4, *ca*
			3739.92	212162	238893	4	6	0.267	0.084	4.14	−0.473	C	4n, *ls*
			3762.63	212162	238732	4	4	0.269	0.057	2.83	−0.64	C	4n, *ls*
			3777.60	212162	238626	4	2	0.252	0.0269	1.34	−0.97	C	4n, *ls*
70		²P° − ²P (34)	*3809.3*	*214210*	*240454*	6	6	0.65	0.142	10.7	**−0.069**	C	3, *ca*
			3803.14	214230	240516	4	4	0.55	0.119	5.9	−0.324	C	*ls*
			3821.68	214170	240329	2	2	0.432	0.095	2.38	−0.72	C	*ls*
			3830.45	214230	240329	4	2	0.215	0.0236	1.19	−1.025	C	*ls*
			3794.48	214170	240516	2	4	0.110	0.0476	1.19	−1.021	C	*ls*

No.	Transition Array	Multiplet	λ(Å)	E_i(cm⁻¹)	E_k(cm⁻¹)	g_i	g_k	A_{ki}(10⁸ sec⁻¹)	f_{ik}	S(at.u.)	log gf	Accuracy	Source
71	$2p^23p'-$ $2p^2(^1D)4s'$	$^2F°-^2D$ (39)	*3272.4*	*228737*	*259287*	14	10	1.20	0.137	20.7	0.284	C	*3, ca*
			3273.52	228747	259286	8	6	1.14	0.137	11.8	0.039	C	*ls*
			3270.98	228723	259287	6	4	1.20	0.128	8.3	−0.114	C	*ls*
			[3270.9]	228723	259287	6	6	0.057	0.0091	0.59	−1.261	C	*ls*
72		$^2D°-^2D$ (44)	*3408.4*	*229956*	*259287*	10	10	0.80	0.140	15.7	0.146	C	*3, ca*
			3407.38	229947	259286	6	6	0.75	0.131	8.8	−0.106	C	*ls*
			3409.84	229968	259287	4	4	0.72	0.126	5.7	−0.298	C	*ls*
			3407.38	229947	259287	6	4	0.080	0.0093	0.63	−1.252	C	*ls*
			3409.84	229968	259286	4	6	0.054	0.0140	0.63	−1.252	C	*ls*
73		$^2P°-^2D$ (62)	*3733.9*	*232513*	*259287*	6	10	0.416	0.145	10.7	−0.060	C	*3, ca*
			3735.94	232527	259286	4	6	0.416	0.130	6.4	−0.282	C	*ls*
			3729.34	232480	259287	2	4	0.349	0.145	3.57	−0.54	C	*ls*
			[3735.9]	232527	259287	4	4	0.069	0.0145	0.71	−1.237	C	*ls*
74	$2p^23d-$ $2p^2(^3P)4p$	$^4F-^4D°$ (45)	*6897.5*	*231429*	*245923*	28	20	0.333	0.170	108	0.68	C	*3, ca*
			6895.29	231530	246029	10	8	0.298	0.170	38.6	0.231	C	*ls*
			6906.54	231428	245903	8	6	0.272	0.146	26.5	0.067	C	*ls*
			6910.75	231350	245816	6	4	0.267	0.127	17.4	−0.117	C	*ls*
			6908.11	231296	245768	4	2	0.332	0.119	10.8	−0.323	C	*ls*
			6846.97	231428	246029	8	8	0.0347	0.0244	4.40	−0.71	C	*ls*
			6869.74	231350	245903	6	6	0.059	0.0415	5.6	−0.60	C	*ls*
			6885.07	231296	245816	4	4	0.067	0.0476	4.32	−0.72	C	*ls*
			[6810.6]	231350	246029	6	8	0.00180	0.00167	0.224	−2.000	C	*ls*
			[6844.1]	231296	245903	4	6	0.00325	0.00343	0.309	−1.86	C	*ls*
75		$^2P-^2P°$ (85)	*6657.3*	*233468*	*248485*	6	6	0.105	0.070	9.2	−0.377	C	*3, ca*
			6627.62	233430	248514	4	4	0.089	0.059	5.1	−0.63	C	*ls*
			[6718.1]	233544	248425	2	2	0.068	0.0461	2.04	−1.035	C	*ls*
			6678.19	233544	248514	2	4	0.0173	0.0232	1.02	−1.334	C	*ls*
			6666.94	233430	248425	4	2	0.0349	0.0116	1.02	−1.333	C	*ls*
76	$2p^23d-$ $2p^2(^3P)4f$	$^4F-^4G°$ (48)	*4093.7*	*231429*	*255850*	28	36	2.60	0.84	317	1.372	C	*3, ca*
			4089.30	231530	255978	10	12	2.62	0.79	106	0.90	C	*ls*
			4097.26	231428	255828	8	10	2.37	0.75	81	0.78	C	*ls*
			4095.63	231350	255759	6	8	2.23	0.75	61	0.65	C	*ls*
			4087.16	231296	255756	4	6	2.24	0.84	45.3	0.53	C	*ls*
			[4114.4]	231530	255828	10	10	0.212	0.054	7.3	−0.269	C	*ls*
			4108.75	231428	255759	8	8	0.349	0.088	9.6	−0.151	C	*ls*
			4096.18	231350	255756	6	6	0.359	0.090	7.3	−0.267	C	*ls*
			[4126.1]	231530	255759	10	8	0.0077	0.00158	0.214	−1.80	C	*ls*
			[4109.3]	231428	255756	8	6	0.0128	0.00244	0.264	−1.71	C	*ls*
77		$^4P-^4D°$ (54)	*4293.8*	*232511*	*255794*	12	20	1.98	0.91	155	1.040	C	*3, ca*
			4303.82	232463	255691	6	8	1.97	0.73	62	0.64	C	*ls*
			4294.82	232536	255813	4	6	1.39	0.57	32.5	0.362	C	*ls*
			[4288.8]	232603	255913	2	4	0.83	0.457	12.9	−0.039	C	*ls*
			4281.40	232463	255813	6	6	0.60	0.164	13.9	−0.006	C	*ls*
			4282.82	232536	255913	4	4	1.06	0.293	16.5	−0.068	C	*ls*
			4288.83	232603	255912	2	2	1.66	0.457	12.9	−0.039	C	*ls*
			[4263.2]	232463	255913	6	4	0.101	0.0184	1.55	−0.96	C	*ls*
			4276.71	232536	255912	4	2	0.334	0.0458	2.58	−0.74	C	*ls*

No.	Transition Array	Multiplet	λ(Å)	E_i(cm⁻¹)	E_k(cm⁻¹)	g_i	g_k	A_{ki}(10⁸ sec⁻¹)	f_{ik}	S(at.u.)	log gf	Accuracy	Source
78		⁴D − ⁴F° (67)	*4278.0*	*232746*	*256115*	20	28	2.12	0.81	229	1.211	C	3, *ca*
			4275.52	232754	256136	8	10	2.12	0.73	82	0.76	C	*ls*
			4276.71	232748	256123	6	8	1.82	0.66	56	0.60	C	*ls*
			4282.96	232746	256088	4	6	1.58	0.65	36.8	0.417	C	*ls*
			4277.40	232712	256084	2	4	1.49	0.82	23.0	0.213	C	*ls*
			4277.90	232754	256123	8	8	0.302	0.083	9.3	−0.179	C	*ls*
			4283.13	232748	256088	6	6	0.51	0.141	11.9	−0.074	C	*ls*
			4283.75	232746	256084	4	4	0.59	0.162	9.2	−0.187	C	*ls*
			[4284.4]	232754	256088	8	6	0.0204	0.00420	0.474	−1.474	C	*ls*
			[4284.0]	232748	256084	6	4	0.0421	0.0077	0.65	−1.334	C	*ls*
79		²F − ²G° (77)	*4341.7*	*232889*	*255915*	14	18	2.31	0.84	168	1.070	C	3, *ca*
			4342.00	232959	255984	8	10	2.31	0.82	93	0.81	C	*ls*
			4340.36	232796	255829	6	8	2.23	0.84	72	0.70	C	*ls*
			[4371.3]	232959	255829	8	8	0.081	0.0232	2.67	−0.73	C	*ls*
80		²P − ²D° (86)	*4488.9*	*233468*	*255739*	6	10	1.81	0.91	81	0.74	C	3, *ca*
			4491.25	233430	255690	4	6	1.81	0.82	48.6	0.52	C	*ls*
			4489.48	233544	255812	2	4	1.51	0.91	27.0	0.262	C	*ls*
			[4466.6]	233430	255812	4	4	0.307	0.092	5.4	−0.435	C	*ls*
81		²D − ²F° (93)	*4606.6*	*234434*	*256136*	10	14	1.82	0.81	123	0.91	C	3, *ca*
			4609.42	234454	256143	6	8	1.82	0.77	70	0.67	C	*ls*
			4602.11	234402	256126	4	6	1.70	0.81	49.2	0.51	C	*ls*
			4613.11	234454	256126	6	6	0.121	0.0385	3.51	−0.64	C	*ls*
82	2p²3d′ − 2p²(¹D)4f′	²F − ²G° (97)	*4060.8*	*251222*	275841	14	18	2.20	0.70	131	0.99	C	3, *ca*
83		²G − ²H° (101)	*4253.9*	*252608*	276109	18	22	2.63	0.87	220	1.196	C	3, 4 *ca*
84	2p²3d − 2p²(³P)5f	⁴P − ⁴D° (56)	[3011.7]	*232511*	[265705]	12	20	0.75	0.169	20.1	0.307	C	3, *ca*
			3013.37	232463	265639	6	8	0.74	0.135	8.0	−0.091	C	*ls*
			[3014.0]	232536	[265705]	4	6	0.52	0.106	4.22	−0.371	C	*ls*
			[3019.8]	232602	[265762]	2	4	0.311	0.085	1.68	−0.77	C	*ls*
			[3007.4]	232463	[265705]	6	6	0.225	0.0305	1.81	−0.74	C	*ls*
			[3008.8]	232536	[265762]	4	4	0.398	0.054	2.14	−0.67	C	*ls*
			[3006.0]	232602	[265859]	2	2	0.63	0.085	1.68	−0.77	C	*ls*
			[3002.2]	232463	[265762]	6	4	0.0376	0.00339	0.201	−1.69	C	*ls*
			[3000.1]	232536	[265859]	4	2	0.126	0.0085	0.335	−1.470	C	*ls*
85		⁴D − ⁴F° (74)	[3008.4]	*232746*	[265977]	20	28	0.84	0.160	31.7	0.51	C	3, *ca*
			3007.08	232754	265999	8	10	0.84	0.143	11.3	0.057	C	*ls*
			3007.74	232748	265985	6	8	0.72	0.130	7.8	−0.106	C	*ls*
			3009.81	232746	[265961]	4	6	0.63	0.128	5.1	−0.289	C	*ls*
			[3009.7]	232712	[265928]	2	4	0.59	0.159	3.16	−0.496	C	*ls*
			3008.28	232754	265985	8	8	0.120	0.0163	1.29	−0.89	C	*ls*
			[3010.0]	232748	[265961]	6	6	0.204	0.0278	1.65	−0.78	C	*ls*
			[3012.8]	232746	[265928]	4	4	0.235	0.0320	1.27	−0.89	C	*ls*
			[3010.5]	232754	[265961]	8	6	0.0081	8.3 × 10⁻⁴	0.066	−2.180	C	*ls*
			[3013.0]	232748	[265928]	6	4	0.0167	0.00152	0.090	−2.040	C	*ls*
86		²F − ²G° (83)	*3032.5*	*232889*	265856	14	18	0.85	0.151	21.1	0.325	C	3, *ca*
			3032.08	232959	265930	8	10	0.85	0.147	11.7	0.069	C	*ls*
			3032.50	232796	265763	6	8	0.82	0.151	9.0	−0.043	C	*ls*
			[3047.5]	232959	265763	8	8	0.0300	0.00417	0.335	−1.476	C	*ls*

Forbidden Transitions

The adopted values are exclusively from Seaton and Osterbrock's calculations [1]. The important effects of configuration interaction are partially taken into account and a reliable estimate of the quadrupole integral is given (see also general introduction).

Reference

[1] Seaton, M. J., and Osterbrock, D. E., Astrophys. J. **125**, 66–83 (1957).

O II. Forbidden Transitions

No.	Transition Array	Multiplet	λ(Å)	E_i(cm^{-1})	E_k(cm^{-1})	g_i	g_k	Type of Transition	A_{ki}(sec^{-1})	S(at.u.)	Accuracy	Source
1	$2p^3 - 2p^3$	$^4S° - ^2D°$ (1 F)										
			3728.91	0.0	26810.7	4	6	m	7.4×10^{-6}	8.5×10^{-8}	C	1
			3728.91	0.0	26810.7	4	6	e	4.1×10^{-5}	1.1×10^{-4}	D	1
			3726.16	0.0	26830.5	4	4	m	1.43×10^{-4}	1.10×10^{-6}	C	1
			3726.16	0.0	26830.5	4	4	e	2.7×10^{-5}	4.5×10^{-5}	D	1
2		$^4S° - ^2P°$										
			[2470.4]	0.0	40466.9	4	4	m	0.060	1.33×10^{-4}	C	1
			[2470.4]	0.0	40466.9	4	4	e	1.5×10^{-7}	3.3×10^{-8}	D	1
			[2470.3]	0.0	40468.4	4	2	m	0.0238	2.66×10^{-5}	C	1
			[2470.3]	0.0	40468.4	4	2	e	7.4×10^{-7}	8.1×10^{-8}	D	1
3		$^2D° - ^2D°$										
			[50.8 × 10^5]	26810.7	26830.5	6	4	m	1.26×10^{-7}	2.40	B	1
			[50.5 × 10^5]	26810.7	26830.5	6	4	e	1.5×10^{-19}	0.0012	D	1
4		$^2D° - ^2P°$ (2 F)										
			7319.4	26810.7	40466.9	6	4	m	0.0091	5.3×10^{-4}	C	1
			7319.4	26810.7	40466.9	6	4	e	0.106	5.30	C	1
			7318.6	26810.7	40468.4	6	2	e	0.0610	1.52	C	1
			7330.7	26830.5	40466.9	4	4	m	0.0160	9.3×10^{-4}	C	1
			7330.7	26830.5	40466.9	4	4	e	0.0450	2.29	C	1
			7329.9	26830.5	40468.4	4	2	m	0.0103	3.01×10^{-4}	C	1
			7329.9	26830.5	40468.4	4	2	e	0.0900	2.27	C	1
5		$^2P° - ^2P°$										
			[6.7 × 10^7]	40466.9	40468.4	4	2	m	6.04×10^{-11}	1.33	C+	1
			[6.7 × 10^7]	40466.9	40468.4	4	2	e	4.9×10^{-24}	5.0×10^{-4}	D	1

O III

Ground State $1s^2\, 2s^2\, 2p^2\, {}^3P_0$

Ionization Potential $54.886\ \mathrm{eV} = 442807\ \mathrm{cm^{-1}}$

Allowed Transitions

List of tabulated lines:

Wavelength [Å]	No.	Wavelength [Å]	No.	Wavelength [Å]	No.
302.34	14	2683.65	36	3284.57	27
303.411	11	2686.14	24	3299.36	17
303.460	11	2687.53	36	3305.77	27
303.515	11	2695.49	36	3312.30	17
303.621	11	2983.78	20	3326.16	40
303.693	11	2992.11	28	3330.40	40
303.799	11	2996.51	28	3332.49	40
305.596	10	2997.71	28	3333.00	23
305.656	10	3004.35	28	3333.40	23
305.703	10	3008.79	28	3336.78	23
305.769	10	3017.63	28	3336.78	40
305.836	10	3023.45	18	3340.74	17
305.879	10	3024.36	28	3344.26	23
320.979	13	3024.57	18	3344.26	40
328.448	12	3035.43	18	3348.05	40
345.309	15	3043.02	18	3350.68	23
373.805	7	3047.13	18	3350.99	23
374.005	7	3059.30	18	3355.92	40
374.075	7	3065.01	38	3362.38	23
374.165	7	3068.06	38	3376.4	39
374.331	7	3068.48	38	3376.82	39
374.436	7	3068.68	38	3377.3	39
395.558	8	3074.15	38	3382.69	39
434.975	9	3074.68	38	3383.5	39
507.391	3	3075.19	38	3383.85	39
507.683	3	3075.95	38	3384.95	39
508.182	3	3083.65	38	3394.26	39
525.795	5	3084.63	38	3395.5	39
597.818	6	3088.04	38	3405.74	31
599.598	4	3095.81	38	3408.13	31
702.332	2	3115.73	29	3415.29	31
702.822	2	3121.71	29	3428.67	31
702.899	2	3132.86	29	3430.60	31
703.850	2	3198.2	42	3444.10	31
832.927	1	3200.95	42	3446.73	37
833.742	1	3202.2	42	3447.22	37
835.096	1	3207.12	42	3448.05	37
835.292	1	3210.2	42	3450.94	37
2454.99	21	3215.97	42	3451.33	37
2558.06	46	3221.2	42	3454.90	37
2597.69	45	3260.98	27	3455.12	37
2605.41	45	3265.46	27	3459.52	37
2609.6	45	3267.31	27	3459.98	37
2665.69	24	3279.97	47	3466.15	37
2674.57	24	3281.94	27	3466.90	37

766–655 O–66—8

Wavelength [Å]	No.	Wavelength [Å]	No.	Wavelength [Å]	No.
3475.2	37	3712.48	22	3816.75	34
3520.7	26	3714.03	30	3961.59	33
3530.7	26	3715.08	30	4072.3	25
3532.8	26	3720.86	22	4073.90	25
3534.3	26	3721.95	22	4081.10	25
3555.3	26	3725.30	30	4088.5	25
3556.92	26	3728.49	41	4103.8	25
3638.70	44	3728.82	41	4118.6	25
3645.20	44	3729.70	41	4440.1	43
3646.84	44	3732.13	30	4447.82	43
3649.20	44	3734.80	22	4461.56	43
3650.70	44	3742.0	41	5268.06	35
3653.00	44	3747.6	41	5500.11	32
3695.37	22	3754.67	16	5592.37	19
3698.70	22	3757.21	16		
3702.75	30	3759.87	16		
3703.37	22	3761.2	41		
3704.73	22	3774.00	16		
3707.24	30	3791.26	16		
3709.52	22	3810.96	16		

Values for the strong $2s^2 2p^2 - 2s2p^3$ transitions, which are very sensitive to configuration interaction, are taken from the calculations of Bolotin et al. [1]. These authors have used analytical one-electron wave functions and include configuration interaction in a crude manner. Thus large uncertainties must be expected. This applies also for the $2p^2 - 2p3s$ and to a lesser extent to the $2p^2 - 2p3d$ transitions, for which only Kelly's self-consistent field calculations [2] are available. In these, configuration interaction has been entirely neglected. For many other transitions the simplified self-consistent field calculations by Kelly [3], in which exchange effects are approximately taken into account, are applied. The results agree within a few percent with the values of the Coulomb approximation and the averaged values are adopted. The accuracy rating of "C" is supported by the good agreement with relative f-value measurements of Berg et al. [4] done with a magnetically driven shock tube.

References

[1] Bolotin, A. B., Levinson, I. B., and Levin, L. I., Soviet Phys.—JETP **2**, 391–395 (1956).
[2] Kelly, P. S., Astrophys. J. **140**, 1247–1268 (1964).
[3] Kelly, P. S., J. Quant. Spectrosc. Radiat. Transfer **4**, 117–148 (1964).
[4] Berg, H. F., Eckerle, K. L., Burris, R. W., and Wiese, W. L., Astrophys. J. **139**, 751–757 (1964).

O III.   Allowed Transitions

No.	Transition Array	Multiplet	$\lambda(Å)$	$E_i(cm^{-1})$	$E_k(cm^{-1})$	g_i	g_k	$A_{ki}(10^8 sec^{-1})$	f_{ik}	S(at.u.)	log gf	Accuracy	Source
1	$2s^2 2p^2 - 2s2p^3$	$^3P - {}^3D°$ (1 uv)	834.50	208.2	120041	9	15	8.4	0.15	3.6	0.12	E	1
			835.292	306.8	120025	5	7	8.4	0.12	1.7	−0.21	E	*ls*
			833.742	113.4	120053	3	5	6.3	0.11	0.90	−0.48	E	*ls*
			832.927	0.0	120059	1	3	4.7	0.15	0.40	−0.84	E	*ls*
			835.096	306.8	120053	5	5	2.1	0.022	0.30	−0.96	E	*ls*
			833.742	113.4	120059	3	3	3.5	0.036	0.30	−0.96	E	*ls*
			835.096	306.8	120059	5	3	0.23	0.0015	0.020	−2.14	E	*ls*

No.	Transition Array	Multiplet	λ(Å)	E_i(cm^{-1})	E_k(cm^{-1})	g_i	g_k	A_{ki}(10^8 sec^{-1})	f_{ik}	S(at.u.)	log gf	Accuracy	Source
2		^{3}P — ^{3}P° (2 uv)	703.36	208.2	142384	9	9	25	0.18	3.8	0.22	E	1
			703.850	306.8	142382	5	5	19	0.14	1.6	−0.16	E	ls
			702.899	113.4	142383	3	3	6.2	0.046	0.32	−0.86	E	ls
			703.850	306.8	142383	5	3	10	0.046	0.53	−0.64	E	ls
			702.822	113.4	142397	3	1	25	0.061	0.42	−0.74	E	ls
			702.899	113.4	142382	3	5	6.2	0.076	0.53	−0.64	E	ls
			702.332	0.0	142383	1	3	8.2	0.18	0.42	−0.74	E	ls
3		^{3}P — ^{3}S° (3 uv)	507.93	208.2	197087	9	3	150	0.19	2.9	0.24	E	1
			508.182	306.8	197087	5	3	82	0.19	1.6	−0.02	E	ls
			507.683	113.4	197087	3	3	50	0.19	0.97	−0.24	E	ls
			507.391	0.0	197087	1	3	17	0.19	0.32	−0.72	E	ls
4		^{1}D — ^{1}D° (7 uv)	599.598	20271	187049	5	5	68	0.37	3.6	0.26	E	1
5		^{1}D — ^{1}P° (8 uv)	525.795	20271	210459	5	3	100	0.25	2.2	0.10	E	1
6		^{1}S — ^{1}P° (13 uv)	597.818	43184	210459	1	3	21	0.35	0.69	−0.46	E	1
7	$2p^2 -$ $2p(^2$P°)$3s$	^{3}P — ^{3}P° (4 uv)	374.12	208.2	267505	9	9	38	0.081	0.90	−0.14	E	2
			374.075	306.8	267633	5	5	29	0.061	0.37	−0.52	E	ls
			374.165	113.4	267376	3	3	9.6	0.020	0.075	−1.22	E	ls
			374.436	306.8	267376	5	3	16	0.020	0.12	−0.99	E	ls
			374.331	113.4	267257	3	1	38	0.027	0.10	−1.09	E	ls
			373.805	113.4	267633	3	5	9.6	0.034	0.12	−0.99	E	ls
			374.005	0.0	267376	1	3	13	0.081	0.10	−1.09	E	ls
8		^{1}D — ^{1}P° (9 uv)	395.558	20271	273080	5	3	68	0.096	0.62	−0.32	E	2
9		^{1}S — ^{1}P° (14 uv)	434.975	43184	273080	1	3	13	0.11	0.16	−0.96	E	2
10	$2p^2 -$ $2p(^2$P°)$3d$	^{3}P — ^{3}D° (5 uv)	305.72	208.2	327302	9	15	180	0.43	3.9	0.58	D −	2
			305.769	306.8	327351	5	7	180	0.36	1.8	0.25	D −	ls
			305.656	113.4	327277	3	5	140	0.32	0.97	−0.02	D −	ls
			305.596	0.0	327228	1	3	100	0.43	0.43	−0.37	D −	ls
			305.836	306.8	327277	5	5	46	0.064	0.32	−0.49	D −	ls
			305.703	113.4	327228	3	3	76	0.11	0.32	−0.49	D −	ls
			305.879	306.8	327228	5	3	5.1	0.0043	0.022	−1.67	D −	ls
11		^{3}P — ^{3}P° (6 uv)	303.66	208.2	329525	9	9	100	0.14	1.3	0.10	D −	2
			303.799	306.8	329468	5	5	76	0.11	0.53	−0.28	D −	ls
			303.515	113.4	329582	3	3	26	0.035	0.11	−0.97	D −	ls
			303.693	306.8	329582	5	3	42	0.035	0.18	−0.75	D −	ls
			303.460	113.4	329643	3	1	100	0.047	0.14	−0.85	D −	ls
			303.621	113.4	329468	3	5	25	0.059	0.18	−0.75	D −	ls
			303.411	0.0	329582	1	3	34	0.14	0.14	−0.85	D −	ls
12		^{1}D — ^{1}D° (10 uv)	328.448	20271	324734	5	5	61	0.099	0.53	−0.31	D −	2
13		^{1}D — ^{1}F° (11 uv)	320.979	20271	331820	5	7	190	0.41	2.2	0.31	D −	2
14		^{1}D — ^{1}P°	[302.34]	20271	332777	5	3	6.4	0.0052	0.026	−1.58	D −	2

No.	Transition Array	Multiplet	λ(Å)	E_i(cm⁻¹)	E_k(cm⁻¹)	g_i	g_k	A_{ki}(10⁸ sec⁻¹)	f_{ik}	S(at.u.)	log gf	Accuracy	Source
15		¹S — ¹P° (15 uv)	345.309	43184	332777	1	3	98	0.53	0.60	−0.28	D −	2
16	2p3s — 2p(²P°)3p	³P° — ³D (2)	*3762.3*	*267505*	*294077*	9	15	1.07	0.377	42.0	0.53	C	3, *ca*
			3759.87	267633	294222	5	7	1.07	0.317	19.6	0.200	C	*ls*
			3754.67	267376	294002	3	5	0.80	0.283	10.5	−0.071	C	*ls*
			3757.21	267257	293865	1	3	0.59	0.378	4.67	−0.423	C	*ls*
			3791.26	267633	294002	5	5	0.260	0.056	3.50	−0.55	C	*ls*
			3774.00	267376	293865	3	3	0.440	0.094	3.50	−0.55	C	*ls*
			3810.96	267633	293865	5	3	0.0284	0.00371	0.233	−1.73	C	*ls*
17		³P° — ³S (3)	*3326.6*	*267505*	*297558*	9	3	1.56	0.086	8.5	−0.110	C	3, *ca*
			3340.74	267633	297558	5	3	0.85	0.085	4.70	−0.369	C	*ls*
			3312.30	267376	297558	3	3	0.52	0.086	2.82	−0.59	C	*ls*
			3299.36	267257	297558	1	3	0.177	0.087	0.94	−1.063	C	*ls*
18		³P° — ³P (4)	*3041.5*	*267505*	*300374*	9	9	2.04	0.283	25.5	0.406	C	3, *ca*
			3047.13	267633	300441	5	5	1.52	0.211	10.6	0.024	C	*ls*
			3035.43	267376	300310	3	3	0.51	0.071	2.12	−0.67	C	*ls*
			3059.30	267633	300310	5	3	0.84	0.070	3.54	−0.454	C	*ls*
			3043.02	267376	300228	3	1	2.03	0.094	2.83	−0.55	C	*ls*
			3023.45	267376	300441	3	5	0.52	0.119	3.54	−0.449	C	*ls*
			3024.57	267257	300310	1	3	0.69	0.284	2.83	−0.55	C	*ls*
19		¹P° — ¹P (5)	5592.37	273080	290957	3	3	0.328	0.154	8.5	−0.336	C	3, *ca*
20		¹P° — ¹D (6)	2983.78	273080	306585	3	5	2.24	0.499	14.7	0.175	C	3, *ca*
21		¹P° — ¹S (19 uv)	2454.99	273080	313801	3	1	4.00	0.120	2.92	−0.442	C	3, *ca*
22	2s2p²3s — 2s2p²(⁴P)3p	⁵P — ⁵D° (21)	*3706.1*	*338741*	*365716*	15	25	1.09	0.375	69	0.75	C	*ca*
			3703.37	338852	365846	7	9	1.10	0.290	24.7	0.308	C	*ls*
			3698.70	338690	365719	5	7	0.73	0.210	12.8	0.021	C	*ls*
			3695.37	338566	365619	3	5	0.384	0.131	4.78	−0.406	C	*ls*
			3720.86	338852	365719	7	7	0.361	0.075	6.4	−0.280	C	*ls*
			3712.48	338690	365619	5	5	0.63	0.131	8.0	−0.184	C	*ls*
			3704.73	338566	365551	3	3	0.81	0.168	6.1	−0.298	C	*ls*
			3734.80	338852	365619	7	5	0.071	0.0106	0.91	−1.130	C	*ls*
			3721.95	338690	365551	5	3	0.270	0.0336	2.06	−0.77	C	*ls*
			3709.52	338566	365516	3	1	1.09	0.075	2.75	−0.65	C	*ls*
23		⁵P — ⁵P° (22)	*3345.9*	*338741*	*368620*	15	15	1.50	0.252	41.6	0.58	C	*ca*
			3350.99	338852	368685	7	7	1.00	0.168	13.0	0.070	C	*ls*
			3344.26	338690	368584	5	5	0.125	0.0210	1.16	−0.98	C	*ls*
			3336.78	338566	368526	3	3	0.377	0.063	2.08	−0.72	C	*ls*
			3362.38	338852	368584	7	5	0.69	0.084	6.5	−0.233	C	*ls*
			3350.68	338690	368526	5	3	0.112	0.113	6.2	−0.248	C	*ls*
			3333.00	338690	368685	5	7	0.51	0.118	6.5	−0.229	C	*ls*
			3333.40	338566	368584	3	5	0.68	0.189	6.2	−0.246	C	*ls*
24		⁵P — ⁵S° (22 uv)	*2678.2*	*338741*	*376068*	15	5	2.99	0.107	14.2	0.206	C	*ca*
			2686.14	338852	376068	7	5	1.38	0.107	6.6	−0.126	C	*ls*
			2674.57	338690	376068	5	5	1.00	0.107	4.71	−0.272	C	*ls*
			2665.69	338566	376068	3	5	0.60	0.107	2.82	−0.494	C	*ls*

No.	Transition Array	Multiplet	λ(Å)	E_i(cm⁻¹)	E_k(cm⁻¹)	g_i	g_k	A_{ki}(10⁸ sec⁻¹)	f_{ik}	S(at.u.)	log gf	Accuracy	Source
25		³P — ³D° (23)	*4081.0*	*350212*	*374709*	9	15	0.94	0.391	47.3	0.55	C	*ca*
			4081.10	350302	374799	5	7	0.94	0.329	22.1	0.217	C	*ls*
			4073.90	350123	374663	3	5	0.71	0.294	11.8	−0.055	C	*ls*
			[4072.3]	350026	374575	1	3	0.52	0.392	5.2	−0.407	C	*ls*
			[4103.8]	350302	374663	5	5	0.232	0.058	3.95	−0.53	C	*ls*
			[4088.5]	350123	374575	3	3	0.389	0.098	3.94	−0.53	C	*ls*
			[4118.6]	350302	374575	5	3	0.0254	0.00388	0.263	−1.71	C	*ls*
26		³P — ³P° (24)	*3544.6*	*350212*	*378416*	9	9	1.46	0.274	28.8	0.392	C	*ca*
			3556.92	350302	378409	5	5	1.08	0.205	12.0	0.010	C	*ls*
			[3532.8]	350123	378421	3	3	0.367	0.069	2.39	−0.69	C	*ls*
			[3555.3]	350302	378421	5	3	0.60	0.068	4.00	−0.467	C	*ls*
			[3530.7]	350123	378438	3	1	1.47	0.092	3.19	−0.56	C	*ls*
			[3534.3]	350123	378409	3	5	0.366	0.114	3.99	−0.465	C	*ls*
			[3520.7]	350026	378421	1	3	0.493	0.275	3.19	−0.56	C	*ls*
27	2p3p — 2p(²P°)3d	³D — ³F° (8)	*3265.9*	*294007*	*324688*	15	21	2.08	0.465	75	0.84	C	*3, ca*
			3265.46	294222	324836	7	9	2.07	0.425	32.0	0.474	C	*ls*
			3260.98	294002	324658	5	7	1.84	0.412	22.1	0.314	C	*ls*
			3267.31	293865	324462	3	5	1.73	0.462	14.9	0.142	C	*ls*
			3284.57	294222	324658	7	7	0.226	0.0366	2.77	−0.59	C	*ls*
			3281.94	294002	324462	5	5	0.317	0.051	2.77	−0.59	C	*ls*
			3305.77	294222	324462	7	5	0.0093	0.00109	0.083	−2.118	C	*ls*
28		³D — ³D° (10)	*3002.6*	*294007*	*327302*	15	15	0.68	0.092	13.6	0.139	C	*3, ca*
			3017.63	294222	327351	7	7	0.59	0.081	5.6	−0.249	C	*ls*
			3004.35	294002	327277	5	5	0.472	0.064	3.16	−0.496	C	*ls*
			2996.51	293865	327228	3	3	0.51	0.069	2.04	−0.68	C	*ls*
			3024.36	294222	327277	7	5	0.104	0.0102	0.71	−1.147	C	*ls*
			3008.79	294002	327228	5	3	0.134	0.0109	0.54	−1.264	C	*ls*
			2997.71	294002	327351	5	7	0.076	0.0144	0.71	−1.143	C	*ls*
			2992.11	293865	327277	3	5	0.082	0.0183	0.54	−1.261	C	*ls*
29		³S — ³P° (12)	*3127.3*	*297558*	*329525*	3	9	1.37	0.60	18.6	0.257	C	*3, ca*
			3132.86	297558	329468	3	5	1.36	0.333	10.3	−0.001	C	*ls*
			3121.71	297558	329582	3	3	1.38	0.201	6.2	−0.220	C	*ls*
			3115.73	297558	329643	3	1	1.39	0.067	2.07	−0.70	C	*ls*
30		³P — ³D° (14)	*3712.5*	*300374*	*327302*	9	15	1.10	0.379	41.7	0.53	C	*3, ca*
			3715.08	300441	327351	5	7	1.10	0.319	19.5	0.203	C	*ls*
			3707.24	300310	327277	3	5	0.83	0.284	10.4	−0.070	C	*ls*
			3702.75	300228	327228	1	3	0.62	0.380	4.63	−0.420	C	*ls*
			3725.30	300441	327277	5	5	0.273	0.057	3.48	−0.55	C	*ls*
			3714.03	300310	327228	3	3	0.459	0.095	3.48	−0.55	C	*ls*
			3732.13	300441	327228	5	3	0.0301	0.00378	0.232	−1.72	C	*ls*
31		³P — ³P° (15)	*3429.4*	*300374*	*329525*	9	9	0.79	0.140	14.2	0.100	C	*3, ca*
			3444.10	300441	329468	5	5	0.59	0.104	5.9	−0.284	C	*ls*
			3415.29	300310	329582	3	3	0.200	0.0350	1.18	−0.98	C	*ls*
			3430.60	300441	329582	5	3	0.330	0.0349	1.97	−0.76	C	*ls*
			3408.13	300310	329643	3	1	0.81	0.0469	1.58	−0.85	C	*ls*
			3428.67	300310	329468	3	5	0.198	0.058	1.97	−0.76	C	*ls*
			3405.74	300228	329582	1	3	0.270	0.141	1.58	−0.85	C	*ls*
32		¹D — ¹D° (16)	5500.11	306585	324734	5	5	0.112	0.051	4.58	−0.60	C	*3, ca*
33		¹D — ¹F° (17)	3961.59	306585	331820	5	7	1.28	0.422	27.5	0.324	C	*3, ca*

No.	Transition Array	Multiplet	λ(Å)	E_i(cm^{-1})	E_k(cm^{-1})	g_i	g_k	A_{ki}(10^8 sec^{-1})	f_{ik}	S(at.u.)	log gf	Accuracy	Source
34		^{1}D $-$ ^{1}P° (18)	3816.75	306585	332777	5	3	0.0402	0.0053	0.331	-1.58	C	3, *ca*
35		^{1}S $-$ ^{1}P° (19)	5268.06	313801	332777	1	3	0.311	0.389	6.7	-0.411	C	3, *ca*
36	$2s2p^23p -$ $2s2p^2(^4$P$)3d$	^{3}S° $-$ ^{3}P (23 uv)	*2691.5*	*363267*	*400410*	3	9	2.10	0.68	18.2	0.312	C	*ca*
			2695.49	363267	400355	3	5	2.09	0.379	10.1	0.056	C	*ls*
			2687.53	363267	400465	3	3	2.11	0.229	6.1	-0.163	C	*ls*
			2683.65	363267	400518	3	1	2.12	0.076	2.02	-0.64	C	*ls*
37		^{5}D° $-$ ^{5}F (25)	*3453.0*	*365716*	*394668*	25	35	1.68	0.420	119	1.021	C	*ca*
			3455.12	365846	394780	9	11	1.67	0.365	37.4	0.52	C	*ls*
			3450.94	365719	394688	7	9	1.40	0.321	25.5	0.351	C	*ls*
			3448.05	365619	394613	5	7	1.15	0.287	16.3	0.157	C	*ls*
			3446.73	365551	394555	3	5	0.94	0.279	9.5	-0.077	C	*ls*
			3447.22	365516	394516	1	3	0.78	0.419	4.76	-0.377	C	*ls*
			3466.15	365846	394688	9	9	0.276	0.0497	5.1	-0.350	C	*ls*
			3459.98	365719	394613	7	7	0.496	0.089	7.1	-0.205	C	*ls*
			3454.90	365619	394555	5	5	0.67	0.120	6.8	-0.223	C	*ls*
			3451.33	365551	394516	3	3	0.78	0.140	4.76	-0.378	C	*ls*
			[3475.2]	365846	394613	9	7	0.0234	0.00330	0.340	-1.53	C	*ls*
			3466.90	365719	394555	7	5	0.066	0.0085	0.68	-1.225	C	*ls*
			3459.52	365619	394516	5	3	0.111	0.0119	0.68	-1.224	C	*ls*
38		^{5}D° $-$ ^{5}D (26)	*3081.0*	*365716*	*398164*	25	25	0.62	0.089	22.5	0.345	C	*ca*
			3088.04	365846	398219	9	9	0.52	0.074	6.8	-0.178	C	*ls*
			3083.65	365719	398137	7	7	0.311	0.0443	3.15	-0.51	C	*ls*
			3075.19	365619	398127	5	5	0.157	0.0222	1.12	-0.95	C	*ls*
			3068.48	365551	398131	3	3	0.234	0.0330	0.225	-1.004	C	*ls*
			3095.81	365846	398137	9	7	0.132	0.0147	1.35	-0.88	C	*ls*
			3084.63	365719	398127	7	5	0.248	0.0253	1.80	-0.75	C	*ls*
			3074.68	365619	398131	5	3	0.365	0.0310	1.57	-0.81	C	*ls*
			3068.06	365551	398135	3	1	0.63	0.0296	0.90	-1.052	C	*ls*
			3075.95	365719	398219	7	9	0.104	0.0190	1.35	-0.88	C	*ls*
			3074.15	365619	398137	5	7	0.180	0.0355	1.80	-0.75	C	*ls*
			3068.68	365551	398127	3	5	0.220	0.052	1.57	-0.81	C	*ls*
			3065.01	365516	398131	1	3	0.210	0.089	0.90	-1.051	C	*ls*
39		^{5}P° $-$ ^{5}D (27)	*3383.8*	*368620*	*398164*	15	25	1.45	0.416	69	0.80	C	*ca*
			3384.95	368685	398219	7	9	1.45	0.321	25.0	0.351	C	*ls*
			3382.69	368584	398137	5	7	0.97	0.233	13.0	0.066	C	*ls*
			[3377.3]	368526	398127	3	5	0.51	0.146	4.85	-0.360	C	*ls*
			3394.26	368685	398137	7	7	0.480	0.083	6.5	-0.237	C	*ls*
			3383.85	368584	398127	5	5	0.85	0.145	8.1	-0.139	C	*ls*
			3376.82	368526	398131	3	3	1.09	0.187	6.2	-0.251	C	*ls*
			[3395.5]	368685	398127	7	5	0.096	0.0118	0.93	-1.082	C	*ls*
			[3383.5]	368584	398131	5	3	0.363	0.0374	2.08	-0.73	C	*ls*
			[3376.4]	368526	398135	3	1	1.46	0.083	2.77	-0.60	C	*ls*
40		^{5}P° $-$ ^{5}P (28)	*3343.6*	*368620*	*398519*	15	15	0.84	0.140	23.1	0.322	C	*ca*
			3355.92	368685	398474	7	7	0.55	0.093	7.2	-0.187	C	*ls*
			3336.78	368584	398544	5	5	0.070	0.0117	0.64	-1.233	C	*ls*
			3326.16	368526	398583	3	3	0.212	0.0352	1.16	-0.98	C	*ls*
			3348.05	368685	398544	7	5	0.388	0.0466	3.60	-0.487	C	*ls*
			3332.49	368584	398583	5	3	0.63	0.063	3.47	-0.50	C	*ls*
			3344.26	368584	398474	5	7	0.278	0.065	3.59	-0.487	C	*ls*
			3330.40	368526	398544	3	5	0.379	0.105	3.45	-0.50	C	*ls*

No.	Transition Array	Multiplet	λ(Å)	E_i(cm^{-1})	E_k(cm^{-1})	g_i	g_k	A_{ki}(10^8 sec^{-1})	f_{ik}	S(at.u.)	log gf	Accuracy	Source
41		^{3}D°—^{3}F (30)	*3730.1*	*374709*	*401510*	15	21	1.58	0.460	85	0.84	C	*ca*
			3728.82	374799	401609	7	9	1.58	0.424	36.4	0.472	C	*ls*
			3728.49	374663	401475	5	7	1.41	0.411	25.2	0.312	C	*ls*
			3729.70	374575	401379	3	5	1.33	0.461	17.0	0.141	C	*ls*
			[3747.6]	374799	401475	7	7	0.174	0.0366	3.16	−0.59	C	*ls*
			[3742.0]	374663	401379	5	5	0.244	0.051	3.16	−0.59	C	*ls*
			[3761.2]	374799	401379	7	5	0.0072	0.00108	0.094	−2.120	C	*ls*
42		^{3}D°—^{3}D (31)	*3210.2*	*374709*	*405851*	15	15	0.66	0.102	16.2	0.186	C	*ca*
			3215.97	374799	405883	7	7	0.58	0.091	6.7	−0.198	C	*ls*
			3207.12	374663	405834	5	5	0.460	0.071	3.74	−0.451	C	*ls*
			3200.95	374575	405805	3	3	0.499	0.077	2.42	−0.64	C	*ls*
			[3221.2]	374799	405834	7	5	0.102	0.0113	0.84	−1.102	C	*ls*
			[3210.2]	374663	405805	5	3	0.165	0.0153	0.81	−1.117	C	*ls*
			[3202.2]	374663	405883	5	7	0.074	0.0159	0.84	−1.099	C	*ls*
			[3198.2]	374575	405834	3	5	0.100	0.0256	0.81	−1.115	C	*ls*
43		^{5}S°—^{5}P (33)	*4452.9*	*376068*	*398519*	5	15	0.490	0.437	32.0	0.340	C	*ca*
			4461.56	376068	398474	5	7	0.486	0.203	14.9	0.007	C	*ls*
			4447.82	376068	398544	5	5	0.492	0.146	10.7	−0.137	C	*ls*
			4440.1	376068	398583	5	3	0.495	0.088	6.4	−0.358	C	*ls*
44		^{3}P°—^{3}D (35)	*3643.9*	*378416*	*405851*	9	15	1.39	0.461	49.8	0.62	C	*ca*
			3638.70	378409	405883	5	7	1.40	0.388	23.2	0.288	C	*ls*
			3646.84	378421	405834	3	5	1.04	0.345	12.4	0.015	C	*ls*
			3653.00	378438	405805	1	3	0.77	0.460	5.5	−0.337	C	*ls*
			3645.20	378409	405834	5	5	0.347	0.069	4.15	−0.462	C	*ls*
			3650.70	378421	405805	3	3	0.58	0.115	4.15	−0.462	C	*ls*
			3649.20	378409	405805	5	3	0.0384	0.00460	0.276	−1.64	C	*ls*
45	2p3d—2p(^{2}P°)4p	^{3}P°—^{3}S (20 uv)	*2601.6*	*329525*	367952	9	3	1.73	0.059	4.52	−0.278	C	3, *ca*
			2597.69	329468	367952	5	3	0.97	0.059	2.51	−0.53	C	*ls*
			2605.41	329582	367952	3	3	0.58	0.059	1.51	−0.75	C	*ls*
			[2609.6]	329643	367952	1	3	0.190	0.058	0.50	−1.235	C	*ls*
46		^{1}F°—^{1}D (21 uv)	2558.06	331820	370901	7	5	1.16	0.081	4.79	−0.245	C	3, *ca*
47	2p4p—2p(^{2}P°)5d	^{1}S—^{1}P° (29)	3279.97	373046	403526	1	3	0.241	0.117	1.26	−0.93	C	3, *ca*

Forbidden Transitions

The adopted values represent, as in the case of C I, the work of Garstang [1], Naqvi [2], and Yamanouchi and Horie [3], who have independently done essentially the same calculations and arrived at very similar results. For the selection of values, the same considerations as for C I have been applied. (Yamanouchi and Horie's result for the $^3P_1 - {}^1D_2$ transition apparently contains a numerical error and is not used).

References

[1] Garstang, R. H., Monthly Notices Roy. Astron. Soc. **111,** 115–124 (1951).
[2] Naqvi, A. M., Thesis Harvard (1951).
[3] Yamanouchi, T., and Horie, H., J. Phys. Soc. Japan **7,** 52–56 (1952).

O III. Forbidden Transitions

No.	Transition Array	Multiplet	$\lambda(\text{Å})$	$E_i(\text{cm}^{-1})$	$E_k(\text{cm}^{-1})$	g_i	g_k	Type of Transition	$A_{ki}(\text{sec}^{-1})$	$S(\text{at.u.})$	Accuracy	Source
1	$2p^2 - 2p^2$	$^3P - {}^3P$										
			$[51.69 \times 10^4]$	113.4	306.8	3	5	m	9.75×10^{-5}	2.50	B	1, 2, 3
			$[51.69 \times 10^4]$	113.4	306.8	3	5	e	7.8×10^{-12}	0.086	C	1
			$[32.59 \times 10^4]$	0	306.8	1	5	e	3.50×10^{-11}	0.383	C	1
			$[88.16 \times 10^4]$	0	113.4	1	3	m	2.62×10^{-5}	2.00	B	1, 2, 3
2		$^3P - {}^1D$ (1 F)										
			5006.84	306.8	20271	5	5	m	0.0210	4.88×10^{-4}	C	1, 2, 3
			5006.84	306.8	20271	5	5	e	4.1×10^{-5}	3.8×10^{-4}	D	1
			4958.91	113.4	20271	3	5	m	0.0071	1.61×10^{-4}	C	1, 2
			4958.91	113.4	20271	3	5	e	6.2×10^{-6}	5.5×10^{-5}	D	1
			4931.8	0	20271	1	5	e	1.9×10^{-6}	1.7×10^{-5}	D	1
3		$^3P - {}^1S$										
			$[2331.6]$	306.8	43183.5	5	1	e	7.1×10^{-4}	2.9×10^{-5}	D	1
			$[2321.1]$	113.4	43183.5	3	1	m	0.230	1.07×10^{-4}	C	1, 3
4		$^1D - {}^1S$ (2 F)										
			4363.21	20271	43183.5	5	1	e	1.60	1.51	C	1

O IV

Ground State $1s^2\,2s^2\,2p\,{}^2P^\circ_{1/2}$

Ionization Potential 77.394 eV $= 624396.5$ cm^{-1}

Allowed Transitions

List of tabulated lines:

Wavelength [Å]	No.	Wavelength [Å]	No.	Wavelength [Å]	No.
238.361	6	3216.31	14	3774.38	13
238.573	6	3348.08	9	3930.63	17
238.58	6	3349.11	9	3942.14	17
279.633	5	3354.31	15	3945.29	17
279.937	5	3362.63	15	3956.82	17
553.328	3	3375.50	15	3974.66	17
554.074	3	3378.09	9	3977.10	17
554.514	3	3381.28	8	3995.17	17
555.262	3	3381.33	8	4568	21
608.395	2	3385.55	8	4652.5	20
609.829	2	3390.37	8	4685.4	20
624.617	4	3396.83	8	4772.57	16
625.130	4	3403.58	12	4779.09	16
625.852	4	3405.97	8	4783.43	16
787.710	1	3409.75	8	4794.22	16
790.103	1	3411.76	12	4798.25	16
790.203	1	3413.71	12	4800.77	16
2494.8	10	3425.57	8	4813.07	16
2511.4	10	3489.84	11	4823.93	16
3063.46	7	3492.2	11	5290.1	18
3071.66	7	3492.24	11	5305.3	18
3177.80	14	3560.42	19	5362.4	18
3180.72	14	3563.36	19	5378.3	18
3180.98	14	3593.1	19		
3185.72	14	3725.81	13		
3188.17	14	3729.03	13		
3188.65	14	3736.78	13		
3194.75	14	3744.73	13		
3199.53	14	3755.82	13		
3209.64	14	3758.45	13		

Values for the $2s^2 2p - 2s 2p^2$ transitions are taken from the calculations of Bolotin and Yutsis [1] who employ analytical one-electron wave functions and include configuration interaction with a relatively crude approximation. For these as well as the $2s 2p^2 - 2p^3$ and $2p - 3s$ transitions large uncertainties must be expected because they are very sensitive to the effects of configuration interaction.

For several other transitions Kelly's self-consistent field calculations [2, 3] (which include exchange effects) are available. In the case of the highly excited lines, they agree within a few percent with the results of the Coulomb approximation and the averaged values are adopted.

References

[1] Bolotin, A. B., and Yutsis, A. P., Zhur. Eksptl. i Teoret. Fiz. **24**, 537–543 (1953). (Translated in "Optical Transition Probabilities," Office of Technical Services, U.S. Department of Commerce, Washington, D.C.)

[2] Kelly, P. S., Astrophys. J. **140**, 1247–1268 (1964).

[3] Kelly, P. S., J. Quant. Spectrosc. Radiat. Transfer **4**, 117–148 (1964).

O IV. Allowed Transitions

No.	Transition Array	Multiplet	$\lambda(\text{Å})$	$E_i(\text{cm}^{-1})$	$E_k(\text{cm}^{-1})$	g_i	g_k	$A_{ki}(10^8 \text{ sec}^{-1})$	f_{ik}	$S(\text{at.u.})$	$\log gf$	Accuracy	Source
1	$2s^2 2p -$ $2s(^1S)2p^2$	$^2P° - {}^2D$ (1 uv)	*789.36*	*257.7*	*126942*	6	10	9.5	0.15	2.3	−0.05	E	1
			790.203	386.5	126936	4	6	9.6	0.13	1.4	−0.27	E	*ls*
			787.710	0.0	126950	2	4	8.0	0.15	0.77	−0.53	E	*ls*
			790.103	386.5	126950	4	4	1.5	0.014	0.15	−1.24	E	*ls*
2		$^2P° - {}^2S$ (2 uv)	*609.35*	*257.7*	*164367*	6	2	54	0.10	1.2	−0.22	E	1
			609.829	386.5	164367	4	2	36	0.10	0.80	−0.40	E	*ls*
			608.395	0.0	164367	2	2	18	0.10	0.40	−0.70	E	*ls*
3		$^2P° - {}^2P$ (3 uv)	*554.37*	*257.7*	*180644*	6	6	83	0.38	4.2	0.36	E	1
			554.514	386.5	180725	4	4	68	0.31	2.3	0.10	E	*ls*
			554.074	0.0	180481	2	2	55	0.25	0.93	−0.29	E	*ls*
			555.262	386.5	180481	4	2	28	0.064	0.47	−0.59	E	*ls*
			553.328	0.0	180725	2	4	14	0.13	0.47	−0.59	E	*ls*
4	$2s2p^2 - 2p^3$	$^4P - {}^4S°$ (6 uv)	*625.41*	*[71379]*	*[231275]*	12	4	72	0.14	3.5	0.23	E	2
			625.852	[71493]	[231275]	6	4	37	0.15	1.8	−0.06	E	*ls*
			625.130	[71308]	[231275]	4	4	25	0.15	1.2	−0.23	E	*ls*
			624.617	[71177]	[231275]	2	4	12	0.14	0.58	−0.55	E	*ls*
5	$2p - (^1S)3s$	$^2P° - {}^2S$ (4 uv)	*279.83*	*257.7*	*357615*	6	2	130	0.050	0.28	−0.52	E	2
			279.937	386.5	357615	4	2	85	0.050	0.19	−0.70	E	*ls*
			279.633	0.0	357615	2	2	43	0.050	0.092	−1.00	E	*ls*
6	$2p - (^1S)3d$	$^2P° - {}^2D$ (5 uv)	*238.50*	*257.7*	*419544*	6	10	350	0.50	2.4	0.48	D−	2
			238.573	386.5	419550	4	6	350	0.45	1.4	0.26	D−	*ls*
			238.361	0.0	419534	2	4	300	0.50	0.79	0.00	D−	*ls*
			[238.58]	386.5	419534	4	4	59	0.050	0.16	−0.70	D−	*ls*
7	$3s - (^1S)3p$	$^2S - {}^2P°$ (1)	*3066.2*	*357615*	*390219*	2	6	1.48	0.62	12.6	0.096	C	3, *ca*
			3063.46	357615	390248	2	4	1.48	0.416	8.4	−0.079	C	*ls*
			3071.66	357615	390161	2	2	1.47	0.208	4.20	−0.382	C	*ls*
8	$2s2p3s -$ $2s(^3P°)2p3p$	$^4P° - {}^4D$ (3)	*3374.3*	*[438698]*	*[468325]*	12	20	1.07	0.303	40.4	0.56	C	*ca*
			3385.55	[438589]	[468499]	6	8	1.06	0.242	16.2	0.162	C	*ls*
			3381.28	[438724]	[468290]	4	6	0.74	0.191	8.5	−0.117	C	*ls*
			3381.33	[438971]	[468154]	2	4	0.442	0.151	3.37	−0.52	C	*ls*
			3409.75	[438589]	[468290]	6	6	0.310	0.054	3.64	−0.489	C	*ls*
			3396.83	[438724]	[468154]	4	4	0.56	0.096	4.31	−0.414	C	*ls*
			3390.37	[438971]	[468075]	2	2	0.88	0.151	3.37	−0.52	C	*ls*
			3425.57	[438589]	[468154]	6	4	0.051	0.0060	0.404	−1.446	C	*ls*
			3405.97	[438724]	[468075]	4	2	0.172	0.0149	0.67	−1.224	C	*ls*
9		$^2P° - {}^2D$ (4)	*3350.7*	*452985*	*482821*	6	10	1.23	0.346	22.9	0.317	C	*ca*
			3349.11	453073	482923	4	6	1.23	0.311	13.7	0.094	C	*ls*
			3348.08	452808	482668	2	4	1.03	0.345	7.6	−0.162	C	*ls*
			3378.09	453073	482668	4	4	0.201	0.0344	1.53	−0.86	C	*ls*
10		$^2P° - {}^2S$ (5)	*2505.8*	*452985*	*492880*	6	2	3.04	0.095	4.72	−0.243	C	*ca*
			[2511.4]	453073	492880	4	2	2.01	0.095	3.15	−0.420	C	*ls*
			[2494.8]	452808	492880	2	2	1.02	0.096	1.57	−0.72	C	*ls*
11	$2s2p3s' -$ $2s2p(^1P°)3p'$	$^2P° - {}^2D$ (14)	*3490.9*	*518688*	*547326*	6	10	0.99	0.301	20.8	0.257	C	*ca*
			3489.84	518690	547336	4	6	0.99	0.272	12.5	0.037	C	*ls*
			3492.24	518684	547311	2	4	0.82	0.300	6.9	−0.222	C	*ls*
			[3492.2]	518684	547311	4	4	0.165	0.0302	1.39	−0.92	C	*ls*

No.	Transition Array	Multiplet	$\lambda(\text{Å})$	$E_i(\text{cm}^{-1})$	$E_k(\text{cm}^{-1})$	g_i	g_k	$A_{ki}(10^8$ $\text{sec}^{-1})$	f_{ik}	$S(\text{at.u.})$	log gf	Accuracy	Source
12	$3p-(^1\text{S})3d$	$^2\text{P}°-^2\text{D}$ (2)	3409.1	390219	419544	6	10	1.15	0.334	22.5	0.302	C	3, *ca*
			3411.76	390248	419550	4	6	1.15	0.300	13.5	0.080	C	*ls*
			3403.58	390161	419534	2	4	0.96	0.335	7.5	−0.174	C	*ls*
			3413.71	390248	419534	4	4	0.191	0.0334	1.50	−0.87	C	*ls*
13	$2s2p3p-$ $2s2p(^3\text{P}°)3d$	$^4\text{D}-^4\text{F}°$ (6)	3733.4	[468325]	[495103]	20	28	0.80	0.235	58	0.67	C	*ca*
			3736.78	[468499]	[495253]	8	10	0.80	0.209	20.6	0.224	C	*ls*
			3729.03	[468290]	[495099]	6	8	0.69	0.193	14.2	0.063	C	*ls*
			3725.81	[468154]	[494986]	4	6	0.61	0.190	9.3	−0.120	C	*ls*
			3725.81	[468075]	[494908]	2	4	0.57	0.236	5.8	−0.325	C	*ls*
			3758.45	[468499]	[495099]	8	8	0.112	0.0237	2.35	−0.72	C	*ls*
			3744.73	[468290]	[494986]	6	6	0.194	0.0407	3.01	−0.61	C	*ls*
			3736.78	[468154]	[494908]	4	4	0.224	0.0469	2.31	−0.73	C	*ls*
			3774.38	[468075]	[494986]	8	6	0.0075	0.00121	0.120	−2.015	C	*ls*
			3755.82	[468290]	[494908]	6	4	0.0158	0.00222	0.165	−1.87	C	*ls*
14		$^4\text{D}-^4\text{D}°$ (7)	3197.4	[468325]	[499591]	20	20	0.338	0.052	10.9	0.015	C	*ca*
			3209.64	[468499]	[499647]	8	8	0.286	0.0442	3.74	−0.451	C	*ls*
			3194.75	[468290]	[499582]	6	6	0.194	0.0296	1.87	−0.75	C	*ls*
			3185.72	[468154]	[499535]	4	4	0.136	0.0207	0.87	−1.081	C	*ls*
			3180.72	[468075]	[499506]	2	2	0.173	0.0263	0.55	−1.280	C	*ls*
			3216.31	[468499]	[499582]	8	6	0.063	0.0073	0.62	−1.232	C	*ls*
			3199.53	[468290]	[499535]	6	4	0.118	0.0120	0.76	−1.142	C	*ls*
			3188.65	[468154]	[499506]	4	2	0.172	0.0131	0.55	−1.281	C	*ls*
			3188.17	[468290]	[499647]	6	8	0.0485	0.0098	0.62	−1.229	C	*ls*
			3180.98	[468154]	[499582]	4	6	0.080	0.0181	0.76	−1.139	C	*ls*
			3177.80	[468075]	[499535]	2	4	0.087	0.0263	0.55	−1.279	C	*ls*
15		$^4\text{S}-^4\text{P}°$ (8)	3367.6	[474218]	[503904]	4	12	0.69	0.350	15.5	0.146	C	*ca*
			3375.50	[474218]	[503835]	4	6	0.68	0.175	7.8	−0.154	C	*ls*
			3362.63	[474218]	[503948]	4	4	0.69	0.117	5.2	−0.328	C	*ls*
			3354.31	[474218]	[504022]	4	2	0.69	0.058	2.58	−0.63	C	*ls*
16		$^4\text{P}-^4\text{D}°$ (9)	4792.5	[478731]	[499591]	12	20	0.303	0.174	32.9	0.320	C	*ca*
			4798.25	[478811]	[499647]	6	8	0.303	0.139	13.2	−0.078	C	*ls*
			4783.43	[478682]	[499582]	4	6	0.213	0.110	6.9	−0.358	C	*ls*
			4772.57	[478588]	[499535]	2	4	0.128	0.087	2.74	−0.76	C	*ls*
			4813.07	[478811]	[499582]	6	6	0.090	0.0311	2.96	−0.73	C	*ls*
			4794.22	[478682]	[499535]	4	4	0.161	0.056	3.51	−0.65	C	*ls*
			4779.09	[478588]	[499506]	2	2	0.254	0.087	2.74	−0.76	C	*ls*
			4823.93	[478811]	[499535]	6	4	0.0148	0.00345	0.329	−1.68	C	*ls*
			4800.77	[478682]	[499506]	4	2	0.050	0.0087	0.55	−1.46	C	*ls*
17		$^4\text{P}-^4\text{P}°$ (10)	3971.4	[478731]	[503904]	12	12	0.314	0.074	11.6	−0.050	C	*ca*
			3995.17	[478811]	[503835]	6	6	0.215	0.051	4.06	−0.51	C	*ls*
			3956.82	[478682]	[503948]	4	4	0.0425	0.0100	0.52	−1.399	C	*ls*
			3930.63	[478588]	[504022]	2	2	0.053	0.0124	0.322	−1.61	C	*ls*
			3977.10	[478811]	[503948]	6	4	0.140	0.0221	1.74	−0.88	C	*ls*
			3945.29	[478682]	[504022]	4	2	0.266	0.0310	1.61	−0.91	C	*ls*
			3974.66	[478682]	[503835]	4	6	0.094	0.0332	1.74	−0.88	C	*ls*
			3942.14	[478588]	[503948]	2	4	0.133	0.062	1.61	−0.91	C	*ls*
18		$^2\text{D}-^2\text{D}°$ (11)	5339.5	482821	501544	10	10	0.075	0.0319	5.6	−0.497	C	*ca*
			5362.4	482923	501566	6	6	0.069	0.0299	3.16	−0.75	C	*ls*
			5305.3	482668	501511	4	4	0.069	0.0291	2.03	−0.93	C	*ls*
			[5378.3]	482923	501511	6	4	0.0074	0.00213	0.226	−1.89	C	*ls*
			[5290.1]	482668	501566	4	6	0.0052	0.00324	0.226	−1.89	C	*ls*

No.	Transition Array	Multiplet	λ(Å)	E_i(cm⁻¹)	E_k(cm⁻¹)	g_i	g_k	$A_{ki}(10^8$ sec⁻¹)	f_{ik}	S(at.u.)	log gf	Accuracy	Source
19		²D — ²F° (12)	*3563.0*	*482821*	*510879*	10	14	1.15	0.306	35.9	0.486	C	*ca*
			3563.36	482923	510979	6	8	1.15	0.291	20.5	0.242	C	*ls*
			3560.42	482668	510746	4	6	1.08	0.307	14.4	0.089	C	*ls*
			[3593.1]	482923	510746	6	6	0.075	0.0145	1.03	−1.060	C	*ls*
20		²S — ²P° (13)	*4674.4*	*492880*	*514267*	2	6	0.297	0.292	9.0	−0.234	C	*ca*
			[4685.4]	492880	514217	2	4	0.295	0.194	6.0	−0.411	C	*ls*
			[4652.5]	492880	514368	2	2	0.301	0.098	2.99	−0.71	C	*ls*
21	5f — (¹S)6d	²F° — ²D (15)	4568	552490	[574375]	14	10	0.124	0.0278	5.9	−0.410	C	*ca*

Forbidden Transitions

Naqvi's calculation [1] of the one possible transition in the ground state configuration $2p$ is the only available source. The line strength should be quite accurate, since it does not sensitively depend on the choice of the interaction parameters.

Reference

[1] Naqvi, A. M., Thesis Harvard (1951).

O IV.   Forbidden Transitions

No.	Transition Array	Multiplet	λ(Å)	E_i(cm⁻¹)	E_k(cm⁻¹)	g_i	g_k	Type of Transition	A_{ki}(sec⁻¹)	S(at.u.)	Accuracy	Source
1	2p — 2p	²P° — ²P°	[25.87 × 10⁴]	0	386.5	2	4	m	5.18 × 10⁻⁴	1.33	B	1

O v

Ground State $\qquad$ $1s^2\,2s^2\,{}^1S_0$

Ionization Potential $\qquad$ $113.873\ \mathrm{eV} = 918702\ \mathrm{cm}^{-1}$

Allowed Transitions

List of tabulated lines:

Wavelength [Å]	No.	Wavelength [Å]	No.	Wavelength [Å]	No.
172.168	2	3230	18	5114	10
192.751	8	3239	12	5343	21
192.80	8	3245	18	5352	21
192.800	8	3249	18	5376	21
192.906	8	3264	18	5417	21
192.91	8	3275.67	12	5432	21
192.92	8	3298	18	5473	21
215.034	6	3692	17	5573	15
215.104	6	3701	17	5582	15
215.245	6	3703	17	5584	15
220.352	9	3717	17	5600	15
248.459	7	3726	17	5606	15
629.732	1	3747	17	5608	15
758.677	3	3762	17	6329	22
759.440	3	4120	11	6767	20
760.229	3	4121.7	19	6790	20
760.445	3	4123	11	6819	20
761.131	3	4123.90	11	6830	20
762.001	3	4135.9	19	6878	20
774.522	5	4151	11	6909	20
				7438	24
1371.29	4	4158.76	19		
3058.68	13	4179	11		
3144.68	14	4211	11		
3222	12	4522	23		
3222	18	4554.28	16		

Values for the $2s^2 - 2s2p$ and $2s2p - 2p^2$ transition arrays are taken from the self-consistent field calculations of Weiss [1]. These calculations do not include the important effects of configuration interaction; hence large uncertainties must be expected. The average of the dipole length and velocity approximations is adopted [1]. Accuracies within 50 percent are indicated by the following comparison: Weiss [1] has undertaken refined calculations, including configuration interaction, for the same transitions in Be I — the first member of this isoelectronic sequence — in addition to calculations of the type done for this ion. In all cases the agreement with the average of the dipole length and velocity approximations is close.

For the remaining low-lying transitions Kelly's approximate Hartree-Fock calculations [2] are adopted, while for the moderately excited transitions Kelly's values are averaged with the Coulomb approximation, with which they agree quite well.

References

[1] Weiss, A. W., private communication (1964).
[2] Kelly, P. S., J. Quant. Spectrosc. Radiat. Transfer **4**, 117–148 (1964).

O v. Allowed Transitions

No.	Transition Array	Multiplet	$\lambda(\text{Å})$	$E_i(\text{cm}^{-1})$	$E_k(\text{cm}^{-1})$	g_i	g_k	$A_{ki}(10^8\ \text{sec}^{-1})$	f_{ik}	$S(\text{at.u.})$	$\log gf$	Accuracy	Source
1	$2s^2 -$ $2s(^2S)2p$	$^1S - ^1P^\circ$ (1 uv)	629.732	0	158798	1	3	30	0.53	1.1	-0.28	D	1
2	$2s^2 -$ $2s(^2S)3p$	$^1S - ^1P^\circ$ (2 uv)	172.168	0	580826	1	3	450	0.59	0.34	-0.23	D	2
3	$2s2p - 2p^2$	$^3P^\circ - ^3P$ (3 uv)	*760.36*	[82413]	[213929]	9	9	21	0.18	4.1	0.21	D	1
			760.445	[82564]	[214066]	5	5	16	0.14	1.7	-0.17	D	ls
			760.229	[82258]	[213797]	3	3	5.2	0.045	0.34	-0.87	D	ls
			762.001	[83564]	[213797]	5	3	8.6	0.045	0.56	-0.65	D	ls
			761.131	[82258]	[213642]	3	1	21	0.060	0.45	-0.75	D	ls
			758.677	[82258]	[214066]	3	5	5.2	0.075	0.56	-0.65	D	ls
			759.440	[82121]	[213797]	1	3	6.9	0.18	0.45	-0.74	D	ls
4		$^1P^\circ - ^1D$ (7 uv)	1371.29	158798	231722	3	5	6.7	0.32	4.3	-0.03	D	1
5		$^1P^\circ - ^1S$ (8 uv)	774.522	158798	287909	3	1	21	0.062	0.48	-0.73	D	1
6	$2s2p -$ $2s(^2S)3s$	$^3P^\circ - ^3S$ (4 uv)	*215.18*	[82413]	[547150]	9	3	211	0.0488	0.311	-0.358	C	2
			215.245	[82564]	[547150]	5	3	117	0.0488	0.173	-0.61	C	ls
			215.104	[82258]	[547150]	3	3	71	0.0490	0.104	-0.83	C	ls
			215.034	[82121]	[547150]	1	3	23.5	0.0489	0.0346	-1.311	C	ls
7		$^1P^\circ - ^1S$ (9 uv)	248.459	158798	561278	3	1	137	0.0424	0.104	-0.90	C	2
8	$2s2p -$ $2s(^2S)3d$	$^3P^\circ - ^3D$ (5 uv)	*192.85*	[82413]	[600943]	9	15	680	0.64	3.63	0.76	C	2
			192.906	[82564]	[600956]	5	7	680	0.53	1.69	0.425	C	ls
			192.800	[82258]	[600936]	3	5	510	0.478	0.91	0.157	C	ls
			192.751	[82121]	[600926]	1	3	380	0.64	0.403	-0.197	C	ls
			[192.91]	[82564]	[600936]	5	5	171	0.095	0.303	-0.321	C	ls
			[192.80]	[82258]	[600926]	3	3	286	0.159	0.303	-0.321	C	ls
			[192.92]	[82564]	[600926]	5	3	19.0	0.0064	0.0202	-1.498	C	ls
9		$^1P^\circ - ^1D$ (10 uv)	220.352	158798	612617	3	5	458	0.56	1.21	0.222	C	2
10	$2s3s -$ $2s(^2S)3p$	$^1S - ^1P^\circ$ (1)	5114	547150	580826	1	3	0.253	0.298	5.01	-0.526	C+	2, ca
11	$2p3s -$ $2p(^2P^\circ)3p$	$^3P^\circ - ^3D$ (4)	*4130.4*	[653435]	[677639]	9	15	0.483	0.206	25.2	0.268	C	ca
			4123.90	[653605]	[677847]	5	7	0.487	0.174	11.8	-0.061	C	ls
			4120	[653262]	[677532]	3	5	0.365	0.155	6.3	-0.333	C	ls
			4123	[653100]	[677333]	1	3	0.270	0.206	2.80	-0.69	C	ls
			4179	[653605]	[677532]	5	5	0.117	0.0305	2.10	-0.82	C	ls
			4151	[653262]	[677333]	3	3	0.198	0.051	2.10	-0.81	C	ls
			4211	[653605]	[677333]	5	3	0.0127	0.00202	0.140	-1.99	C	ls
12		$^3P^\circ - ^3S$ (5)	*3257.5*	[653435]	[684124]	9	3	1.01	0.053	5.2	-0.318	C	ca
			3275.67	[653605]	[684124]	5	3	0.55	0.053	2.87	-0.57	C	ls
			3239	[653262]	[684124]	3	3	0.342	0.054	1.72	-0.79	C	ls
			3222	[653100]	[684124]	1	3	0.116	0.054	0.57	-1.268	C	ls
13		$^1P^\circ - ^1D$ (6)	3058.68	664486	697170	3	5	1.30	0.305	9.2	-0.039	C	ca
14	$2s3p -$ $2s(^2S)3d$	$^1P^\circ - ^1D$ (2)	3144.68	580826	612617	3	5	1.05	0.258	8.02	-0.111	C+	2, ca

No.	Transition Array	Multiplet	$\lambda(\text{Å})$	$E_i(\text{cm}^{-1})$	$E_k(\text{cm}^{-1})$	g_i	g_k	$A_{ki}(10^8\ \text{sec}^{-1})$	f_{ik}	$S(\text{at.u.})$	log gf	Accuracy	Source
15		³P° — ³D (3)	5590.0	[583059]	[600943]	9	15	0.176	0.138	22.8	0.093	C+	2, ca
			5600	[583097]	[600956]	5	7	0.175	0.115	10.6	−0.240	C+	ls
			5582	[583020]	[600936]	3	5	0.133	0.103	5.70	−0.508	C+	ls
			5573	[582984]	[600926]	1	3	0.0987	0.138	2.53	−0.861	C+	ls
			5606	[583097]	[600936]	5	5	0.0437	0.0206	1.90	−0.987	C+	ls
			5584	[583020]	[600926]	3	3	0.0737	0.0345	1.90	−0.986	C+	ls
			5608	[583097]	[600926]	5	3	0.00486	0.00138	0.127	−2.163	C+	ls
16	2p3p — 2p(²P°)3d	¹P — ¹D° (7)	4554.28	672965	694646	3	5	0.233	0.121	5.4	−0.440	C	ca
17		³D — ³D° (8)	3727.5	[667639]	[704459]	15	15	0.155	0.0323	6.0	−0.314	C	ca
			3747	[677847]	[704527]	7	7	0.136	0.0286	2.47	−0.70	C	ls
			3717	[677532]	[704424]	5	5	0.109	0.0226	1.38	−0.95	C	ls
			3701	[677333]	[704360]	3	3	0.119	0.0244	0.89	−1.135	C	ls
			3762	[677847]	[704424]	7	5	0.0235	0.00356	0.309	−1.60	C	ls
			3726	[677532]	[704360]	5	3	0.0388	0.00484	0.297	−1.62	C	ls
			3703	[677532]	[704527]	5	7	0.0176	0.0051	0.309	−1.60	C	ls
			3692	[677333]	[704424]	3	5	0.0239	0.0081	0.297	−1.61	C	ls
18		³D — ³P° (9)	3268.4	[677639]	[708226]	15	9	0.0264	0.00254	0.410	−1.419	C	ca
			3298	[677847]	[708154]	7	5	0.0216	0.00251	0.191	−1.75	C	ls
			3249	[677532]	[708296]	5	3	0.0201	0.00191	0.102	−2.021	C	ls
			3222	[677333]	[708379]	3	1	0.0276	0.00143	0.0455	−2.368	C	ls
			3264	[677532]	[708154]	5	5	0.00397	6.3×10^{-4}	0.0341	−2.499	C	ls
			3230	[677333]	[708296]	3	3	0.0068	0.00107	0.0341	−2.494	C	ls
			3245	[677333]	[708379]	3	5	2.70×10^{-4}	7.1×10^{-5}	0.00228	−3.67	C	ls
19		³S — ³P° (11)	4147.9	[684124]	[708226]	3	9	0.259	0.200	8.2	−0.222	C	ca
			4158.76	[684124]	[708154]	3	5	0.257	0.111	4.56	−0.478	C	ls
			4135.9	[684124]	[708296]	3	3	0.261	0.067	2.73	−0.70	C	ls
			4121.7	[684124]	[708379]	3	1	0.264	0.0224	0.91	−1.173	C	ls
20		³P — ³D° (12)	6816.6	[689793]	[704459]	9	15	0.075	0.088	17.7	−0.103	C	ca
			6830	[689890]	[704527]	5	7	0.075	0.073	8.3	−0.435	C	ls
			6790	[689700]	[704424]	3	5	0.057	0.066	4.42	−0.70	C	ls
			6767	[689586]	[704360]	1	3	0.0430	0.088	1.97	−1.053	C	ls
			6878	[689890]	[704424]	5	5	0.0183	0.0130	1.47	−1.188	C	ls
			6819	[689700]	[704360]	3	3	0.0313	0.0218	1.47	−1.184	C	ls
			6909	[689890]	[704360]	5	3	0.00201	8.6×10^{-4}	0.098	−2.364	C	ls
21		³P — ³P° (13)	5423.6	[689793]	[708226]	9	9	0.87	0.384	62	0.54	C	ca
			5473	[689890]	[708154]	5	5	0.64	0.285	25.7	0.154	C	ls
			5376	[689700]	[708296]	3	3	0.223	0.097	5.1	−0.54	C	ls
			5432	[689890]	[708296]	5	3	0.361	0.096	8.6	−0.320	C	ls
			5352	[689700]	[708379]	3	1	0.91	0.130	6.9	−0.410	C	ls
			5417	[689700]	[708154]	3	5	0.218	0.160	8.6	−0.318	C	ls
			5343	[689586]	[708296]	1	3	0.304	0.390	6.9	−0.409	C	ls
22		¹D — ¹F° (14)	6329	697170	712967	5	7	0.136	0.114	11.9	−0.243	C	ca
23		¹D — ¹P° (15)	4522	697170	719277	5	3	0.0110	0.00203	0.151	−1.99	C	ca
24	2s4s — 2s(²S)4p	³S — ³P° (17)	7438	[722666]	[736107]	3	9	0.287	0.715	52.5	0.331	C+	2, ca

Forbidden Transitions

Naqvi's calculations [1] are the only available source. The results for the $^3P° - {}^3P°$ transitions are essentially independent of the choice of the interaction parameters. For the $^3P° - {}^1P°$ transitions, Naqvi has used empirical term intervals, i.e., the effects of configuration interaction should be partially included.

Reference

[1] Naqvi, A. M., Thesis Harvard (1951).

O V.   Forbidden Transitions

No.	Transition Array	Multiplet	$\lambda(\text{Å})$	$E_i(\text{cm}^{-1})$	$E_k(\text{cm}^{-1})$	g_i	g_k	Type of Transition	$A_{ki}(\text{sec}^{-1})$	$S(\text{at.u.})$	Accuracy	Source
1	$2s2p -$ $2s(^2S)2p$	$^3P° - {}^3P°$										
			$[73.13 \times 10^4]$	$[82121.2]$	$[82257.9]$	1	3	m	4.60×10^{-5}	2.00	B	1
			$[32.65 \times 10^4]$	$[82257.9]$	$[82564.1]$	3	5	m	3.87×10^{-4}	2.50	B	1
2		$^3P° - {}^1P°$										
			$[1304.2]$	$[82121.2]$	158798	1	3	m	0.064	1.57×10^{-5}	C	1
			$[1306.5]$	$[82257.9]$	158798	3	3	m	16.9	0.00420	C	1
			$[1311.8]$	$[82564.1]$	158798	5	3	m	0.078	1.96×10^{-5}	C	1

O VI

Ground State $1s^2\, 2s\ {}^2S_{1/2}$

Ionization Potential 138.080 eV $= 1113999.5$ cm^{-1}

Allowed Transitions

List of tabulated lines:

Wavelength [Å]	No.	Wavelength [Å]	No.	Wavelength [Å]	No.
129.786	5	1031.95	1	4751	14
129.87	5	1037.63	1	5112	16
129.872	5	3068	8	5279	18
150.088	2	3314	10	5298	19
150.124	2	3426	12	5410	17
172.935	4	3438	13	5602	15
173.082	4	3509	11	11744	7
173.09	4	3622	9	11892	7
183.937	3	3811.35	6	11964	7
184.117	3	3834.24	6		

The values taken from Weiss' calculations [1] are estimated to be accurate to within 10% because of the very close agreement between his dipole length and dipole velocity approximations. The values calculated with the length approximation are adopted. The Coulomb approximation should be quite reliable for the highly excited transitions and is given perference over Kelly's approximate Hartree-Fock calculations [2], with which it sometimes disagrees.

References

[1] Weiss, A. W., Astrophys. J. **138,** 1262–1276 (1963).
[2] Kelly, P. S., J. Quant. Spectrosc. Radiat. Transfer **4,** 117–148 (1964).

O VI. Allowed Transitions

No.	Transition Array	Multiplet	λ(Å)	E_i(cm⁻¹)	E_k(cm⁻¹)	g_i	g_k	A_{ki}(10⁸ sec⁻¹)	f_{ik}	S(at.u.)	log gf	Accuracy	Source
1	2s − 2p	²S − ²P° (1 uv)	1033.8	0.0	96730	2	6	4.08	0.196	1.33	− 0.407	A	1
			1031.95	0.0	96908	2	4	4.09	0.131	0.887	− 0.583	A	ls
			1037.63	0.0	96375	2	2	4.02	0.0648	0.443	− 0.887	A	ls
2	2s − 3p	²S − ²P° (2 uv)	150.10	0.0	666218	2	6	259	0.262	0.259	− 0.281	B+	1
			150.088	0.0	666270	2	4	259	0.175	0.173	− 0.456	B+	ls
			150.124	0.0	666113	2	2	259	0.0874	0.0864	− 0.757	B+	ls
3	2p − 3s	²P° − ²S (3 uv)	184.06	96730	640040	6	2	170	0.0287	0.104	− 0.764	B+	1
			184.117	96908	640040	4	2	113	0.0287	0.093	− 0.939	B+	ls
			183.937	96375	640040	2	2	56.7	0.0287	0.0347	− 1.241	B+	ls
4	2p − 3d	²P° − ²D (4 uv)	173.03	96730	674657	6	10	884	0.662	2.26	0.599	B+	1
			173.082	96908	674677	4	6	886	0.597	1.36	0.378	B+	ls
			172.935	96375	674626	2	4	737	0.661	0.753	0.121	B+	ls
			[173.09]	96908	674626	4	4	147	0.0662	0.151	− 0.577	B+	ls
5	2p − 4d	²P° − ²D (5 uv)	129.84	96730	866893	6	10	287	0.121	0.310	− 0.139	B	ca
			129.872	96908	866902	4	6	285	0.108	0.185	− 0.364	B	ls
			129.786	96375	866880	2	4	239	0.121	0.103	− 0.618	B	ls
			[129.87]	96908	866880	4	4	47.6	0.0120	0.0206	− 1.317	B	ls
6	3s − 3p	²S − ²P° (1)	3818.9	640040	666218	2	6	0.510	0.335	8.41	− 0.175	B	1
			3811.35	640040	666270	2	4	0.513	0.224	5.61	− 0.350	B	ls
			3834.24	640040	666113	2	2	0.503	0.111	2.80	− 0.654	B	ls
7	3p − 3d	²P° − ²D (1)	11847	666218	674657	6	10	0.0137	0.0481	11.3	− 0.540	B	1
			[11892]	666270	674677	4	6	0.0136	0.0433	6.78	− 0.762	B	ls
			[11744]	666113	674626	2	4	0.0118	0.0488	3.77	− 1.011	B	ls
			[11964]	666270	674626	4	4	0.00223	0.00478	0.753	− 1.719	B	ls
8	6s − 7p	²S − ²P° (2)	3068	1000080	1032630	2	6	0.874	0.370	7.47	− 0.131	B	ca
9	6p − 7s	²P° − ²S (3)	3622	1003130	1030780	6	2	2.72	0.178	12.7	0.029	B	ca
10	6p − 7d	²P° − ²D (4)	3314	1003130	1033324	6	10	2.02	0.554	36.3	0.522	B	ca
11	6d − 7p	²D − ²P° (5)	3509	1004178	1032630	10	6	0.860	0.0952	11.0	− 0.021	B	ca
12	6d − 7f	²D − ²F° (6)	3426	1004178	[1033382]	10	14	3.34	0.824	92.9	0.916	B	ca
13	6f − 7d	²F° − ²D (7)	3438	[1004265]	1033324	14	10	0.337	0.0426	6.75	− 0.225	B	ca
14	7s − 8p	²S − ²P° (10)	4751	1030780	1051724	2	6	0.423	0.429	13.4	− 0.067	B	ca
15	7p − 8s	²P° − ²S (11)	5602	1032630	[1050543]	6	2	1.38	0.216	23.9	0.113	B	ca

No.	Transition Array	Multiplet	$\lambda(\text{Å})$	$E_i(\text{cm}^{-1})$	$E_k(\text{cm}^{-1})$	g_i	g_k	$A_{ki}(10^8 \text{ sec}^{-1})$	f_{ik}	$S(\text{at.u.})$	$\log gf$	Accuracy	Source
16	$7p-8d$	$^2P°-{}^2D$ (12)	5112	1032630	1052296	6	10	0.923	0.603	60.9	0.559	B	*ca*
17	$7d-8p$	$^2D-{}^2P°$ (13)	5410	1033324	1051724	10	6	0.491	0.129	23.0	0.111	B	*ca*
18	$7d-8f$	$^2D-{}^2F°$ (14)	5279	1033324	[1052280]	10	14	1.64	0.960	167	0.982	B	*ca*
19	$7f-8d$	$^2F°-{}^2D$ (15)	5298	[1033382]	1052296	14	10	0.255	0.0766	18.7	0.030	B	2

O VII

Ground State $1s^2 \ {}^1S_0$

Ionization Potential $739.114 \text{ eV} = 5963000 \text{ cm}^{-1}$

Allowed Transitions

The results of extensive non-relativistic variational calculations by Weiss [1] are used.   Values have been calculated in both the dipole length and dipole velocity approximations and agree to within 1 percent, except for the $3p \ ^1P° - 3d \ ^1D$ transition where agreement is not as good.   The average of the two approximations is adopted [1].

Reference

[1] Weiss, A. W., private communication (1964).

O VII.   Allowed Transitions

No.	Transition Array	Multiplet	$\lambda(\text{Å})$	$E_i(\text{cm}^{-1})$	$E_k(\text{cm}^{-1})$	g_i	g_k	$A_{ki}(10^8\text{sec}^{-1})$	f_{ik}	$S(\text{at. u.})$	$\log gf$	Accuracy	Source
1	$1s^2-1s2p$	$^1S-{}^1P°$	[21.602]	0	4629200	1	3	33000	0.694	0.0494	-0.158	A	1
2	$1s^2-1s3p$	$^1S-{}^1P°$	[18.627]	0	5368550	1	3	9370	0.146	0.00897	-0.835	A	1
3	$1s2s-1s2p$	$^1S-{}^1P°$	[2475.4]	[4588814]	4629200	1	3	0.246	0.0679	0.553	-1.168	A	1
4	$1s2s-1s3p$	$^1S-{}^1P°$	[128.25]	[4588814]	5368550	1	3	504	0.373	0.158	-0.428	A	1
5	$1s2p-1s3d$	$^1P°-{}^1D$	[135.77]	4629200	[5365734]	3	5	1530	0.705	0.945	0.325	A	1
6	$1s3d-1s3p$	$^1D-{}^1P°$	[35500]?	[5365734]	5368550	5	3	6.99×10^{-4}	0.00792	4.62	-1.402	C+	1
7	$1s2s-1s2p$	$^3S-{}^3P°$	[1630.3]	4525270	[4586610]	3	9	0.794	0.0949	1.53	-0.546	A	1
8	$1s2s-1s3p$	$^3S-{}^3P°$	[120.33]	4525270	5356300	3	9	533	0.347	0.413	0.018	A	1
9	$1s2p-1s3d$	$^3P°-{}^3D$	[128.46]	[4586610]	5365070	9	15	1620	0.666	2.54	0.778	A	1
10	$1s3p-1s3d$	$^3P°-{}^3D$	[11399]?	5356300	5365070	9	15	0.0113	0.0367	12.4	-0.481	A	1

FLUORINE

F I.

Ground State $1s^2 2s^2 2p^5\ ^2P^\circ_{3/2}$

Ionization Potential   17.418 eV $= 140524.5$ cm^{-1}

Allowed Transitions
List of tabulated lines:

Wavelength [Å]	No.	Wavelength [Å]	No.	Wavelength [Å]	No.
6239.64	3	6909.82	2	7489.14	5
6348.50	3	6966.35	6	7514.93	1
6413.66	3	7037.45	6	7552.24	1
6708.27	2	7127.88	6	7573.41	1
6773.97	2	7202.37	6	7607.17	4
6795.52	2	7311.02	5	7754.70	4
6834.26	2	7331.95	1	7800.22	4
6856.02	2	7398.68	1		
6870.22	2	7425.64	1		
6902.46	2	7482.72	1		

Since there are no numerical data available for this spectrum, values for the prominent lines have been calculated from the Coulomb approximation by Bates and Damgaard. This method is expected to give fairly reliable results as judged from other atomic systems of similar complexity, where comparison data have been available.

F I. Allowed Transitions

No.	Transition Array	Multi-plet	λ(Å)	E_i(cm^{-1})	E_k(cm^{-1})	g_i	g_k	$A_{ki}(10^8$ sec$^{-1})$	f_{ik}	S(at.u.)	log gf	Accu-racy	Source
1	$2p^43s -$ $2p^4(^3P)3p$	$^4P - ^4P^\circ$ (1)	7490.3	102571	115918	12	12	0.35	0.29	86	0.54	D	ca
			7398.68	102407	115919	6	6	0.25	0.21	30	0.09	D	ls
			7482.72	102681	116042	4	4	0.047	0.039	3.9	-0.81	D	ls
			7514.93	102841	116144	2	2	0.058	0.049	2.4	-1.01	D	ls
			7331.95	102407	116042	6	4	0.17	0.089	13	-0.27	D	ls
			7425.64	102681	116144	4	2	0.30	0.12	12	-0.31	D	ls
			7552.24	102681	115919	4	6	0.10	0.13	13	-0.28	D	ls
			7573.41	102841	116042	2	4	0.14	0.24	12	-0.31	D	ls
2		$^4P - ^4D^\circ$ (2)	6859.2	102571	117146	12	20	0.45	0.53	140	0.80	D	ca
			6856.02	102407	116988	6	8	0.45	0.42	57	0.40	D	ls
			6902.46	102681	117165	4	6	0.31	0.33	30	0.12	D	ls
			6909.82	102841	117309	2	4	0.18	0.26	12	-0.28	D	ls
			6773.97	102407	117165	6	6	0.14	0.095	13	-0.24	D	ls
			6834.26	102681	117309	4	4	0.24	0.17	15	-0.17	D	ls
			6870.22	102841	117393	2	2	0.38	0.27	12	-0.27	D	ls
			6708.27	102407	117309	6	4	0.024	0.011	1.4	-1.19	D	ls
			6795.52	102681	117393	4	2	0.077	0.027	2.4	-0.97	D	ls

No.	Transition Array	Multi-plet	λ(Å)	E_i(cm⁻¹)	E_k(cm⁻¹)	g_i	g_k	A_{ki}(10⁸ sec⁻¹)	f_{ik}	S(at.u.)	log gf	Accu-racy	Source
3		⁴P — ⁴S° (3)	6304.2	102571	118429	12	4	0.56	0.11	28	0.12	D	ca
			6239.64	102407	118429	6	4	0.29	0.11	14	−0.18	D	ls
			6348.50	102681	118429	4	4	0.18	0.11	9.3	−0.35	D	ls
			6413.66	102841	118429	2	4	0.090	0.11	4.7	−0.65	D	ls
4		²P — ²D° (4)	7759.4	104840	117724	6	10	0.35	0.53	80	0.50	D	ca
			7754.70	104732	117624	4	6	0.35	0.47	48	0.27	D	ls
			7800.22	105057	117874	2	4	0.29	0.53	27	0.02	D	ls
			7607.17	104732	117874	4	4	0.061	0.053	5.3	−0.67	D	ls
5		²P — ²S° (5)	7369.3	104840	118406	6	2	0.40	0.11	16	−0.18	D	ca
			7311.02	104732	118406	4	2	0.27	0.11	11	−0.36	D	ls
			7489.14	105057	118406	2	2	0.13	0.11	5.4.	−0.66	D	ls
6		²P — ²P° (6)	7067.02	104840	118986	6	6	0.46	0.34	48	0.31	D	ca
			7037.45	104732	118938	4	4	0.38	0.28	26	0.05	D	ls
			7127.88	105057	119083	2	2	0.30	0.23	11	−0.35	D	ls
			6966.35	104732	119083	4	2	0.16	0.056	5.2	−0.65	D	ls
			7202.37	105057	118938	2	4	0.072	0.11	5.3	−0.65	D	ls

Forbidden Transitions

Naqvi's calculation [1] of the one possible transition in the ground state configuration $2p^5$ is the only available source. The line strength should be quite accurate, since it does not sensitively depend on the choice of the interaction parameters.

Reference

[1] Naqvi, A. M., Thesis Harvard (1951).

F I. Forbidden Transitions

No.	Transition Array	Multiplet	λ(Å)	E_i(cm⁻¹)	E_k(cm⁻¹)	g_i	g_k	Type of Transition	A_{ki}(sec⁻¹)	S(at. u.)	Accu-racy	Source
1	$2p^5 - 2p^5$	²P° — ²P°	[24.75 × 10⁴]	0.0	404.0	4	2	m	0.00118	1.33	B	1

Ground State $\qquad$ $1s^2 2s^2 2p^4 \, ^3P_2$

Ionization Potential $\qquad$ $34.98 \text{ eV} = 282190.2 \text{ cm}^{-1}$

Allowed Transitions

List of tabulated lines:

Wavelength [Å]	No.	Wavelength [Å]	No.	Wavelength [Å]	No.
605.67	1	3535.2	5	4103.09	9
606.27	1	3536.84	5	4103.3	9
606.81	1	3538.6	5	4103.53	9
606.95	1	3541.77	5		
607.48	1			4103.72	9
		3544.5	5	4103.87	9
608.06	1	3546.1	5	4104.1	9
3202.74	7	3640.89	10	4109.17	4
3501.42	8	3640.9	10	4112.7	4
3501.5	8	3641.99	10		
3501.6	8			4113.1	4
		3642.80	10	4116.55	4
3502.9	8	3847.09	2	4117.1	4
3502.95	8	3849.99	2	4118.8	4
3503.10	8	3851.67	2	4119.22	4
3505.4	8	4024.73	3		
3505.6	8			4246.16	11
		4025.01	3	4299.18	6
3505.61	8	4025.50	3	4446.9	12

For one of the strongest ultraviolet transitions a value calculated by Varsavsky [1] from a screening approximation is available and listed. Because the strong effects of configuration interaction have been neglected, this number should be quite uncertain. (In general, Varsavsky's values have a tendency to be too large.) Values obtained with the Coulomb approximation are presented for all prominent transitions in the visible and near ultraviolet. The indicated accuracies are estimated from extrapolation with equivalent transitions of O I, for which experimental and theoretical comparison data are available.

Reference

[1] Varsavsky, C. M., Astrophys. J. Suppl. Ser. 6, 75–108 (1961).

F II. Allowed Transitions

No.	Transition Array	Multiplet	λ(Å)	E_i(cm^{-1})	E_k(cm^{-1})	g_i	g_k	A_{ki}(10^8 sec^{-1})	f_{ik}	S(at.u.)	log gf	Accuracy	Source
1	$2s^2 2p^4 -$ $2s 2p^5$	$^3P - ^3P°$ (1 uv)	606.85	169	164955	9	9	100	0.56	10	0.70	E	1
			606.81	0	164798	5	5	78	0.43	4.3	0.33	E	ls
			606.95	342	165107	3	3	26	0.14	0.86	−0.37	E	ls
			605.67	0	165107	5	3	43	0.14	1.4	−0.15	E	ls
			606.27	342	165281	3	1	100	0.18	1.1	−0.26	E	ls
			608.06	342	164798	3	5	25	0.23	1.4	−0.16	E	ls
			607.48	491	165107	1	3	33	0.55	1.1	−0.26	E	ls
2	$2p^3 3s -$ $2p^3(^4S°)3p$	$^5S° - ^5P$ (1)	3848.9	[176654]	[202628]	5	15	1.3	0.84	54	0.62	D	ca
			3847.09	[176654]	[202641]	5	7	1.3	0.39	25	0.29	D	ls
			3849.99	[176654]	[202621]	5	5	1.3	0.28	18	0.15	D	ls
			3851.67	[176654]	[202610]	5	3	1.3	0.17	11	−0.08	D	ls

No.	Transition Array	Multiplet	λ(Å)	E_i(cm^{-1})	E_k(cm^{-1})	g_i	g_k	A_{ki}(10^8 sec^{-1})	f_{ik}	S(at.u.)	log gf	Accuracy	Source
3		³S° − ³P (2)	4025.0	182865	207703	3	9	1.2	0.90	36	0.43	D	ca
			4024.73	182865	207705	3	5	1.2	0.50	20	0.18	D	ls
			4025.50	182865	207700	3	3	1.2	0.30	12	−0.04	D	ls
			4025.01	182865	207703	3	1	1.2	0.10	4.0	−0.52	D	ls
4	2p³3s′ − 2p³(²D°)3p′	³D° − ³D (5)	4113.7	211881	236183	15	15	1.8	0.45	92	0.83	D	ca
			4109.17	211867	236196	7	7	1.6	0.40	38	0.45	D	ls
			4116.55	211888	236173	5	5	1.2	0.32	21	0.20	D	ls
			4119.22	211901	236170	3	3	1.3	0.34	14	0.01	D	ls
			[4113.1]	211867	236173	7	5	0.28	0.050	4.8	−0.45	D	ls
			[4117.1]	211888	236170	5	3	0.45	0.068	4.6	−0.47	D	ls
			[4112.7]	211888	236196	5	7	0.20	0.071	4.8	−0.45	D	ls
			[4118.8]	211901	236173	3	5	0.27	0.11	4.6	−0.47	D	ls
5		³D° − ³P (6)	3539.8	211881	240123	15	9	2.1	0.23	40	0.54	D	ca
			3541.77	211867	240093	7	5	1.7	0.23	19	0.21	D	ls
			3536.84	211888	240153	5	3	1.5	0.17	10	−0.06	D	ls
			[3535.2]	211901	240180	3	1	2.1	0.13	4.5	−0.42	D	ls
			[3544.5]	211888	240093	5	5	0.31	0.058	3.4	−0.54	D	ls
			[3538.6]	211901	240153	3	3	0.51	0.096	3.4	−0.54	D	ls
			[3546.1]	211901	240093	3	5	0.021	0.0064	0.23	−1.71	D	ls
6		¹D° − ¹F (7)	4299.18	215070	238324	5	7	1.7	0.64	45	0.51	D	ca
7		¹D° − ¹D (8)	3202.74	215070	246284	5	5	1.4	0.21	11	0.02	D	ca
8	2p³3p − 2p³(⁴S°)3d	⁵P − ⁵D° (3)	3504.0	[202628]	[231159]	15	25	2.86	0.88	152	1.120	C	ca
			3505.61	[202641]	[231158]	7	9	2.86	0.68	55	0.68	C	ls
			3503.10	[202621]	[231159]	5	7	1.91	0.491	28.3	0.390	C	ls
			[3501.6]	[202610]	[231160]	3	5	1.00	0.307	10.6	−0.036	C	ls
			[3505.6]	[202641]	[231159]	7	7	0.95	0.175	14.2	0.089	C	ls
			3502.95	[202621]	[231160]	5	5	1.67	0.307	17.7	0.186	C	ls
			[3501.5]	[202610]	[231161]	3	3	2.15	0.395	13.7	0.074	C	ls
			[3505.4]	[202641]	[231160]	7	5	0.190	0.0251	2.02	−0.76	C	ls
			[3502.9]	[202621]	[231161]	5	3	0.72	0.079	4.55	−0.404	C	ls
			3501.42	[202610]	[231161]	3	1	2.86	0.175	6.1	−0.279	C	ls
9		³P − ³D° (4)	4103.4	207703	232066	9	15	2.05	0.86	105	0.89	C	ca
			4103.53	207705	232067	5	7	2.05	0.72	48.8	0.56	C	ls
			4103.09	207700	232065	3	5	1.54	0.65	26.2	0.287	C	ls
			4103.72	207703	232064	1	3	1.14	0.86	11.6	−0.065	C	ls
			4103.87	207705	232065	5	5	0.51	0.129	8.7	−0.190	C	ls
			[4103.3]	207700	232064	3	3	0.85	0.215	8.7	−0.190	C	ls
			[4104.1]	207705	232064	5	3	0.057	0.0086	0.58	−1.366	C	ls
10	2p³3p′ − 2p³(²D°)3d′	³F − ³F° (11)	3641.7	237509	264961	21	21	0.147	0.0292	7.3	−0.213	C −	ca
			3640.89	237508	264966	9	9	0.137	0.0273	2.95	−0.61	C −	ls
			3641.99	237509	264959	7	7	0.123	0.0245	2.06	−0.77	C −	ls
			3642.80	237509	264953	5	5	0.130	0.0259	1.55	−0.89	C −	ls
			3641.99	237508	264959	9	7	0.0118	0.00182	0.197	−1.79	C −	ls
			3642.80	237509	264953	7	5	0.0163	0.00231	0.194	−1.79	C −	ls
			[3640.9]	237509	264966	7	9	0.0092	0.00234	0.196	−1.79	C −	ls
			3641.99	237509	264959	5	7	0.0116	0.00324	0.194	−1.79	C −	ls
11	2p³3d − 2p³(⁴S°)4f	⁵D° − ⁵F (9)	4246.16	[231159]	[254703]	25	25	2.47	0.93	326	1.368	C	ca
12		³D° − ³F (10)	4446.9	232066	254547	15	21	2.35	0.97	214	1.165	C	ca

Forbidden Transitions

The adopted values represent the results of calculations by Garstang [1] and Naqvi [2], which are very similar in character. Garstang's evaluation of the quadrupole integral s_q is considered the more refined one; therefore, the quadrupole line strengths are taken from his paper. Naqvi, in his calculations of magnetic dipole lines, retains the spin-spin and spin-other-orbit integral in the transformation coefficients, while Garstang neglects it. Thus, Naqvi's values are chosen, whenever this becomes significant. When this refinement is not sensitive, the two authors agree. For the $^3P - {}^1S$ transition the important effects of configuration interaction are most appropriately taken into account by Garstang's method, so that his values are used. (Further explanations are found in the general introduction.)

References

[1] Garstang, R. H., Monthly Notices Roy. Astron. Soc. **111**, 115–124 (1951).
[2] Naqvi, A. M., Thesis Harvard (1951).

F II.   Forbidden Transitions

No.	Transition Array	Multi-plet	λ(Å)	E_i(cm^{-1})	E_k(cm^{-1})	g_i	g_k	Type of Transition	A_{ki}(sec^{-1})	S(at.u.)	Accuracy	Source
1	$2p^4 - 2p^4$	$^3P - {}^3P$										
			$[29.25 \times 10^4]$	0.0	341.8	5	3	m	8.97×10^{-4}	2.50	B	1, 2
			$[29.25 \times 10^4]$	0.0	341.8	5	3	e	2.30×10^{-10}	0.88	C	1
			$[20.38 \times 10^4]$	0.0	490.6	5	1	e	1.80×10^{-9}	0.376	C	1
			$[67.19 \times 10^4]$	341.8	490.6	3	1	m	1.78×10^{-4}	2.00	B	1, 2
2		$^3P - {}^1D$ (1 F)										
			4789.5	0.0	20873	5	5	m	3.81	7.8×10^{-4}	C	2
			4789.5	0.0	20873	5	5	e	9.6×10^{-5}	7.2×10^{-4}	D	1
			4869.3	341.8	20873	3	5	m	0.0121	2.59×10^{-4}	C	2
			4869.3	341.8	20873	3	5	e	1.3×10^{-5}	1.1×10^{-4}	D	1
			$[4904.8]$	490.6	20873	1	5	e	4.1×10^{-6}	3.5×10^{-5}	D	1
3		$^3P - {}^1S$										
			$[2225.5]$	0.0	44919	5	1	e	0.0016	5.2×10^{-5}	D	1
			$[2246.6]$	341.8	44919	3	1	m	0.490	2.06×10^{-4}	C	1
4		$^1D - {}^1S$ (2 F)										
			4157.5	20873	44919	5	1	e	2.10	1.55	C	1

F III.

Ground State	$1s^2 2s^2 2p^3\ {}^4S^{\circ}_{3/2}$
Ionization Potential	62.646 eV $= 505410$ cm^{-1}

Allowed Transitions

After having written introductory remarks for 9.2 elements, we must confess that this becomes a rather cumbersome exercise in style. Since we expect that this introduction will share the fate of most introductions (namely be ignored) and since there is nothing new to say on this ion (for scientific content see F I) we might as well give the few readers of this introduction some good advice:

If there is no other data source,
Use the Coulomb approximation, of course.
The results should be certainly fine
For any moderately or highly excited line.

F III. Allowed Transitions

No.	Transition Array	Multi-plet	λ(Å)	E_i(cm^{-1})	E_k(cm^{-1})	g_i	g_k	A_{ki}(10^8 sec^{-1})	f_{ik}	S(at.u.)	log gf	Accu-racy	Source
1	2p²3s − 2p²(³P)3p	⁴P − ⁴D° (1)	3124.4	317043	349040	12	20	1.6	0.40	48	0.67	D	ca
			3121.52	317238	349264	6	8	1.6	0.31	19	0.27	D	ls
			3115.67	316919	349005	4	6	1.1	0.25	10	−0.01	D	ls
			3113.58	316707	348815	2	4	0.67	0.19	4.0	−0.41	D	ls
			3146.96	317238	349005	6	6	0.47	0.070	4.3	−0.38	D	ls
			3134.21	316919	348815	4	4	0.84	0.12	5.1	−0.30	D	ls
			3124.76	316707	348701	2	2	1.3	0.19	4.0	−0.41	D	ls
			3165.86	317238	348815	6	4	0.077	0.0077	0.48	−1.34	D	ls
			3145.54	316919	348701	4	2	0.26	0.019	0.80	−1.11	D	ls
2		²P − ²D° (2)	3176.9	324746	356214	6	10	1.7	0.42	26	0.40	D	ca
			3174.13	324874	356370	4	6	1.7	0.38	16	0.18	D	ls
			3174.73	324490	355980	2	4	1.4	0.42	8.7	−0.08	D	ls
			3213.97	324874	355980	4	4	0.27	0.041	1.8	−0.78	D	ls
3	2p²3p′ − 2p²(¹D)3d′	²D° − ²F (3)	3039.3	380265	413158	10	14	2.75	0.53	53	0.73	C	ca
			3039.25	380243	413136	6	8	2.75	0.51	30.4	0.483	C	ls
			3039.75	380299	413187	4	6	2.56	0.53	21.3	0.329	C	ls
			3034.54	380243	413187	6	6	0.184	0.0254	1.52	−0.82	C	ls
4		²P° − ²D (4)	3150.6	384440	416171	6	10	1.39	0.344	21.4	0.315	C	ca
			3154.39	384485	416178	4	6	1.38	0.309	12.9	0.093	C	ls
			3142.78	384351	416161	2	4	1.16	0.344	7.1	−0.162	C	ls
			3156.11	384485	416161	4	4	0.230	0.0344	1.43	−0.86	C	ls

Forbidden Transitions

Naqvi's [1] calculations are the only available source. The values should not be quite as reliable as for other ions of the p^3 configuration (O II, Ne IV) since the important configuration interaction effects (see general introduction) are neglected.

Reference

[1] Naqvi, A. M., Thesis Harvard (1951).

F III. Forbidden Transitions

No.	Transition Array	Multi-plet	λ(Å)	E_i(cm^{-1})	E_k(cm^{-1})	g_i	g_k	Type of Transition	A_{ki}(sec^{-1})	S(at.u.)	Accu-racy	Source
1	2p³ − 2p³	⁴S° − ²D°										
			[2933.1]	0	34084	4	6	m	1.08 × 10⁻⁵	6.1 × 10⁻⁸	C −	1
			[2933.1]	0	34084	4	6	e	1.2 × 10⁻⁴	9.3 × 10⁻⁵	D −	1
			[2930.0]	0	34120	4	4	m	0.00134	4.98 × 10⁻⁶	C −	1
			[2930.0]	0	34120	4	4	e	7.5 × 10⁻⁵	3.8 × 10⁻⁵	D −	1
2		⁴S° − ²P°										
			[1939.6]	0	51558	4	4	m	0.256	2.77 × 10⁻⁴	C −	1
			[1939.6]	0	51558	4	4	e	2.7 × 10⁻⁸	1.8 × 10⁻⁹	D −	1
			[1939.6]	0	51558	4	2	m	0.102	5.5 × 10⁻⁵	C −	1
			[1939.6]	0	51558	4	2	e	7.4 × 10⁻⁷	2.4 × 10⁻⁸	D −	1
3		²D° − ²D°										
			[27.8 × 10⁵]	34084	34120	6	4	m	7.55 × 10⁻⁷	2.40	B	1
			[27.8 × 10⁵]	34084	34120	6	4	e	1.8 × 10⁻¹⁸	7.2 × 10⁻⁴	D −	1

F III. Forbidden Transitions—*Continued*

No.	Transition Array	Multiplet	$\lambda(\text{Å})$	$E_i(\text{cm}^{-1})$	$E_k(\text{cm}^{-1})$	g_i	g_k	Type of Transition	$A_{ki}(\text{sec}^{-1})$	$S(\text{at.u.})$	Accuracy	Source
4		$^2D^\circ - {}^2P^\circ$ (1F)										
			5721.2	34084	51558	6	4	m	0.0280	7.8×10^{-4}	C −	1
			5721.2	34084	51558	6	4	e	0.15	2.2	D	1
			[5721.2]	34084	51558	6	2	e	0.088	0.64	D	1
			5733.0	34120	51558	4	4	m	0.0494	0.00138	C −	1
			5733.0	34120	51558	4	4	e	0.065	0.96	D	1
			[5733.0]	34120	51558	4	2	m	0.0309	4.32×10^{-4}	C −	1
			[5733.0]	34120	51558	4	2	e	0.13	0.96	D	1

F IV.

Ground State $\qquad\qquad\qquad\qquad\qquad\qquad\qquad\qquad\qquad$ $1s^2 2s^2 2p^2\ {}^3P_0$

Ionization Potential $\qquad\qquad\qquad\qquad\qquad\qquad$ $87.14\ \text{eV} = 703020\ \text{cm}^{-1}$

Allowed Transitions

The results of calculations by Bolotin et al. [1] are listed. These authors have employed relatively simple wave functions and include the important effects of configuration interaction in a crude manner. Thus, their results should be quite uncertain, but they are nevertheless included since these transitions are expected to be among the strongest for this ion.

Reference

[1] Bolotin, A. B., Levinson, I. B., and Levin, L. I., Soviet Phys.—JETP **2**, 391–395 (1956).

F IV. Allowed Transitions

No.	Transition Array	Multiplet	$\lambda(\text{Å})$	$E_i(\text{cm}^{-1})$	$E_k(\text{cm}^{-1})$	g_i	g_k	$A_{ki}(10^8\ \text{sec}^{-1})$	f_{ik}	$S(\text{at.u.})$	$\log gf$	Accuracy	Source
1	$2s^2 2p^2 - 2s 2p^3$	$^3P - {}^3D^\circ$	678.18	416	147870	9	15	11	0.13	2.6	0.07	E	1
			[679.21]	613	147842	5	7	11	0.11	1.2	−0.27	E	ls
			[677.21]	225	147889	3	5	8.5	0.097	0.65	−0.54	E	ls
			[676.12]	0	147902	1	3	6.3	0.13	0.29	−0.89	E	ls
			[679.00]	613	147889	5	5	2.8	0.020	0.22	−1.01	E	ls
			[677.15]	225	147902	3	3	4.8	0.033	0.22	−1.01	E	ls
			[678.94]	613	147902	5	3	0.30	0.0013	0.014	−2.20	E	ls
2		$^3P - {}^3P^\circ$	572.00	416	175242	9	9	32	0.16	2.7	0.16	E	1
			[572.66]	613	175237	5	5	24	0.12	1.1	−0.23	E	ls
			[571.37]	225	175242	3	3	8.3	0.041	0.23	−0.91	E	ls
			[572.64]	613	175242	5	3	14	0.040	0.38	−0.70	E	ls
			[571.30]	225	175264	3	1	33	0.053	0.30	−0.80	E	ls
			[571.39]	225	175237	3	5	8.3	0.067	0.38	−0.69	E	ls
			[570.64]	0	175242	1	3	11	0.16	0.30	−0.80	E	ls
3		$^3P - {}^3S^\circ$	420.38	416	238297	9	3	180	0.16	2.0	0.16	E	1
			[420.73]	613	238297	5	3	100	0.16	1.1	−0.10	E	ls
			[420.04]	225	238297	3	3	61	0.16	0.67	−0.31	E	ls
			[419.64]	0	238297	1	3	20	0.16	0.22	−0.80	E	ls
4		$^1D - {}^1D^\circ$	[491.00]	25241	228908	5	5	86	0.31	2.5	0.19	E	1
5		$^1D - {}^1P^\circ$	[430.76]	25241	257390	5	3	130	0.21	1.5	0.02	E	1
6		$^1S - {}^1P^\circ$	[490.57]	53544	257390	1	3	27	0.30	0.48	−0.53	E	1

Forbidden Transitions

The adopted values represent the results of calculations by Garstang [1] and Naqvi [2], which are very similar in character. Garstang's evaluation of the quadrupole integral s_q is considered the more refined one; therefore, the quadrupole line strengths are taken from his paper. The results for the magnetic dipole lines agree, except for the $^3P - {}^1S$ transition. For this line, the important effects of configuration interaction are more appropriately taken into account by Garstang's approach of using the experimental term intervals, so that his values are used. (Further explanations are found in the general introduction.)

References

[1] Garstang, R. H., Monthly Notices Roy. Astron. Soc. **111**, 115–124 (1951).
[2] Naqvi, A. M., Thesis Harvard (1951).

F IV. Forbidden Transitions

No.	Transition Array	Multiplet	λ(Å)	E_i(cm^{-1})	E_k(cm^{-1})	g_i	g_k	Type of Transition	A_{ki}(sec^{-1})	S(at.u.)	Accuracy	Source
1	$2p^2 - 2p^2$	$^3P - {}^3P$										
			$[44.39 \times 10^4]$	0.0	225.2	1	3	m	2.05	2.00	B	1, 2
			$[16.30 \times 10^4]$	0.0	613.4	1	5	e	5.0×10^{-10}	0.171	C	1
			$[25.75 \times 10^4]$	225.2	613.4	3	5	m	7.89×10^{-4}	2.50	B	1, 2
			$[25.75 \times 10^4]$	225.2	613.4	3	5	e	1.20×10^{-10}	0.405	C	1
2		$^3P - {}^1D$ (1 F)										
			[3960.7]	0.0	25241	1	5	e	6.4×10^{-6}	1.9×10^{-5}	D	1
			3996.3	225.2	25241	3	5	m	0.0342	4.05×10^{-4}	C	1, 2
			3996.3	225.2	25241	3	5	e	2.1×10^{-5}	6.4×10^{-5}	D	1
			4059.3	613.4	25241	5	5	m	0.098	0.00122	C	1, 2
			4059.3	613.4	25241	5	5	e	1.3×10^{-4}	4.3×10^{-5}	D	1
3		$^3P - {}^1S$										
			[1875.5]	225.2	53544	3	1	m	1.10	2.69×10^{-4}	C	1
			[1889.3]	613.4	53544	5	1	e	0.0023	3.3×10^{-5}	D	1
4		$^1D - {}^1S$ (2 F)										
			3532.2	25241	53544	5	1	e	2.10	0.69	C	1

F V.

Ground State $\cdot 1s^2 2s^2 2p\ {}^2P^{\circ}_{1/2}$

Ionization Potential   114.214 eV $=$ 921450 cm^{-1}

Allowed Transitions

The two available sources are quantum mechanical calculations by Bolotin and Yutsis [1] and Naqvi and Victor [2]. The important transitions covered by Bolotin and Yutsis are very sensitive to the effects of configuration interaction, which are only approximately included in their calculations. For the result of Naqvi and Victor, obtained from the charge expansion method, an accuracy within 25 percent is indicated from comparisons of this work with other material for equivalent transitions within this isoelectronic sequence.

References

[1] Bolotin, A. B., and Yutsis, A. P., Zhur. Eksptl. i Teoret. Fiz. **24,** 537–543 (1953) (Translated in "Optical Transition Probabilities," Office of Technical Services, U.S. Department of Commerce, Washington, D.C.).

[2] Naqvi, A. M., and Victor, G. A., Technical Documentary Report No. RTD TDR–63–3118 (1964).

F v.   Allowed Transitions

No.	Transition Array	Multi-plet	$\lambda(\text{Å})$	$E_i(\text{cm}^{-1})$	$E_k(\text{cm}^{-1})$	g_i	g_k	$A_{ki}(10^8$ $\text{sec}^{-1})$	f_{ik}	$S(\text{at.u.})$	$\log gf$	Accu-racy	Source
1	$2s^2 2p -$ $2s2p^2$	$^2P° - {}^2D$	656.22	497	152885	6	10	12	0.13	1.7	−0.10	E	1
			[657.33]	746	152876	4	6	12	0.12	1.0	−0.34	E	ls
			[654.03]	0	152898	2	4	10	0.13	0.57	−0.58	E	ls
			[657.24]	746	152898	4	4	2.0	0.013	0.11	−1.29	E	ls
2		$^2P° - {}^2S$	507.44	497	197565	6	2	67	0.086	0.86	−0.29	E	1
			[508.08]	746	197565	4	2	44	0.085	0.57	−0.47	E	ls
			[506.16]	0	197565	2	2	23	0.087	0.29	−0.76	E	ls
3		$^2P° - {}^2P$	465.78	497	215192	6	6	100	0.33	3.0	0.29	E	1
			[465.98]	746	215348	4	4	85	0.28	1.7	0.04	E	ls
			[465.37]	0	214881	2	2	67	0.22	0.67	−0.36	E	ls
			[467.00]	746	214881	4	2	33	0.054	0.33	−0.67	E	ls
			[464.36]	0	215348	2	4	17	0.11	0.33	−0.67	E	ls
4	$3s - (^1S)3p$	$^2S - {}^2P°$	2454.2	524751	565485	2	6	2.24	0.61	9.8	0.084	C	2
			[2450.7]	524751	565544	2	4	2.24	0.403	6.5	−0.094	C	ls
			[2461.3]	524751	565367	2	2	2.22	0.202	3.27	−0.394	C	ls

Forbidden Transitions

Naqvi's calculation [1] of the one possible transition in the ground state configuration $2p$ is the only available source. The line strength should be quite accurate, since it does not sensitively depend on the choice of the interaction parameters.

Reference

[1] Naqvi, A. M., Thesis Harvard (1951).

F V.   Forbidden Transitions

No.	Transition Array	Multiplet	$\lambda(\text{Å})$	$E_i(\text{cm}^{-1})$	$E_k(\text{cm}^{-1})$	g_i	g_k	Type of Transition	$A_{ki}(\text{sec}^{-1})$	$S(\text{at. u.})$	Accu-racy	Source
1	$2p - 2p$	$^2P° - {}^2P°$	13.40×10^4	0	746	2	4	m	0.00373	1.33	B	1

Ground State $1s^2 2s^2\ {}^1S_0$

Ionization Potential   157.117 eV $= 1267581$ cm^{-1}

Allowed Transitions

The results of the charge expansion calculations by Naqvi and Victor [1] are utilized whenever comparison of this work with other data in the isoelectronic sequence indicates a fair reliability of this material. Values for the $2s2p - 2p^2$ transition array are available from the self-consistent field calculations by Weiss [2]. These calculations do not include the important effects of configuration interaction; hence, fairly large uncertainties must be expected. The average of the dipole length and velocity approximations [2] is adopted and accuracies within 50 percent are indicated from comparisons possible for the first member of this isoelectronic sequence.

References

[1] Naqvi, A. M., and Victor, G. A., Technical Documentary Report No. RTD TDR−63−3118 (1964).
[2] Weiss, A. W., private communication (1964).

Fvi.   Allowed Transitions

No.	Transition Array	Multiplet	$\lambda(\text{Å})$	$E_i(\text{cm}^{-1})$	$E_k(\text{cm}^{-1})$	g_i	g_k	$A_{ki}(10^8$ sce$^{-1})$	f_{ik}	S(at.u.)	$\log gf$	Accuracy	Source
1	$2s^2 - 2s(^2S)2p$	$^1S - {}^1P°$	[535.21]	0	186841	1	3	48	0.62	1.1	−0.20	E	1
2	$2s^2 - 2s(^2S)3p$	$^1S - {}^1P°$	[126.93]	0	787833	1	3	660	0.48	0.20	−0.32	E	1
3	$2s2p - 2p^2$	$^3P° - {}^3P$	646.27	97152	251886	9	9	25	0.16	3.0	0.15	D	2
			[646.38]	97437	252145	5	5	18	0.11	1.2	−0.25	D	ls
			[646.10]	96861	251635	3	3	6.3	0.039	0.25	−0.93	D	ls
			[648.52]	97437	251635	5	3	10	0.039	0.42	−0.71	D	ls
			[647.33]	96861	251341	3	1	25	0.052	0.33	−0.81	D	ls
			[643.98]	96861	252145	3	5	6.4	0.066	0.42	−0.70	D	ls
			[645.02]	96601	251635	1	3	8.3	0.16	0.33	−0.81	D	ls
4		$^1P° - {}^1D$	[1139.5]	186841	274597	3	5	8.2	0.27	3.0	−0.10	D	2
5		$^1P° - {}^1S$	[651.11]	186841	340424	3	1	26	0.054	0.35	−0.79	D	2
6	$2s3s - 2s(^2S)3p$	$^1S - {}^1P°$	[4264.8]	764392	787833	1	3	0.326	0.267	3.75	−0.57	C	1

Forbidden Transitions

Naqvi's calculations [1] are the only available source. The results for the $^3P° - {}^3P°$ transitions are essentially independent of the choice of the interaction parameters. For the $^3P° - {}^1P°$ transitions, Naqvi uses empirical term intervals, i.e., the effects of configuration interaction should be partially included.

Reference

[1] Naqvi, A. M., Thesis Harvard (1951).

F VI. Forbidden Transitions

No.	Transition Array	Multiplet	$\lambda(\text{Å})$	$E_i(\text{cm}^{-1})$	$E_k(\text{cm}^{-1})$	g_i	g_k	Type of Transition	$A_{ki}(\text{sec}^{-1})$	$S(\text{at. u.})$	Accuracy	Source
1	$2s2p -$ $2s(^2S)2p$	$^3P° - ^3P°$	$[38.5 \times 10^4]$	96601	96861	1	3	m	3.16×10^{-4}	2.00	B	1
			$[17.36 \times 10^4]$	96861	97437	3	5	m	0.00258	2.50	B	1
2		$^3P° - ^1P°$										
			$[1108.2]$	96601	186841	1	3	m	0.268	4.05×10^{-5}	C	1
			$[1111.4]$	96861	186841	3	3	m	44.2	0.0068	C	1
			$[1118.5]$	97437	186841	5	3	m	0.324	5.1×10^{-5}	C	1

F VII.

Ground State $1s^2 2s\ ^2S_{1/2}$

Ionization Potential $185.139\ \text{eV} = 1493656\ \text{cm}^{-1}$

Allowed Transitions

List of tabulated lines:

Wavelength [Å]	No.	Wavelength [Å]	No.	Wavelength [Å]	No.
86.732	3	127.81	5	890.762	1
97.262	6	134.71	4		
97.354	6	134.88	4	3246.6	7
112.94	2			3276.6	7
112.98	2	335.17	8	7958.9	11
		391.73	10	9524.8	9
127.65	5	392.16	10	9702.3	9
127.80	5	883.097	1		
				9787.8	9

For F VII, an ion of the Lithium sequence, theoretical data from the self-consistent field calculations by Weiss [1] and the variational calculations by Flannery and Stewart [2], both done in the dipole length and velocity approximations, as well as an experimental result from the lifetime measurement of Berkner et al. [3], are available. The agreement for the $2s - 2p$ transition, which is covered by all three methods, is within an impressive 10 percent. Errors smaller than 25 percent are estimated from the close agreement between the dipole length and velocity approximations. The dipole length values are chosen.

References

[1] Weiss, A. W., Astrophys. J. **138**, 1262–1276 (1963).
[2] Flannery, M. R., and Stewart, A. L., Monthly Notices Roy. Astron. Soc. **126**, 387–392 (1963).
[3] Berkner, K. H., Cooper, W. L., Kaplan, S. N., and Pyle, R. V., Phys. Letters **16**, 35 (1965).

No.	Transition Array	Multi-plet	λ(Å)	E_i(cm^{-1})	E_k(cm^{-1})	g_i	g_k	A_{ki}(10^8 sec^{-1})	f_{ik}	S(at.u.)	log gf	Accu-racy	Source
1	2s–2p	^{2}S–^{2}P°	885.64	0	112913	2	6	4.77	0.168	0.981	−0.473	B	1, 2, 3
			883.097	0	113238	2	4	4.81	0.112	0.654	−0.648	B	*ls*
			890.762	0	112263	2	2	4.69	0.0558	0.327	−0.953	B	*ls*
2	2s–3p	^{2}S–^{2}P°	112.95	0	885324	2	6	499	0.286	0.213	−0.242	B+	1, 2
			[112.94]	0	885418	2	4	499	0.191	0.142	−0.418	B+	*ls*
			[112.98]	0	885136	2	2	499	0.0954	0.0710	−0.719	B+	*ls*
3	2s–4p	^{2}S–^{2}P°	[86.732]	0	1152977	2	6	214	0.0725	0.0414	−0.839	C+	2
4	2p–3s	^{2}P°–^{2}S	134.82	112913	854625	6	2	264	0.0240	0.0638	−0.842	C+	1, 2
			[134.88]	113238	854625	4	2	175	0.0239	0.0425	−1.019	C+	*ls*
			[134.71]	112263	854625	2	2	88.3	0.0240	0.0213	−1.319	C+	*ls*
5	2p–3d	^{2}P°–^{2}D	127.75	112913	895686	6	10	1630	0.666	1.68	0.602	B	1
			[127.80]	113238	895722	4	6	1630	0.600	1.01	0.380	B	*ls*
			[127.65]	112263	895632	2	4	1360	0.666	0.560	0.125	B	*ls*
			[127.81]	113238	895632	4	4	272	0.0665	0.112	−0.575	B	*ls*
6	2p–4s	^{2}P°–^{2}S	97.323	112913	1140416	6	2	99	0.00468	0.0090	−1.55	C	2
			[97.354]	113238	1140416	4	2	66	0.00468	0.0060	−1.73	C	*ls*
			[97.262]	112263	1140416	2	2	33.0	0.00468	0.00300	−2.028	C	*ls*
7	3s–3p	^{2}S–^{2}P°	3256.5	854625	885324	2	6	0.604	0.288	6.18	−0.239	B+	1, 2
			[3246.6]	854625	885418	2	4	0.610	0.193	4.12	−0.414	B+	*ls*
			[3276.6]	854625	885136	2	2	0.593	0.0955	2.06	−0.719	B+	*ls*
8	3s–4p	^{2}S–^{2}P°	[335.17]	854625	1152977	2	6	63.7	0.322	0.710	−0.192	B	2
9	3p–3d	^{2}P°–^{2}D	9648.0	885324	895686	6	10	0.0186	0.0432	8.23	−0.587	B	1
			[9702.3]	885418	895722	4	6	0.0183	0.0387	4.94	−0.811	B	*ls*
			[9524.8]	885136	895632	2	4	0.0161	0.0437	2.74	−1.059	B	*ls*
			[9787.8]	885418	895632	4	4	0.00297	0.00426	0.549	−1.769	B	*ls*
10	3p–4s	^{2}P°–^{2}S	392.02	885324	1140416	6	2	58.3	0.0448	0.347	−0.571	B	2
			[392.16]	885418	1140416	4	2	38.8	0.0447	0.231	−0.747	B	*ls*
			[391.73]	885136	1140416	2	2	19.5	0.0450	0.116	−1.046	B	*ls*
11	4s–4p	^{2}S–^{2}P°	[7958.9]	1140416	1152977	2	6	0.140	0.399	20.9	−0.098	B	2

F VIII.

Ground State $\qquad$ $1s^2\ {}^1S_0$

Ionization Potential $\qquad$ $953.60\ \text{eV} = 7693400\ \text{cm}^{-1}$

Allowed Transitions

The results of extensive non-relativistic variational calculations by Weiss [1] are used. Values have been calculated in both the dipole length and dipole velocity approximations and agree to within 1 percent, except for the $3p\ {}^1P^\circ - 3d\ {}^1D$ transition where agreement is not as good. The average of the two approximations is adopted [1].

Reference

[1] Weiss, A. W., private communication (1964).

F VIII. Allowed Transitions

No.	Transition Array	Multiplet	$\lambda(\text{Å})$	$E_i(\text{cm}^{-1})$	$E_k(\text{cm}^{-1})$	g_i	g_k	$A_{ki}(10^8\ \text{sec}^{-1})$	f_{ik}	$S(\text{at.u.})$	$\log gf$	Accuracy	Source
1	$1s^2 - 1s2p$	${}^1S - {}^1P^\circ$	[16.807]	0	5949900	1	3	5.59×10^4	0.710	0.0393	-0.149	A	1
2	$1s^2 - 1s3p$	${}^1S - {}^1P^\circ$	[14.458]	0	6916590	1	3	1.57×10^4	0.148	0.00704	-0.830	A	1
3	$1s2s - 1s2p$	${}^1S - {}^1P^\circ$	[2149.9]	[5903400]	5949900	1	3	0.288	0.0599	0.424	-1.223	A	1
4	$1s2s - 1s3p$	${}^1S - {}^1P^\circ$	[98.698]	[5903400]	6916590	1	3	867	0.380	0.123	-0.420	A	1
5	$1s2p - 1s3d$	${}^1P^\circ - {}^1D$	[103.80]	5949900	[6913300]	3	5	2610	0.703	0.721	0.324	A	1
6	$1s3d - 1s3p$	${}^1D - {}^1P^\circ$	[30390]?	[6913300]	6916590	5	3	8.52×10^{-4}	0.00708	3.54	-1.451	C+	1
7	$1s2s - 1s2p$	${}^3S - {}^3P^\circ$	[1422.9]	[5829640]	[5899920]	3	9	0.915	0.0833	1.17	-0.602	A	1
8	$1s2s - 1s3p$	${}^3S - {}^3P^\circ$	[93.213]	[5829640]	[6902450]	3	9	914	0.357	0.329	0.030	A	1
9	$1s2p - 1s3d$	${}^3P^\circ - {}^3D$	[98.756]	[5899920]	6912520	9	15	2750	0.669	1.96	0.780	A	1
10	$1s3p - 1s3d$	${}^3P^\circ - {}^3D$	[9927.8]	[6902450]	6912520	9	15	0.0133	0.0327	9.62	-0.531	A	1

NEON

Ne I.

Ground State $1s^2 2s^2 2p^6\ {}^1S_0$

Ionization Potential $21.559\ \text{eV} = 173932\ \text{cm}^{-1}$

Allowed Transitions

List of tabulated lines:

Wavelength [Å]	No.	Wavelength [Å]	No.	Wavelength [Å]	No.
735.89	2	6717.04	6	23709	14
743.70	1	6929.47	6	23956	16
3454.19	7	7032.41	3	24249	16
3472.57	7	7173.94	6	24339	13
3520.47	8	7245.17	4	24365	14
5852.49	6	7438.90	5	25524	13
5881.90	3	7488.87	9	25855	16
5944.83	3	8377.61	10	26861	14
5975.53	3	8495.36	11	27521	15
6030.00	4	8654.38	12	28533	16
6074.34	4	18210	14	28744	16
6096.16	4	19577	13	29714	16
6128.45	4	19772	13	31860	15
6143.06	3	20350	14	33511	16
6163.59	5	20354	14		
6217.28	3	20565	14		
6266.50	5	21041	16		
6304.79	4	21708	14		
6334.43	3	22530	13		
6382.99	4	22662	13		
6402.25	3	23100	15		
6506.53	4	23260	13		
6532.88	5	23373	15		
6598.95	6	23565	14		
6678.28	6	23636	13		

In the vacuum uv region data are available for the two transitions of the $2p-3s$ array. They have been obtained experimentally from lifetime measurements by Schütz [1], Phelps [2], Korolev et al. [3], and theoretically from SCF calculations including exchange effects by Gold and Knox [4]. In the experiments only one of the two lines is obtained directly whereas the other one is derived using Shortley's [5] calculated intensity ratio. Since the total spread between the results is within a factor of two, uncertainties within 25 percent (class C) are estimated for the averaged values.

Extensive experimental work [6, 7] has been done on the lines of the prominent $3s-3p$ transition array. Ladenburg and Levy, and Pery-Thorne and Chamberlain have used the method of anomalous dispersion; Doherty and Friedrichs measured absolute emission intensities, the former with a conventional shock tube, the latter with a stabilized arc; with a discharge tube Garbuny determined relative intensities in emission and Krebs in absorption. *Relative f*-values have been obtained from the following procedure: the results of the three emission experiments (by Garbuny, Doherty, and Friedrichs) have been employed to obtain the line strengths within the groups of lines with the same upper but different lower levels, since for these cases errors are obviously minimized.

Analogously, the absorption measurements of Krebs and the anomalous dispersion measurements of Ladenburg and Levy, and Pery-Thorne and Chamberlain have supplied the most accurate relative f-values for lines starting with the same lower level but ending in different upper levels. The averaged emission and absorption data have then been combined in a least squares fit procedure to obtain a best set of relative data. It turns out that this set fits most of the original data and the J-file sum rule within 10 percent, but a few deviations of 30 percent are encountered.

Absolute values have been obtained by employing the results of recent extensive lifetime measurements of the $3p$ levels undertaken by Klose [7] with a delayed coincidence technique. An averaged conversion factor has been obtained from fitting the levels p_1, p_2, p_5, p_6, p_7, p_8, and p_9 which were measured by Klose with a high degree of precision. The averaged conversion factor has a standard deviation of only 6 percent. Accuracies within 10 percent for most absolute f-values are indicated (a) from the high experimental precision obtained by Klose which is usually within 4 percent, (b) from the good consistency of the data with the J-file sum rule, (c) from the excellent agreement of the total line strength for this transition array, which is 224, with a value of 230 obtained from the Coulomb approximation, and (d) from the very good agreement of Klose's lifetime results with some preliminary lifetime data by Bennett et al. [8].

For a few lines of the $3s-4p$ array, Klose's lifetime data for $4p$ levels could be utilized to derive transition probabilities. However, these cannot be considered as accurate as before because the contribution of the respective $4s-4p$ transition to the lifetimes could be only approximately taken into account using the data discussed immediately below.

The Coulomb approximation has been applied for obtaining an absolute scale for the $4s-4p$ array. For the breakdown into individual lines the intermediate coupling calculations of Ufford [10] are available. The latter are estimated to be not too reliable, since similar calculations by Shortley [5] for the $3s-3p$ array, as judged from the many experimental comparisons, have had only a fair degree of success.

From Doherty's [9] shock tube experiment some further material is available for the $3p-3d$ array. His absolute values have been renormalized by using the same conversion factor as that for his values of the $3s-3p$ array.

References

[1] Schütz, W., Ann. Physik **18**, 705–720 (1933).

[2] Phelps, A. V., Phys. Rev. **100**, 1230 (1955).

[3] Korolev, F. A., Odintsov, V. I., and Fursova, E. V., Optics and Spectroscopy (U.S.S.R.) **16**, 304–305 (1964).

[4] Gold, A. and Knox, R. S., Phys. Rev. **113**, 834–839 (1959).

[5] Shortley, G. H., Phys. Rev. **47**, 295–300 (1935).

[6] Krebs, K., Z. Physik **101**, 604–642 (1936).
　　Ladenburg, R. and Levy, S., Z. Physik **88**, 461–468 (1934).
　　Pery-Thorne, A. and Chamberlain, J. E., Proc. Phys. Soc. London A **82**, 133–141 (1963).
　　Doherty, L. R., Thesis Michigan (1961).
　　Garbuny, M., Z. Physik **107**, 362–368 (1937).
　　Friedrichs, H., Z. Astrophys. **60**, 176–183 (1964).

[7] Klose, J. Z., Phys. Rev. **141**, 181–186 (1966).

[8] Bennett, Jr., W. R., Kindlmann, P. J., and Mercer, G. N., Applied Optics Supplement 2 of Chemical Lasers, 34–57 (1965).

[9] Doherty, L. R., Thesis Michigan (1961).

[10] Ufford, C. W., Astrophys, J. **85**, 249–250 (1937).

No.	Transition Array	Transition	$\lambda(\text{Å})$	$E_i(\text{cm}^{-1})$	$E_k(\text{cm}^{-1})$	g_i	g_k	$A_{ki}(10^8 \text{ sec}^{-1})$	f_{ik}	S(at.u.)	$\log gf$	Accuracy	Source
1	$2p^6-$ $2p^5(^2P^\circ_{1^1/_2})3s$	$^1S-[1^1/_2]^\circ$ (1 uv)	743.70	0	134461	1	3	0.476	0.0118	0.0290	-1.93	C	1, 2, 3, 4, 5
2	$2p^6-$ $2p^5(^2P^\circ_{^1/_2})3s'$	$^1S-[^1/_2]^\circ$ (2 uv)	735.89	0	135891	1	3	6.64	0.162	0.392	-0.79	C	1, 2, 3, 4, 5
3	$2p^53s-$ $2p^5(^2P^\circ_{1^1/_2})3p$ (1)	$[1^1/_2]^\circ-[\ ^1/_2]$	7032.41	134044	148260	5	3	0.192	0.0854	9.89	-0.370	B$-$	6n, 7
		$[1^1/_2]^\circ-[2^1/_2]$	6402.25	134044	149659	5	7	0.433	0.373	39.3	0.270	B	6n, 7
		$[1^1/_2]^\circ-[1^1/_2]$	6334.43	134044	149826	5	5	0.136	0.0818	8.53	-0.388	B$-$	6n, 7
		$[1^1/_2]^\circ-[1^1/_2]$	6217.28	134044	150124	5	3	0.0777	0.0270	2.76	-0.869	B$-$	6n, 7
		$[1^1/_2]^\circ-[\ ^1/_2]$	6143.06	134044	150318	5	5	0.216	0.122	12.4	-0.214	B$-$	6n, 7
	$2p^5(^2P^\circ_{1^1/_2})3s-$ $2p^5(^2P^\circ_{^1/_2})3p'$ (1)	$[1^1/_2]^\circ-[1^1/_2]$	5975.53	134044	150774	5	3	0.0433	0.0139	1.37	-1.158	B$-$	6n, 7
		$[1^1/_2]^\circ-[1^1/_2]$	5944.83	134044	150860	5	5	0.105	0.0556	5.44	-0.556	C$+$	6n, 7
		$[1^1/_2]^\circ-[\ ^1/_2]$	5881.90	134044	151040	5	3	0.128	0.0398	3.86	-0.701	B$-$	6n, 7
4	$2p^53s-$ $2p^5(^2P^\circ_{1^1/_2})3p$ (3)	$[1^1/_2]^\circ-[\ ^1/_2]$	7245.17	134461	148260	3	3	0.0977	0.0769	5.50	-0.637	B$-$	6n, 7
		$[1^1/_2]^\circ-[2^1/_2]$	6506.53	134461	149826	3	5	0.232	0.245	15.8	-0.133	B$-$	6n, 7
		$[1^1/_2]^\circ-[1^1/_2]$	6382.99	134461	150124	3	3	0.279	0.170	10.7	-0.291	B$-$	6n, 7
		$[1^1/_2]^\circ-[1^1/_2]$	6304.79	134461	150318	3	5	0.0507	0.0504	3.14	-0.821	B$-$	6n, 7
		$[1^1/_2]^\circ-[\ ^1/_2]$	6074.34	134461	150919	3	1	0.617	0.114	6.83	-0.467	C$+$	6n, 7
	$2p^5(^2P^\circ_{1^1/_2})3s-$ $2p^5(^2P^\circ_{^1/_2})3p'$ (3)	$[1^1/_2]^\circ-[1^1/_2]$	6128.45	134461	150774	3	3	0.0327	0.0184	1.11	-1.258	B$-$	6n, 7
		$[1^1/_2]^\circ-[1^1/_2]$	6096.16	134461	150860	3	5	0.169	0.157	9.45	-0.327	C$+$	6n, 7
		$[1^1/_2]^\circ-[\ ^1/_2]$	6030.00	134461	151040	3	3	0.0627	0.0342	2.04	-0.989	B$-$	6n, 7
5	$2p^5(^2P^\circ_{^1/_2})3s'-$ $2p^5(^2P^\circ_{1^1/_2})3p$ (5)	$[\ ^1/_2]^\circ-[\ ^1/_2]$	7438.90	134821	148260	1	3	0.0292	0.0727	1.78	-1.139	B$-$	6n, 7
		$[\ ^1/_2]^\circ-[1^1/_2]$	6532.88	134821	150124	1	3	0.128	0.246	5.28	-0.610	B$-$	6n, 7
	$2p^53s'-$ $2p^5(^2P^\circ_{^1/_2})3p'$ (5)	$[\ ^1/_2]^\circ-[1^1/_2]$	6266.50	134821	150774	1	3	0.223	0.394	8.13	-0.405	B$-$	6n, 7
		$[\ ^1/_2]^\circ-[\ ^1/_2]$	6163.59	134821	151040	1	3	0.160	0.273	5.55	-0.563	B$-$	6n, 7
6	$2p^5(^2P^\circ_{^1/_2})3s'-$ $2p^5(^2P^\circ_{1^1/_2})3p$ (6)	$[\ ^1/_2]^\circ-[2^1/_2]$	7173.94	135891	149826	3	5	0.0365	0.0469	3.33	-0.851	B$-$	6n, 7
		$[\ ^1/_2]^\circ-[1^1/_2]$	6929.47	135891	150318	3	5	0.190	0.228	15.6	-0.165	B$-$	6n, 7
	$2p^53s'-$ $2p^5(^2P^\circ_{^1/_2})3p'$ (6)	$[\ ^1/_2]^\circ-[1^1/_2]$	6717.04	135891	150774	3	3	0.234	0.158	10.5	-0.323	B$-$	6n, 7
		$[\ ^1/_2]^\circ-[1^1/_2]$	6678.28	135891	150860	3	5	0.238	0.265	17.5	-0.099	C$+$	6n, 7
		$[\ ^1/_2]^\circ-[\ ^1/_2]$	6598.95	135891	151040	3	3	0.251	0.164	10.7	-0.308	B$-$	6n, 7
		$[\ ^1/_2]^\circ-[\ ^1/_2]$	5852.49	135891	152973	3	1	0.719	0.123	7.11	-0.433	B	6n, 7
7	$2p^53s-$ $2p^5(^2P^\circ_{1^1/_2})4p$ (2)	$[1^1/_2]^\circ-[2^1/_2]$	3472.57	134044	162833	5	7	0.099	0.0251	1.44	-0.90	C	7
		$[1^1/_2]^\circ-[\ ^1/_2]$	3454.19	134461	163403	3	1	0.085	0.0051	0.173	-1.82	C	7
8	$2p^53s'-$ $2p^5(^2P^\circ_{^1/_2})4p'$ (7)	$[\ ^1/_2]^\circ-[\ ^1/_2]$	3520.47	135891	164288	3	1	0.073	0.00449	0.156	-1.87	C	7

No.	Transition Array	Transition	λ(Å)	E_i(cm⁻¹)	E_k(cm⁻¹)	g_i	g_k	A_{ki}(10⁸ sec⁻¹)	f_{ik}	S(at.u.)	log gf	Accuracy	Source
9	$2p^53p -$ $2p^5(^2P^\circ_{1_{1/2}})3d$	[½]−[1½]°	7488.87	148260	161609	3	5	0.349	0.489	36.2	0.166	C	9n
10		[2½]−[3½]° (12)	8377.61	149659	161592	7	9	0.51	0.69	134	0.69	C	9n
11		[2½]−[3½]° (18)	8495.36	149826	161594	5	7	0.357	0.54	76	0.432	C	9n
12	$2p^53p' -$ $2p^5(^2P^\circ_{1/2})3d'$	[1½]−[2½]° (33)	8654.38	150860	162412	5	7	0.445	0.70	100	0.54	C	9n
13	$2p^54s -$ $2p^5(^2P^\circ_{1_{1/2}})4p$	[1½]°−[½]	[25524]	158603	162520	5	3	0.012	0.073	31	−0.44	D	10n, ca
		[1½]°−[2½]	[23636]	158603	162833	5	7	0.057	0.67	260	0.52	D+	10n, ca
		[1½]°−[2½]	[23260]	158603	162901	5	5	0.0025	0.020	7.8	−0.99	D	10n, ca
		[1½]°−[1½]	[22662]	158603	163015	5	3	0.0058	0.027	10	−0.87	D	10n, ca
		[1½]°−[1½]	[22530]	158603	163040	5	5	0.037	0.28	100	0.15	D	10n, ca
	$2p^5(^2P^\circ_{1_{1/2}})4s -$ $2p^5(^2P^\circ_{1/2})4p'$	[1½]°−[1½]	[19772]	158603	163659	5	3	0.0052	0.018	5.9	−1.04	D	10n, ca
		[1½]°−[1½]	[24339]	158603	163711	5	5	0.021	0.18	73	−0.04	D	10n, ca
		[1½]°−[½]	[19577]	158603	163710	5	3	0.058	0.20	64	−0.00	D	10n, ca
14	$2p^54s -$ $2p^5(^2P^\circ_{1_{1/2}})4p$	[1½]°−[½]	[26861]	158798	162520	3	3	0.015	0.16	43	−0.31	D	10n, ca
		[1½]°−[2½]	[24365]	158798	162901	3	5	0.0015	0.022	5.2	−1.19	D	10n, ca
		[1½]°−[1½]	[23709]	158798	163015	3	3	0.0019	0.016	3.1	−1.32	D	10n, ca
		[1½]°−[1½]	[23565]	158798	163040	3	5	0.021	0.29	68	−0.06	D	10n, ca
		[1½]°−[½]	[21708]	158798	163403	3	1	0.068	0.16	34	−0.32	D+	10n. ca
	$2p^5(^2P^\circ_{1/2})4s -$ $2p^5(^2P^\circ_{1/2})4p'$	[1½]°−[1½]	[20565]	158798	163659	3	3	0.026	0.16	33	−0.31	D	10n, ca
		[1½]°−[1½]	[20350]	158798	163711	3	5	0.054	0.56	110	0.22	D	10n, ca
		[1½]°−[½]	[20354]	158798	163710	3	3	0.025	0.15	31	−0.34	D	10n, ca
		[1½]°−[½]	[18210]	158798	164289	3	1	0.0087	0.014	2.6	−1.36	D	10n, ca
15	$2p^5(^2P^\circ_{1/2})4s' -$ $2p^5(^2P^\circ_{1_{1/2}})4p$	[½]°−[½]	[31860]	159382	162520	1	3	0.0054	0.25	26	−0.61	D	10n, ca
		[½]°−[1½]	[27521]	159382	163015	1	3	0.0075	0.26	23	−0.59	D	10n, ca
	$2p^54s' -$ $2p^5(^2P^\circ_{1/2})4p'$	[½]°−[1½]	[23373]	159382	163659	1	3	0.027	0.67	52	−0.17	D	10n, ca
		[½]°−[½]	[23100]	159382	163710	1	3	0.0055	0.13	10	−0.88	D	10n, ca
16	$2p^5(^2P^\circ_{1/2})4s' -$ $2p^5(^2P^\circ_{1_{1/2}})4p$	[½]°−[½]	[33511]	159537	162520	3	3	0.0020	0.034	11	−0.99	D	10n, ca
		[½]°−[2½]	[29714]	159537	162901	3	5	0.027	0.59	170	0.25	D	10n, ca
		[½]°−[1½]	[28744]	159537	163015	3	3	0.021	0.26	74	−0.11	D	10n, ca
		[½]°−[1½]	[28533]	159537	163040	3	5	0.0023	0.046	13	−0.86	D	10n, ca
		[½]°−[½]	[25855]	159537	163403	3	1	0.0030	0.010	2.6	−1.52	D	10n, ca
	$2p^54s' -$ $2p^5(^2P^\circ_{1/2})4p'$	[½]°−[1½]	[24249]	159537	163659	3	3	0.0095	0.084	20	−0.60	D	10n, ca
		[½]°−[½]	[23956]	159537	163710	3	3	0.0029	0.025	5.9	−1.12	D	10n, ca
		[½]°−[½]	[21041]	159537	164288	3	1	0.075	0.17	34	−0.30	D+	10n, ca

Ne II.

Ground State $1s^2 2s^2 2p^5\ ^2P^\circ_{3/2}$

Ionization Potential 41.07 eV $= 331350$ cm^{-1}

Allowed Transitions

List of tabulated lines:

Wavelength [Å]	No.	Wavelength [Å]	No.	Wavelength [Å]	No.
460.725	1	3166.2	4	3357.90	24
462.338	1	3169.30	28	3360.63	3
2846.4	23	3173.58	25	3362.89	24
2853.5	7	3176.16	28	3367.05	24
2858.0	22	3187.60	4	3367.20	31
2870.0	19	3188.74	26	3371.87	34
2873.0	22	3190.86	25	3374.10	24
2876.4	22	3194.61	28	3378.28	13
2876.5	19	3198.62	25	3379.39	24
		3198.88	25	3386.24	24
2878.1	23	3208.3	27	3388.46	31
2888.4	19	3208.99	26	3390.56	24
2889.0	20	3209.38	28	3392.7	34
2891.5	22	3213.70	25	3392.78	13
2895.0	19	3214.38	26	3393.2	33
2896.3	7	3217.4	28	3397.5	31
2897.1	19	3218.21	25	3414.82	32
2906.8	22	3220.0	27	3416.87	33
2907.7	20	3230.16	16	3417.71	32
2910.4	19	3230.5	16	3453.10	33
2916.2	21	3231.97	16	3456.68	40
2925.7	22	3232.3	28	3463.1	12
2933.7	21	3232.38	16	3475.25	46
2934.3	20	3243.34	27	3477.69	33
2935.3	21	3244.15	26	3479.5	17
2951.1	21	3248.15	27	3480.8	17
2953.0	21	3255.39	35	3481.96	11
2955.7	6	3263.43	27	3503.61	40
3001.65	6	3269.86	27	3522.72	46
3015.7	5	3270.79	3	3538.3	12
3017.34	18	3297.74	3	3542.90	45
3027.04	18	3309.78	13	3544.2	30
3028.7	18	3310.55	35	3546.22	39
3028.84	6	3311.30	3	3551.2	37
3034.48	18	3314.60	34	3554.39	30
3037.73	18	3319.75	15	3557.84	11
3045.58	18	3320.29	24	3561.23	42
3047.57	18	3323.75	13	3565.84	45
3054.69	18	3327.16	3	3568.53	14
3097.5	29	3329.20	24	3571.26	42
3118.02	28	3330.78	31	3574.23	14
3132.22	25	3334.8	34	3574.3	39
3135.8	29	3334.87	3	3574.64	14
3135.82	4	3344.43	3	3590.47	43
3136.5	4	3345.49	15	3594.18	45
3151.16	28	3345.88	24	3612.35	38
3154.82	26	3345.88	15	3628.06	51
3160.0	29	3353.36	35	3632.75	44
3164.46	25	3355.05	3	3643.89	10
3165.70	25	3356.35	32	3644.86	51

Wavelength [Å]	No.	Wavelength [Å]	No.	Wavelength [Å]	No.
3659.93	44	3790.96	41	4290.40	54
3664.09	2	3800.02	49	4323.3	53
3679.80	51	3806.30	41	4346.9	54
3694.22	2	3818.44	49	4365.72	54
3697.09	51	3829.77	49	4369.77	53
3701.81	50	3903.9	9	4379.50	53
3709.64	2	3942.3	9	4385.00	53
3713.09	10	3999.5	9	4391.94	54
3721.86	47	4217.15	52	4397.94	53
3726.9	50	4219.76	52	4409.30	54
3727.08	10	4220.92	52	4413.20	54
3732.7	47	4224.75	52	4428.54	54
3734.94	2	4231.60	52	4430.90	53
3744.66	50	4234.3	52	4441.1	8
3751.26	2	4239.95	52	4442.67	53
3753.83	48	4242.20	52	4446.46	53
3754.9	36	4249.2	54	4492.4	54
3766.29	2	4250.68	52	4502.52	53
3776.9	41	4257.82	52		
3777.16	2	4280.3	53		

Aside from the multiplet $2s^2 2p^5\,^2P° - 2s2p^6\,^2S$ in the vacuum uv for which a quantum mechanical calculation (screening approximation) has been carried out by Varsavsky [1], the main source of theoretical information on the spectrum are the extensive calculations by Garstang [2] for lines of the $3s-3p$ and $3p-3d$ arrays. He has calculated the relative line strengths under the assumption of intermediate coupling and has used the Coulomb approximation to obtain the transition integrals for the absolute values. However, for the $3s-3p$ array Koopman's [3] relative line strengths obtained from intensity measurements with an electrically driven shock tube agree with LS-coupling better than with the intermediate coupling values. Therefore, Koopman's relative values are averaged with LS-coupling results and put on an absolute scale by using the Coulomb approximation. On the other hand, comparison with the very incomplete experimental intensity data [3] for the $3p-3d$ array indicates that intermediate coupling fits much better here than LS-coupling and gives in may cases drastic improvements. Thus Garstang's results are exclusively used for this array as well as for all intercombination lines. Some lines marked D- should be considered inferior in quality to the rest, since Garstang finds them very sensitive to the choice of parameters.

In addition, the f-values for the three strongest multiplets of the $3d-4f$ array have been calculated with the Coulomb approximation using LS-coupling for the multiplet components.

References

[1] Varsavsky, C. M., Astrophys. J. Suppl. Ser. 6, No. 53, 75–108 (1961).
[2] Garstang, R. H., Monthly Notices Roy. Astron. Soc. **114,** 118–133 (1954).
[3] Koopman, D. W., J. Opt. Soc. Am. **54,** 1354–1358 (1964).

Ne II. Allowed Transitions

No.	Transition Array	Multi-plet	λ(Å)	E_i(cm^{-1})	E_k(cm^{-1})	g_i	g_k	A_{ki}(10^8 sec^{-1})	f_{ik}	S(at.u.)	log gf	Accu-racy	Source
1	$2s^2 2p^5 -$ $2s^2 p^6$	^{2}P° $-$ ^{2}S (1 uv)	*461.28*	*260.07*	217050	6	2	310	0.33	3.0	0.29	E	1
			460.725	0.00	217050	4	2	210	0.33	2.0	0.12	E	*ls*
			462.388	782	217050	2	2	100	0.33	1.0	-0.18	E	*ls*
2	$2p^4 3s -$ $2p^4(^3$P$)3p$	^{4}P $-$ ^{4}P° (1)	*3717.2*	*219442*	*246337*	12	12	1.3	0.27	39	0.50	D	*ca*
			3694.22	219133	246195	6	6	0.96	0.20	14	0.07	D	3, *ls*
			3734.94	219651	246417	4	4	0.20	0.041	2.0	-0.78	D	3, *ls*
			3751.26	219950	246600	2	2	0.19	0.039	0.98	-1.10	D	3, *ls*
			3664.09	219133	246417	6	4	0.67	0.090	6.6	-0.27	D	3, *ls*
			3709.64	219651	246600	4	2	1.1	0.11	5.6	-0.34	D	3, *ls*
			3766.29	219651	246195	4	6	0.32	0.10	5.0	-0.39	D	3, *ls*
			3777.16	219950	246417	2	4	0.43	0.18	4.6	-0.43	D	3, *ls*
3		^{4}P $-$ ^{4}D° (2)	*3336.8*	*219442*	*249402*	12	20	1.8	0.51	67	0.79	D	*ca*
			3334.87	219133	249111	6	8	1.8	0.41	27	0.39	D	3, *ls*
			3355.05	219651	249448	4	6	1.3	0.33	15	0.13	D	3, *ls*
			3360.63	219950	249698	2	4	0.73	0.25	5.5	-0.30	D	3, *ls*
			3297.74	219133	249448	6	6	0.53	0.087	5.7	-0.28	D	3, *ls*
			3327.16	219651	249618	4	4	0.98	0.17	7.0	-0.17	D	3, *ls*
			3344.43	219950	249842	2	2	1.5	0.25	5.6	-0.30	D	3, *ls*
			3270.79	219133	249698	6	4	0.12	0.013	0.85	-1.11	D	3, *ls*
			3311.30	219651	249842	4	2	0.30	0.023	1.0	-1.04	D	3, *ls*
4		^{4}P $-$ ^{2}D° (3)											
			3135.82	219133	251013	6	6	0.0065	9.6×10^{-4}	0.059	-2.24	D	2
			[3136.5]	219651	251525	4	4	0.0049	7.2×10^{-4}	0.030	-2.54	D	2
			3187.60	219651	251013	4	6	0.016	0.0036	0.15	-1.84	D	2
			[3166.2]	219950	251525	2	4	0.0042	0.0013	0.026	-2.60	D	2
5		^{4}P $-$ ^{2}S°											
			[3015.7]	219651	252801	4	2	0.013	9.1×10^{-4}	0.036	-2.44	D	2
6		^{4}P $-$ ^{4}S° (4)	*2982.94*	*219442*	252956	12	4	2.5	0.11	13	0.12	D	*ca*
			[2955.7]	219133	252956	6	4	1.2	0.10	5.9	-0.22	D	3, *ls*
			3001.65	219651	252956	4	4	0.78	0.11	4.2	-0.37	D	3, *ls*
			3028.84	219950	252956	2	4	0.57	0.16	3.1	-0.50	D	3, *ls*
7		^{4}P $-$ ^{2}P°											
			[2853.5]	219133	254167	6	4	0.025	0.0020	0.12	-1.91	D	2
			[2896.3]	219651	254167	4	4	0.020	0.0025	0.096	-2.00	D	2
8		^{2}P $-$ ^{4}P°											
			[4441.1]	224089	246600	4	2	0.0034	5.1×10^{-4}	0.030	-2.69	D	2
9		^{2}P $-$ ^{4}D°											
			[3942.3]	224089	249448	4	6	0.012	0.0041	0.21	-1.79	D	2
			[3903.9]	224089	249698	4	4	8.4×10^{-4}	1.9×10^{-4}	0.0099	-3.11	D	2
			[3999.5]	224702	249698	2	4	0.0037	0.0018	0.046	-2.45	D	2
10		^{2}P $-$ ^{2}D° (5)	*3713.0*	*224293*	*251218*	6	10	1.3	0.45	33	0.43	D	*ca*
			3713.09	224089	251013	4	6	1.3	0.40	20	0.21	D	3, *ls*
			3727.08	224702	251525	2	4	1.0	0.43	11	-0.07	D	3, *ls*
			3643.89	224089	251525	4	4	0.23	0.046	2.2	-0.74	D	3, *ls*
11		^{2}P $-$ ^{2}S° (6)	*3506.9*	*224293*	252801	6	2	1.5	0.095	6.6	-0.25	D	*ca*
			3481.96	224089	252801	4	2	1.2	0.11	5.0	-0.36	D	3, *ls*
			3557.84	224702	252801	2	2	0.37	0.070	1.6	-0.85	D	3, *ls*

No.	Transition Array	Multiplet	λ(Å)	E_i(cm⁻¹)	E_k(cm⁻¹)	g_i	g_k	A_{ki}(10⁸ sec⁻¹)	f_{ik}	S(at.u.)	log gf	Accuracy	Source
12		²P — ⁴S°											
			[3463.1]	224089	252956	4	4	0.028	0.0051	0.23	−1.69	D	2
			[3538.3]	224702	252956	2	4	0.0090	0.0034	0.079	−2.17	D	2
13		²P — ²P° (7)	3341.8	224293	254209	6	6	1.8	0.30	19	0.25	D	ca
			3323.75	224089	254167	4	4	1.4	0.24	11	−0.02	D	3, ls
			3378.28	224702	254294	2	2	1.3	0.23	5.1	0.34	D	3, ls
			3309.78	224089	254294	4	2	0.46	0.037	1.6	−0.83	D	3, ls
			3392.78	224702	254167	2	4	0.29	0.098	2.2	−0.71	D	3, ls
14	2p⁴3s′ — 2p⁴(¹D)3p′	²D — ²F° (9)	3571.1	246398	274392	10	14	1.3	0.36	42	0.56	D	ca
			3568.53	246397	274411	6	8	1.3	0.33	24	0.30	D	3, ls
			3574.64	246400	274367	4	6	1.3	0.37	18	0.17	D	3, ls
			3574.23	246397	274367	6	6	0.092	0.018	1.3	−0.97	D	3, ls
15		²D — ²P° (10)	3336.9	246398	276357	10	6	1.7	0.17	19	0.23	D	ca
			3345.49	246397	276279	6	4	1.5	0.17	11	0.01	D	3, ls
			3319.75	246400	276514	4	2	1.7	0.14	6.2	−0.24	D	3, ls
			3345.88	246400	276279	4	4	0.17	0.028	1.3	−0.95	D	3, ls
16		²D — ²D° (11)	3231.1	246398	277339	10	10	1.9	0.29	31	0.47	D	ca
			3230.16	246397	277346	6	6	1.8	0.27	18	0.22	D	3, ls
			3232.38	246400	277328	4	4	1.7	0.26	11	0.02	D	3, ls
			3231.97	246397	277328	6	4	0.19	0.020	1.3	−0.93	D	3, ls
			[3230.5]	246400	277346	4	6	0.13	0.029	1.3	−0.93	D	3, ls
17	2p⁴3s″ — 2p⁴(¹S)3p″	²S — ²P°	3480.3	276678	305403	2	6	1.6	0.86	20	0.24	D	ca
			[3480.8]	276678	305399	2	4	1.6	0.58	13	0.06	D	2
			[3479.5]	276678	305409	2	2	1.6	0.29	6.6	−0.24	D	2
18	2p⁴3p — 2p⁴(³P)3d	⁴P° — ⁴D (8)	3039.3	246337	279230	12	20	3.2	0.74	89	0.95	D	ca
			3034.48	246195	279139	6	8	3.1	0.57	34	0.53	D	2
			3047.57	246417	279221	4	6	1.8	0.37	15	0.17	D	2
			3054.69	246600	279327	2	4	0.93	0.26	5.2	−0.28	D	2
			3027.04	246195	279221	6	6	1.5	0.20	12	0.08	D	2
			3037.73	246417	279327	4	4	2.0	0.28	11	0.05	D	2
			3045.58	246600	279425	2	2	2.5	0.35	7.0	−0.15	D	2
			3017.34	246195	279327	6	4	0.35	0.032	1.9	−0.72	D	2
			[3028.7]	246417	279425	4	2	0.84	0.058	2.3	−0.64	D	2
19		⁴P° — ⁴F	[2897.1]	246195	280703	6	8	0.042	0.0071	0.41	−1.37	D	2
			[2870.0]	246195	281028	6	6	0.11	0.014	0.77	−1.09	D	2
			[2876.5]	246195	280950	6	4	0.18	0.015	0.86	−1.04	D	2
			[2888.4]	246417	281028	4	6	0.015	0.0029	0.11	−1.94	D	2
			[2895.0]	246417	280950	4	4	0.016	0.0021	0.079	−2.08	D	2
			[2910.4]	246600	280950	2	4	0.43	0.11	2.1	−0.66	D	2
20		⁴P° — ²F	[2934.3]	246195	280264	6	8	0.0030	5.1 × 10⁻³	0.030	−2.51	D	2
			[2907.7]	246417	280799	4	6	0.039	0.0075	0.29	−1.52	D	2
			[2889.0]	246195	280799	6	6	0.015	0.0019	0.11	−1.94	D	2
21		⁴P° — ²D	[2933.7]	246195	280271	6	6	0.068	0.0087	0.51	−1.28	D	2
			[2916.2]	246195	280476	6	4	0.047	0.0040	0.23	−1.62	D	2
			[2953.0]	246417	280271	4	6	0.012	0.0023	0.089	−2.04	D	2
			[2935.3]	246417	280476	4	4	0.032	0.0041	0.16	−1.79	D	2
			[2951.1]	246600	280476	2	4	0.023	0.0061	0.12	−1.92	D	2

No.	Transition Array	Multiplet	λ(Å)	E_i(cm⁻¹)	E_k(cm⁻¹)	g_i	g_k	A_{ki}(10⁸ sec⁻¹)	f_{ik}	S(at.u.)	log gf	Accuracy	Source
22		⁴P°−⁴P	*2880.2*	*246337*	*281046*	12	12	1.7	0.21	24	0.40	D	*ca*
			[2858.0]	246195	281174	6	6	0.91	0.11	6.3	−0.18	D	2
			[2891.5]	246417	280992	4	4	0.097	0.012	0.47	−1.31	D	2
			[2925.7]	246600	280770	2	2	0.52	0.067	1.3	−0.87	D	2
			[2873.0]	246195	280992	6	4	0.46	0.038	2.2	−0.64	D	2
			[2906.8]	246417	280770	4	2	1.6	0.10	3.9	−0.39	D	2
			[2876.4]	246417	281174	4	6	0.84	0.16	5.9	−0.21	D	2
			[2906.8]	246600	280992	2	4	0.75	0.19	3.6	−0.42	D	2
23		⁴P°−²P											
			[2878.1]	246600	281335	2	2	0.067	0.0083	0.16	−1.78	D	2
			[2846.4]	246600	281722	2	4	0.035	0.0084	0.16	−1.77	D	2
24		⁴D°−⁴D (12)	*3351.7*	*249402*	*279230*	20	20	0.79	0.13	29	0.42	D	*ca*
			3329.20	249111	279139	8	8	0.87	0.15	13	0.07	D	2
			3357.90	249448	279221	6	6	0.55	0.093	6.1	−0.26	D	2
			3374.10	249698	279327	4	4	0.38	0.065	2.9	−0.59	D	2
			3379.39	249842	279425	2	2	0.35	0.060	1.3	−0.92	D	2
			3320.29	249111	279221	8	6	0.13	0.017	1.5	−0.87	D	2
			3345.88	249448	279327	6	4	0.22	0.024	1.6	−0.83	D	2
			3362.89	249698	279425	4	2	0.30	0.025	1.1	−0.99	D	2
			3367.05	249448	279139	6	8	0.035	0.0079	0.53	−1.32	D	2
			3386.24	249698	279221	4	6	0.067	0.017	0.77	−1.16	D−	2
			3390.56	249842	279327	2	4	0.078	0.027	0.60	−1.27	D	2
25		⁴D°−⁴F (13)	*3202.5*	*249402*	*280619*	20	28	2.5	0.55	120	1.04	D	*ca*
			3218.21	249111	280174	8	10	3.6	0.70	59	0.75	D	2
			3198.62	249448	280703	6	8	2.2	0.45	29	0.44	D	2
			3190.86	249698	281028	4	6	0.73	0.17	7.0	−0.18	D	2
			3213.70	249842	280950	2	4	1.8	0.56	12	0.05	D	2
			3164.46	249111	280703	8	8	0.22	0.033	2.7	−0.58	D	2
			3165.70	249448	281028	6	6	0.19	0.028	1.7	−0.78	D−	2
			3198.88	249698	280950	4	4	0.59	0.090	3.8	−0.44	D−	2
			3132.22	249111	281028	8	6	0.022	0.0024	0.20	−1.72	D−	2
			3173.58	249448	280950	6	4	0.0017	1.7 × 10⁻⁴	0.011	−2.98	D−	2
26		⁴D°−²F (14)											
			3208.99	249111	280264	8	8	0.12	0.018	1.5	−0.84	D	2
			3188.74	249448	280799	6	6	0.32	0.048	3.0	−0.54	D−	2
			3154.82	249111	280799	8	6	0.0022	2.5 × 10⁻⁴	0.021	−2.70	D−	2
			3244.15	249448	280264	6	8	1.1	0.22	14	0.13	D	2
			3214.38	249698	280799	4	6	1.6	0.38	16	0.18	D−	2
27		⁴D°−²D (15)											
			3243.34	249448	280271	6	6	0.18	0.029	1.8	−0.76	D−	2
			3248.15	249698	280476	4	4	0.14	0.022	0.94	−1.06	D	2
			3269.86	249698	280271	4	6	0.48	0.12	5.0	−0.33	D−	2
			3263.43	249842	280476	2	4	0.36	0.12	2.5	−0.64	D	2
			[3222.0]	249448	280476	6	4	0.020	0.0020	0.13	−1.92	D	2
			[3208.3]	249111	280271	8	6	0.0091	0.0010	0.089	−2.07	D	2
28		⁴D°−⁴P (16)	*3159.3*	*249402*	*281046*	20	12	0.39	0.035	7.2	−0.16	D	*ca*
			3118.02	249111	281174	8	6	0.11	0.013	1.0	−0.99	D	2
			3169.30	249448	280992	6	4	0.17	0.017	1.1	−0.99	D−	2
			[3217.4]	249698	280770	4	2	0.13	0.0098	0.42	−1.41	D	2
			3151.16	249448	281174	6	6	0.066	0.0016	0.099	−2.02	D−	2
			3194.61	249698	280992	4	4	0.14	0.021	0.088	−1.08	D−	2
			[3232.3]	249842	280770	2	2	0.033	0.0051	0.11	−1.99	D	2
			3176.16	249698	281174	4	6	0.034	0.0078	0.33	−1.50	D	2
			3209.38	249842	280992	2	4	0.51	0.16	3.3	−0.50	D−	2

No.	Transition Array	Multi-plet	λ(Å)	E_i(cm^{-1})	E_k(cm^{-1})	g_i	g_k	A_{ki}(10^8 sec^{-1})	f_{ik}	S(at.u.)	log gf	Accu-racy	Source
29		^{4}D°–^{2}P											
			[3135.8]	249842	281722	2	4	0.020	0.0058	0.12	−1.94	D	2
			[3160.0]	249698	281335	4	2	0.019	0.0014	0.059	−2.25	D	2
			[3097.5]	249448	281722	6	4	0.015	0.0015	0.089	−2.06	D	2
30		^{2}D°–^{4}D (18)											
			3554.39	251013	279139	6	8	0.013	0.0034	0.24	−1.69	D	2
			[3544.2]	251013	279221	6	6	0.0037	7.0 × 10^{-4}	0.049	−2.38	D	2
31		^{2}D°–^{4}F (19)											
			3367.20	251013	280703	6	8	1.0	0.24	16	0.15	D	2
			3388.46	251525	281028	4	6	2.0	0.51	23	0.31	D	2
			3330.78	251013	281028	6	6	0.12	0.020	1.3	−0.93	D	2
			[3397.5]	251525	280950	4	4	0.049	0.0084	0.38	−1.47	D	2
32		^{2}D°–^{2}F (20)	3414.9	251218	280493	10	14	1.4	0.34	38	0.53	D	ca
			3417.71	251013	280264	6	8	2.0	0.47	32	0.45	D	2
			3414.82	251525	280799	4	6	0.41	0.11	4.8	−0.37	D−	2
			3356.35	251013	280799	6	6	0.11	0.019	1.3	−0.93	D−	2
33		^{2}D°–^{2}D (21)	3431.3	251218	280353	10	10	0.85	0.15	17	0.18	D	ca
			3416.87	251013	280271	6	6	0.67	0.12	7.9	−0.15	D	2
			3453.10	251525	280476	4	4	0.59	0.11	4.8	−0.38	D	2
			[3393.2]	251013	280476	6	4	0.022	0.0025	0.17	−1.82	D	2
			3477.69	251525	280271	4	6	0.34	0.091	4.2	−0.44	D−	2
34		^{2}D°–^{4}P (22)											
			3314.60	251013	281174	6	6	0.026	0.0042	0.28	−1.60	D	2
			3371.87	251525	281174	4	6	0.12	0.032	1.4	−0.89	D	2
			[3392.7]	251525	280992	4	4	0.14	0.025	1.1	−1.00	D	2
			[3334.8]	251013	280992	6	4	0.030	0.0033	0.22	−1.70	D	2
35		^{2}D°–^{2}P (23)	3291.6	251218	281590	10	6	0.098	0.0095	1.0	−1.02	D	ca
			3255.39	251013	281722	6	4	0.12	0.013	0.81	−1.12	D	2
			3353.63	251525	281335	4	2	0.048	0.0040	0.18	−1.79	D	2
			3310.55	251525	281722	4	4	0.0061	0.0010	0.044	−2.40	D	2
36		^{2}S°–^{4}D											
			[3754.9]	252801	279425	2	2	0.0095	0.0020	0.050	−2.40	D	2
37		^{2}S°–^{4}F (24)											
			3551.52	252801	280950	2	4	0.055	0.021	0.49	−1.38	D	2
38		^{2}S°–^{2}D (26)											
			3612.35	252801	280476	2	4	0.22	0.087	2.1	−0.76	D	2
39		^{2}S°–^{4}P (27)											
			3546.22	252801	280992	2	4	0.021	0.0081	0.19	−1.79	D	2
			[3574.3]	252801	280770	2	2	0.046	0.0088	0.21	−1.75	D	2
40		^{2}S°–^{2}P (28)	3472.5	252801	281590	2	6	1.3	0.70	16	0.15	D	ca
			3456.68	252801	281722	2	4	1.0	0.36	8.2	−0.14	D	2
			3503.61	252801	281335	2	2	1.9	0.34	7.9	−0.16	D	2

No.	Transition Array	Multiplet	$\lambda(\text{Å})$	$E_i(\text{cm}^{-1})$	$E_k(\text{cm}^{-1})$	g_i	g_k	$A_{ki}(10^8 \text{ sec}^{-1})$	f_{ik}	$S(\text{at.u.})$	$\log gf$	Accuracy	Source
41		$^4S^\circ - {}^4D$ (30)											
			3806.30	252956	279221	4	6	0.013	0.0043	0.22	-1.76	D	2
			3790.96	252956	279327	4	4	0.017	0.0036	0.18	-1.85	D	2
			[3776.9]	252956	279425	4	2	0.0074	8.0×10^{-4}	0.040	-2.50	D	2
42		$^4S^\circ - {}^4F$ (31)											
			3561.23	252956	281028	4	6	0.11	0.031	1.5	-0.91	D	2
			3571.26	252956	280950	4	4	0.43	0.083	3.9	-0.48	D$-$	2
43		$^4S^\circ - {}^2F$ (32)											
			3590.47	252956	280799	4	6	0.087	0.025	1.2	-0.99	D$-$	2
44		$^4S^\circ - {}^2D$ (33)											
			3659.93	252956	280271	4	6	0.11	0.033	1.6	-0.88	D$-$	2
			3632.75	252956	280476	4	4	0.090	0.018	0.85	-1.15	D	2
45		$^4S^\circ - {}^4P$ (34)	*3559.0*	252956	*281046*	4	12	1.1	0.63	30	0.40	D	*ca*
			3542.90	252956	281174	4	6	1.3	0.35	16	0.15	D	2
			3565.84	252956	280992	4	4	0.82	0.16	7.3	-0.20	D	2
			3594.18	252956	280770	4	2	1:3	0.12	5.9	-0.30	D	2
46		$^4S^\circ - {}^2P$ (35)											
			3475.25	252956	281722	4	4	0.0047	8.5×10^{-4}	0.039	-2.47	D	2
			3522.72	252956	281335	4	2	0.011	0.0011	0.050	-2.37	D	2
47		$^2P^\circ - {}^4F$ (37)											
			3721.86	254167	281028	4	6	0.036	0.011	0.55	-1.35	D$-$	2
			[3732.7]	254167	280950	4	4	0.030	0.0062	0.31	-1.60	D	2
48		$^2P^\circ - {}^2F$ (38)											
			3753.83	254167	280799	4	6	0.55	0.18	8.7	-0.15	D$-$	2
49		$^2P^\circ - {}^2D$ (39)	*3824.0*	*254209*	*280353*	6	10	0.94	0.35	26	0.32	D	*ca*
			3829.77	254167	280271	4	6	0.88	0.29	15	0.06	D	2
			3818.44	254294	280476	2	4	0.69	0.30	7.6	-0.22	D	2
			3800.02	254167	280476	4	4	0.35	0.076	3.8	-0.52	D	2
50		$^2P^\circ - {}^4P$ (40)											
			3701.81	254167	281174	4	6	0.25	0.077	3.7	-0.51	D	2
			3744.66	254294	280992	2	4	0.22	0.091	2.2	-0.74	D	2
			[3726.9]	254167	280992	4	4	0.092	0.019	0.94	-1.12	D	2
51		$^2P^\circ - {}^2P$ (41)	*3651.2*	*254209*	*281590*	6	6	1.2	0.24	17	0.15	D	*ca*
			3628.06	254167	281722	4	4	0.57	0.11	5.3	-0.35	D	2
			3697.09	254294	281335	2	2	0.34	0.070	1.7	-0.86	D	2
			3679.80	254167	281335	4	2	0.36	0.037	1.8	-0.83	D	2
			3644.86	254294	281722	2	4	0.85	0.34	8.2	-0.17	D	2

No.	Transition Array	Multi-plet	λ(Å)	E_i(cm^{-1})	E_k(cm^{-1})	g_i	g_k	A_{ki}(10^8 sec^{-1})	f_{ik}	S(at.u.)	log gf	Accu-racy	Source
52	$2p^43d-$ $2p^4(^3P)4f$	$^4D-^4D°$ (52)	4229.6	279230	302866	20	20	0.39	0.10	29	0.32	D	ca
			4219.76	279139	302831	8	8	0.33	0.089	9.8	−0.15	D	ls
			4231.60	279221	302846	6	6	0.22	0.060	5.0	−0.45	D	ls
			4239.95	279327	302905	4	4	0.15	0.042	2.3	−0.78	D	ls
			4242.20	279425	302991	2	2	0.19	0.052	1.5	−0.98	D	ls
			4217.15	279139	302846	8	6	0.074	0.015	1.6	−0.93	D	ls
			4220.92	279221	302905	6	4	0.14	0.024	2.0	−0.84	D	ls
			4224.57	279327	302991	4	2	0.19	0.026	1.4	−0.99	D	ls
			[4234.3]	279221	302831	6	8	0.055	0.020	1.7	−0.93	D	ls
			4250.68	279327	302846	4	6	0.090	0.036	2.0	−0.84	D	ls
			4257.82	279425	302905	2	4	0.096	0.052	1.5	−0.98	D	ls
53		$^4F-^4F°$ (56)	4394.5	280619	303368	28	28	0.26	0.076	31	0.33	D	ca
			4397.94	280174	302906	10	10	0.24	0.070	10	−0.16	D	ls
			4379.50	280703	303531	8	8	0.20	0.058	6.7	−0.33	D	ls
			4385.00	281028	303827	6	6	0.18	0.053	4.6	−0.50	D	ls
			4430.90	280950	303512	4	4	0.21	0.062	3.6	−0.61	D	ls
			[4280.3]	280174	303531	10	8	0.028	0.0062	0.88	−1.21	D	ls
			[4323.3]	280703	303827	8	6	0.048	0.010	1.2	−1.09	D	ls
			4446.46	281028	303512	6	4	0.052	0.010	0.91	−1.21	D	ls
			4502.52	280703	302906	8	10	0.021	0.0081	0.96	−1.19	D	ls
			4442.67	281028	303531	6	8	0.035	0.014	1.2	−1.08	D	ls
			4369.77	280950	303827	4	6	0.035	0.015	0.88	−1.21	D	ls
54		$^4F-^4G°$ (57)	4360.8	280619	303544	28	36	2.4	0.89	360	1.39	D	ca
			4290.40	280174	303476	10	12	2.5	0.83	120	0.92	D	ls
			4391.94	280703	303465	8	10	2.2	0.79	91	0.80	D	ls
			4409.30	281028	303701	6	8	2.0	0.79	69	0.68	D	ls
			4413.20	280950	303602	4	6	2.0	0.89	52	0.55	D	ls
			[4292.4]	280174	303465	10	10	0.20	0.056	7.9	−0.25	D	ls
			[4346.9]	280703	303701	8	8	0.33	0.093	11	−0.13	D	ls
			4428.54	281028	303602	6	6	0.33	0.096	8.4	−0.24	D	ls
			[4249.2]	280174	303701	10	8	0.0073	0.0016	0.22	−1.80	D	ls
			4365.72	280703	303602	8	6	0.012	0.0026	0.30	−1.68	D	ls

Forbidden Transitions

Naqvi's calculation [1] of the one possible transition in the ground state configuration $2p^5$ is the only available source. The line strength should be quite accurate, since it does not sensitively depend on the choice of the interaction parameters.

Reference

[1] Naqvi, A. M., Thesis Harvard (1951).

Ne II. Forbidden Transitions

No.	Transition Array	Multiplet	λ(Å)	E_i(cm^{-1})	E_k(cm^{-1})	g_i	g_k	Type of Transition	A_{ki}(sec^{-1})	S(at.u.)	Accu-racy	Source
1	$2p^5-2p^5$	$^2P°-^2P°$	[12.78×10^4]	0	782	4	2	m	0.00859	1.33	B	1

Ne III.

Ground State $1s^22s^22p^4\,{}^3P_2$

Ionization Potential $63.5\text{ eV} = 512312\text{ cm}^{-1}$

Allowed Transitions

List of tabulated lines:

Wavelength [Å]	No.	Wavelength [Å]	No.	Wavelength [Å]	No.
227.24	13	283.894	5	2163.5	17
227.42	12	301.124	7	2163.7	17
227.49	12	308.559	9	2163.77	17
227.57	13	313.048	4	2412.73	18
227.72	13	313.677	4	2412.94	18
227.73	12	313.92	4	2413.18	18
227.76	12	379.308	2	2413.54	18
227.82	12	427.840	3	2413.78	18
227.90	12	488.103	1	2590.04	14
228.85	11	488.868	1	2593.60	14
228.88	11	489.501	1	2595.68	14
228.91	11	489.641	1	2610.03	16
229.19	11	490.310	1	2611.42	16
229.22	11	491.050	1	2612.5	16
229.34	11	2086.96	19	2613.41	16
251.145	10	2087.44	19	2614.51	16
251.558	10	2088.92	19	2615.87	16
251.726	10	2089.43	19	2677.90	15
267.059	6	2092.44	19	2678.64	15
267.516	6	2095.54	19		
267.709	6	2159.44	17		
282.50	8	2159.60	17		
283.178	5	2160.88	17		
283.206	5	2161.04	17		
283.690	5	2161.22	17		

The values for the majority of the transitions are taken from the self-consistent field calculations (with exchange) by Weiss[1]. These calculations do not include the important effects of configuration interaction; hence, fairly large uncertainties must be expected in most cases. The average of the dipole length and velocity approximations is adopted [1].

For the $2s^22p^4\,{}^1S - 2s2p^5\,{}^1P°$ transition a value is available from the calculations of Bolotin et al. [2] which include configuration interaction in a limited way. Again, large uncertainties are to be expected.

References

[1] Weiss, A. W., private communication (1965).
[2] Bolotin, A. B., Shironas, I. I., and Braiman, M. Yu., Vilniaus Valstybinio v. Kapsuko vardo universiteto Mokslo Darbai, **33**, matematika, fizika, **9**, 107–112 (1960).

Ne III. Allowed Transitions

No.	Transition Array	Multiplet	λ(Å)	E_i(cm^{-1})	E_k(cm^{-1})	g_i	g_k	A_{ki}(10^8 sec^{-1})	f_{ik}	S(at.u.)	log gf	Accuracy	Source
1	$2s^2 2p^4 -$ $2s2p^5$	$^3P - {}^3P°$ (1 uv)	489.54	317	204589	9	9	71	0.26	3.7	0.36	E	1
			489.501	0	204292	5	5	52	0.19	1.5	-0.03	E	ls
			489.641	643	204879	3	3	18	0.064	0.31	-0.72	E	ls
			488.103	0	204879	5	3	30	0.063	0.51	-0.50	E	ls
			488.868	643	205204	3	1	71	0.085	0.41	-0.59	E	ls
			491.050	643	204292	3	5	17	0.11	0.51	-0.50	E	ls
			490.310	927	204879	1	3	23	0.25	0.41	-0.60	E	ls
2		$^1D - {}^1P°$ (6 uv)	379.308	25841	289479	5	3	210	0.27	1.7	0.13	E	1
3		$^1S - {}^1P°$ (9 uv)	427.840	55747	289479	1	3	16	0.13	0.19	-0.87	E	2
4	$2p^4 -$ $2p^3(^4S°)3s$	$^3P - {}^3S°$ (2 uv)	313.35	317	319445	9	3	81	0.040	0.37	-0.45	E	1
			313.048	0	319445	5	3	46	0.041	0.21	-0.69	E	ls
			313.677	643	319445	3	3	26	0.039	0.12	-0.93	E	ls
			313.92	927	319445	1	3	9.0	0.040	0.041	-1.40	E	ls
5	$2p^4 -$ $2p^3(^2D°)3s'$	$^3P - {}^3D°$ (3 uv)	283.41	317	353167	9	15	28	0.057	0.48	-0.29	E	1
			283.206	0	353148	5	7	28	0.047	0.22	-0.63	E	ls
			283.690	643	353177	3	5	21	0.043	0.12	-0.89	E	ls
			283.894	927	353197	1	3	16	0.057	0.053	-1.25	E	ls
			283.178	0	353177	5	5	7.1	0.0086	0.040	-1.37	E	ls
			283.690	643	353197	3	3	12	0.014	0.040	-1.37	E	ls
			283.178	0	353197	5	3	0.80	5.8×10^{-4}	0.0027	-2.54	E	ls
6	$2p^4 -$ $2p^3(^2P°)3s''$	$^3P - {}^3P°$ (4 uv)	267.29	317	374448	9	9	32	0.034	0.27	-0.51	E	1
			267.059	0	374434	5	5	23	0.025	0.11	-0.90	E	ls
			267.516	643	374461	3	3	8.1	0.0087	0.023	-1.58	E	ls
			267.059	0	374461	5	3	13	0.0086	0.038	-1.36	E	ls
			267.516	643	374478	3	1	32	0.011	0.030	-1.47	E	ls
			267.516	643	374434	3	5	8.0	0.014	0.038	-1.37	E	ls
			267.709	927	374461	1	3	11	0.034	0.030	-1.47	E	ls
7	$2p^4 -$ $2p^3(^2D°)3s'$	$^1D - {}^1D°$ (7 uv)	301.124	25841	357930	5	5	71	0.097	0.48	-0.32	E	1
8	$2p^4 -$ $2p^3(^2P°)3s''$	$^1D - {}^1P°$ (8 uv)	282.50	25841	379834	5	3	45	0.032	0.15	-0.79	E	1
9	$2p^4 -$ $2p^3(^2P°)3s''$	$^1S - {}^1P°$ (10 uv)	308.559	55747	379834	1	3	32	0.14	0.14	-0.86	E	1
10	$2p^4 -$ $2p^3(^4S°)3d$	$^3P - {}^3D°$ (5 uv)	251.33	317	398203	9	15	140	0.21	1.6	0.29	D$-$	1
			251.145	0	398211	5	7	140	0.18	0.75	-0.04	D$-$	ls
			251.558	643	398197	3	5	100	0.16	0.40	-0.32	D$-$	ls
			251.726	927	398193	1	3	76	0.22	0.18	-0.66	D$-$	ls
			251.145	0	398197	5	5	33	0.031	0.13	-0.80	D$-$	ls
			251.558	643	398193	3	3	55	0.052	0.13	-0.80	D$-$	ls
			251.145	0	398193	5	3	3.8	0.0022	0.0089	-1.97	D$-$	ls
11	$2p^4 -$ $2p^3(^2D°)3d'$	$^3P - {}^3D°$	229.06	317	436891	9	15	73	0.096	0.65	-0.06	D$-$	1
			[228.91]	0	436845	5	7	72	0.080	0.30	-0.40	D$-$	ls
			[229.22]	643	436914	3	5	54	0.071	0.16	-0.67	D$-$	ls
			[229.34]	927	436959	1	3	40	0.095	0.072	-1.02	D$-$	ls
			[228.88]	0	436914	5	5	18	0.014	0.054	-1.14	D$-$	ls
			[229.19]	643	436959	3	3	30	0.024	0.054	-1.15	D$-$	ls
			[228.85]	0	436959	5	3	2.0	9.6×10^{-4}	0.0036	-2.32	D$-$	ls

No.	Transition Array	Multi-plet	λ(Å)	E_i(cm⁻¹)	E_k(cm⁻¹)	g_i	g_k	A_{ki}(10⁸ sec⁻¹)	f_{ik}	S(at.u.)	log gf	Accu-racy	Source
12		³P — ³P°	227.62	317	439646	9	9	160	0.12	0.83	0.04	D —	1
			[227.49]	0	439586	5	5	120	0.093	0.35	−0.33	D —	*ls*
			[227.76]	643	439708	3	3	39	0.031	0.069	−1.04	D —	*ls*
			[227.42]	0	439708	5	3	69	0.032	0.12	−0.80	D —	*ls*
			[227.73]	643	439760	3	1	160	0.041	0.092	−0.91	D —	*ls*
			[227.82]	643	439586	3	5	41	0.053	0.12	−0.80	D —	*ls*
			[227.90]	927	439708	1	3	52	0.12	0.092	−0.91	D —	*ls*
13		³P — ³S°	227.40	317	440065	9	3	210	0.055	0.37	−0.31	D —	1
			[227.24]	0	440065	5	3	120	0.056	0.21	−0.55	D —	*ls*
			[227.57]	643	440065	3	3	69	0.053	0.12	−0.80	D —	*ls*
			[227.72]	927	440065	1	3	23	0.055	0.041	−1.26	D —	*ls*
14	2p³3s — 2p³(⁴S°)3p	⁵S° — ⁵P (11 uv)	2592.3	[314148]	[352712]	5	15	2.5	0.76	32	0.58	D	*ca*
			2590.04	[314148]	[352746]	5	7	2.5	0.36	15	0.25	D	*ls*
			2593.60	[314148]	[352693]	5	5	2.5	0.25	11	0.10	D	*ls*
			2595.68	[314148]	[352662]	5	3	2.5	0.15	6.5	−0.12	D	*ls*
15		³S° — ³P (12 uv)	2678.2	319445	356773	3	9	2.4	0.78	20	0.37	D	*ca*
			2677.90	319445	356777	3	5	2.4	0.43	11	0.11	D	*ls*
			2678.64	319445	356766	3	3	2.4	0.26	6.8	−0.11	D	*ls*
			2677.90	319445	356777	3	1	2.4	0.086	2.3	−0.59	D	*ls*
16	2p³3s′ — 2p³(²D°)3p′	³D° — ³F	2612.4	353167	391435	15	21	2.4	0.34	44	0.71	D	*ca*
			2610.03	353148	391450	7	9	2.4	0.32	19	0.34	D	*ls*
			2613.41	353177	391430	5	7	2.1	0.31	13	0.18	D	*ls*
			2615.87	353197	391414	3	5	2.0	0.34	8.9	0.01	D	*ls*
			2611.42	353148	391430	7	7	0.27	0.027	1.6	−0.72	D	*ls*
			2614.51	353177	391414	5	5	0.37	0.038	1.6	−0.72	D	*ls*
			[2612.5]	353148	391414	7	5	0.011	7.8×10^{-4}	0.047	−2.26	D	*ls*
17	2p³3p — 2p³(⁴S°)3d	⁵P — ⁵D°	2163.77	[352746]	[398947]	7	9	6.5	0.59	29.4	0.62	C —	*ca, ls*
			2161.22	[352693]	[398949]	5	7	4.36	0.428	15.2	0.330	C —	*ca, ls*
			2159.60	[352662]	[398952]	3	5	2.30	0.268	5.7	−0.096	C —	*ca, ls*
			[2163.7]	[352746]	[398949]	7	7	2.25	0.158	7.9	0.044	C —	*ca, ls*
			2161.04	[352693]	[398952]	5	5	3.82	0.267	9.5	0.126	C —	*ca, ls*
			2159.44	[352662]	[398956]	3	3	4.92	0.344	7.3	0.014	C —	*ca, ls*
			[2163.5]	[352746]	[398952]	7	5	0.450	0.0227	1.12	−0.80	C —	*ca, ls*
			2160.88	[352693]	[398956]	5	3	1.64	0.069	2.45	−0.464	C —	*ca, ls*
18		³P — ³D°	2413.0	356773	398203	9	15	4.87	0.71	51	0.80	C —	*ca*
			2412.73	356777	398212	5	7	4.87	0.59	23.6	0.473	C —	*ls*
			2412.94	356766	398197	3	5	3.65	0.53	12.7	0.202	C —	*ls*
			2413.78	356777	398193	1	3	2.70	0.71	5.6	−0.150	C —	*ls*
			2413.54	356777	398197	5	5	1.22	0.106	4.22	−0.275	C —	*ls*
			2413.18	356766	398193	3	3	2.03	0.177	4.22	−0.275	C —	*ls*
			2413.78	356777	398193	5	3	0.135	0.0071	0.281	−1.451	C —	*ls*
19	2p³3p′ — 2p³(²D°)3d′	³D — ³D°	2091.7	389099	436891	15	15	3.92	0.257	26.6	0.59	C —	*ca*
			2095.54	389139	436845	7	7	3.47	0.228	11.0	0.204	C —	*ls*
			2089.43	389069	436914	5	5	2.73	0.179	6.2	−0.048	C —	*ls*
			2086.96	389058	436959	3	3	2.96	0.194	3.99	−0.236	C —	*ls*
			2092.44	389139	436914	7	5	0.61	0.0286	1.38	−0.70	C —	*ls*
			2087.44	389069	436959	5	3	0.99	0.0387	1.33	−0.71	C —	*ls*
			2092.44	389069	436845	5	7	0.435	0.0400	1.38	−0.70	C —	*ls*
			2088.92	389058	436914	3	5	0.59	0.064	1.33	−0.71	C —	*ls*

Forbidden Transitions

The adopted valués represent, as in the case of F II, the work of Garstang [1] and Naqvi [2], who independently have done essentially the same calculations and have arrived at very similar results. For the selection of values, the same considerations as for F II have been applied.

References

[1] Garstang, R. H., Monthly Notices Roy. Astron. Soc. **111**, 115–124 (1951).
[2] Naqvi, A. M., Thesis Harvard (1951).

Ne III. Forbidden Transitions

No.	Transition Array	Multi-plet	$\lambda(\text{Å})$	$E_i(\text{cm}^{-1})$	$E_k(\text{cm}^{-1})$	g_i	g_k	Type of Transition	$A_{ki}(\text{sec}^{-1})$	$S(\text{at.u.})$	Accu-racy	Source
1	$2p^4-2p^4$	$^3P-^3P$										
			$[15.55 \times 10^4]$	0	642.9	5	3	m	0.00599	2.50	B	1, 2
			$[15.55 \times 10^4]$	0	642.9	5	3	e	2.60×10^{-9}	0.422	C	1
			$[10.79 \times 10^4]$	0	927	5	1	e	2.03×10^{-8}	0.176	C	1
			$[36.19 \times 10^4]$	642.9	927	3	1	m	0.00115	2.00	B	1, 2
2		$^3P-^1D$ (1 F)										
			3868.74	0	25841	5	5	m	0.170	0.00182	C	2
			3868.74	0	25841	5	5	e	3.0×10^{-4}	7.7×10^{-4}	D	1
			3967.51	642.9	25841	3	5	m	0.052	6.1×10^{-4}	C	2
			3967.51	642.9	25841	3	5	e	3.8×10^{-5}	1.1×10^{-4}	D	1
			$[4012.7]$	927	25841	1	5	e	1.2×10^{-5}	3.7×10^{-5}	D	1
3		$^3P-^1S$										
			$[1793.8]$	0	55747	5	1	e	0.0051	5.6×10^{-5}	D	1
			$[1814.8]$	642.9	55747	3	1	m	2.20	4.87×10^{-4}	C	1
4		$^1D-^1S$ (2 F)										
			3342.9	25841	55747	5	1	e	2.80	0.70	C	1

Ne IV.

Ground State $1s^2 2s^2 2p^3\ {}^4S^o_{3/2}$

Ionization Potential $97.02\ \text{eV} = 782768\ \text{cm}^{-1}$

Allowed Transitions

List of tabulated lines:

Wavelength [Å]	No.	Wavelength [Å]	No.	Wavelength [Å]	No.
208.485	7	541.124	1	2262.08	14
208.734	7	542.076	1	2264.54	14
208.899	7	543.884	1	2285.79	12
212.556	8	2018.44	13	2293.14	12
357.831	3	2022.19	13	2293.49	12
358.70	3	2029.2	13	2350.84	9
387.13	6	2033.5	13	2352.52	9
388.23	6	2174.4	10	2357.96	9
421.584	5	2176.1	10	2362.68	9
469.77	2	2188.0	10	2363.28	11
469.817	2	2192.6	10	2365.49	11
469.865	2	2203.88	10	2372.16	9
521.730	4	2206.4	10	2384.20	9
521.74	4	2220.81	10	2384.95	9
521.810	4	2258.02	14	2404.28	11
				2405.19	9

The values for several of the transitions are taken from the self-consistent field calculations (with exchange) by Weiss [1]. These calculations do not include the important effects of configuration interaction; hence, fairly large uncertainties must be expected. The average of the dipole length and velocity approximations is adopted [1].

For the $2s^2 2p^3\ {}^2P^o - 2s2p^4\ {}^2D, {}^2S$ transitions values are available from the calculations of Levinson et al. [2] which include configuration interaction in a limited way. Again, large uncertainties are to be expected.

References

[1] Weiss, A. W., private communication (1965).
[2] Levinson, I. B., Bolotin, A. B., and Levin, L. I., Trudy Vil'nyusskogo un. 5, 49–55 (1956).

Ne IV. Allowed Transitions

No.	Transition Array	Multiplet	λ(Å)	E_i(cm^{-1})	E_k(cm^{-1})	g_i	g_k	A_{ki}(10^8 sec^{-1})	f_{ik}	S(at.u.)	log gf	Accuracy	Source
1	$2s^22p^3-$ $2s2p^4$	$^4S°-^4P$ (1 uv)	542.82	0	184222	4	12	25	0.34	2.4	0.13	E	1
			543.884	0	183860	4	6	25	0.17	1.2	−0.17	E	ls
			542.076	0	184477	4	4	25	0.11	0.80	−0.35	E	ls
			541.124	0	184799	4	2	25	0.056	0.40	−0.65	E	ls
2		$^2D°-^2D$ (4 uv)	469.84	[40968]	[253808]	10	10	51	0.17	2.6	0.23	E	1
			469.817	[40950]	[253799]	6	6	49	0.16	1.5	−0.01	E	ls
			469.817	[40995]	[253822]	4	4	46	0.15	0.94	−0.22	E	ls
			[469.77]	[40950]	[253822]	6	4	4.9	0.011	0.10	−1.19	E	ls
			469.865	[40995]	[253799]	4	6	3.3	0.016	0.10	−1.19	E	ls
3		$^2D°-^2P$ (5 uv)	358.40	[40968]	[319985]	10	6	150	0.18	2.1	0.25	E	1
			358.70	[40950]	[319751]	6	4	140	0.18	1.3	0.04	E	ls
			357.831	[40995]	[320452]	4	2	150	0.15	0.70	−0.23	E	ls
			358.70	[40995]	[319751]	4	4	15	0.030	0.14	−0.93	E	ls
4		$^2P°-^2D$ (8 uv)	521.78	[62155]	[253808]	6	10	7.7	0.052	0.54	−0.50	E	2
			521.810	[62157]	[253799]	4	6	7.6	0.047	0.32	−0.73	E	ls
			521.730	[62150]	[253822]	2	4	6.4	0.052	0.18	−0.98	E	ls
			[521.74]	[62157]	[253822]	4	4	1.3	0.0052	0.036	−1.68	E	ls
5		$^2P°-^2S$ (9 uv)	421.584	[62155]	[299351]	6	2	120	0.11	0.92	−0.18	E	2
6		$^2P°-^2P$ (10 uv)	387.85	[62155]	[319985]	6	6	75	0.17	1.3	0.01	E	1
			388.23	[62157]	[319751]	4	4	62	0.14	0.72	−0.25	E	ls
			387.13	[62150]	[320452]	2	2	51	0.11	0.29	−0.64	E	ls
			387.13	[62157]	[320452]	4	2	24	0.027	0.14	−0.96	E	ls
			388.23	[62150]	[319751]	2	4	12	0.055	0.14	−0.96	E	ls
7	$2p^3-$ $2p^2(^3P)3s$	$^4S°-^4P$ (2 uv)	208.63	0	479309	4	12	48	0.095	0.26	−0.42	E	1
			208.485	0	479662	4	6	48	0.047	0.13	−0.72	E	ls
			208.734	0	479083	4	4	48	0.032	0.087	−0.90	E	ls
			208.899	0	478701	4	2	48	0.016	0.043	−1.20	E	ls
8	$2p^3-$ $2p^2(^1D)3s'$	$^2D°-^2D$ (6 uv)	212.556	[40968]	[511681]	10	10	74	0.050	0.35	−0.30	E	1
9	$2p^23s-$ $2p^2(^3P)3p$	$^4P-^4D°$	2361.5	479309	521643	12	20	2.5	0.34	32	0.62	D	ca
			2357.96	479662	522058	6	8	2.5	0.28	13	0.22	D	ls
			2352.52	479083	521578	4	6	1.7	0.22	6.7	−0.06	D	ls
			2350.84	478701	521226	2	4	1.0	0.17	2.7	−0.46	D	ls
			2384.95	479662	521578	6	6	0.72	0.061	2.9	−0.43	D	ls
			2372.16	479083	521226	4	4	1.3	0.11	3.4	−0.36	D	ls
			2362.68	478701	521013	2	2	2.0	0.17	2.7	−0.47	D	ls
			2405.19	479662	521226	6	4	0.12	0.0067	0.32	−1.39	D	ls
			2384.20	479083	521013	4	2	0.40	0.017	0.53	−1.17	D	ls
10		$^4P-^4P°$	2197.5	479309	524802	12	12	3.1	0.23	20	0.43	D	ca
			2203.88	479662	525022	6	6	2.2	0.16	6.8	−0.03	D	ls
			[2192.6]	479083	524677	4	4	0.42	0.030	0.86	−0.92	D	ls
			[2188.0]	478701	524391	2	2	0.52	0.037	0.54	−1.13	D	ls
			2220.81	479662	524677	6	4	1.4	0.067	2.9	−0.40	D	ls
			[2206.4]	479083	524391	4	2	2.5	0.093	2.7	−0.43	D	ls
			[2176.1]	479083	525022	4	6	0.96	0.10	2.9	−0.39	D	ls
			[2174.4]	478701	524677	2	4	1.3	0.19	2.7	−0.42	D	ls

766–655 O–66—11

No.	Transition Array	Multi-plet	$\lambda(\text{Å})$	$E_i(\text{cm}^{-1})$	$E_k(\text{cm}^{-1})$	g_i	g_k	$A_{ki}(10^8$ $\text{sec}^{-1})$	f_{ik}	$S(\text{at.u.})$	$\log gf$	Accu-racy	Source
11		$^2P - ^2D°$	*2366.7*	[*488934*]	[*531174*]	6	10	2.6	0.37	17	0.35	D	*ca*
			2363.28	[489161]	[531462]	4	6	2.7	0.33	10	0.12	D	*ls*
			2365.49	[488479]	[530741]	2	4	2.2	0.37	5.7	−0.13	D	*ls*
			2404.28	[489161]	[530741]	4	4	0.42	0.036	1.1	−0.84	D	*ls*
12	$2p^23s' -$ $2p^2(^1D)3p'$	$^2D - ^2F°$	*2289.1*	[*511681*]	[*555353*]	10	14	2.8	0.30	23	0.48	D	*ca*
			2285.79	[511678]	[555413]	6	8	2.8	0.29	13	0.24	D	*ls*
			2293.49	[511685]	[555273]	4	6	2.6	0.30	9.2	0.08	D	*ls*
			2293.14	[511678]	[555273]	6	6	0.18	0.014	0.65	−1.06	D	*ls*
13		$^2D - ^2D°$	*2031.7*	[*511681*]	[*560885*]	10	10	4.0	0.25	17	0.39	D	*ca*
			2022.19	[511678]	[560846]	6	6	3.8	0.23	9.3	0.14	D	*ls*
			2018.44	[511685]	[560943]	4	4	3.7	0.22	6.0	−0.05	D	*ls*
			[2029.2]	[511678]	[560943]	6	4	0.40	0.017	0.66	−1.00	D	*ls*
			[2033.5]	[511685]	[560846]	4	6	0.27	0.025	0.66	−1.00	D	*ls*
14	$2p^23s'' -$ $2p^2(^1S)3p''$	$^6S - ^6P°$	*2260.8*	[*538500*]	[*582718*]	6	18	2.7	0.63	28	0.58	D	*ca*
			2258.02	[538500]	[582773]	6	8	2.7	0.28	12	0.23	D	*ls*
			2262.08	[538500]	[582693]	6	6	2.7	0.21	9.4	0.10	D	*ls*
			2264.54	[538500]	[582645]	6	4	2.7	0.14	6.2	−0.08	D	*ls*

Forbidden Transitions

Garstang's 1960 calculations [1] are exclusively used, since it is felt that the important effects of configuration interaction are partially taken into account in this work and a reliable estimate of the quadrupole integral is provided (see also general introduction).

Reference

[1] Garstang, R. H., Monthly Notices Roy. Astron. Soc. **120**, 201 (1960).

Ne IV. Forbidden Transitions

No.	Transition Array	Multi-plet	$\lambda(\text{Å})$	$E_i(\text{cm}^{-1})$	$E_k(\text{cm}^{-1})$	g_i	g_k	Type of Transition	$A_{ki}(\text{sec}^{-1})$	$S(\text{at.u.})$	Accu-racy	Source
1	$2p^3 - 2p^3$	$^4S° - ^2D°$	[2441.3]	0	40950	4	6	m	1.80×10^{-4}	5.8×10^{-7}	C	1
			[2441.3]	0	40950	4	6	e	4.1×10^{-4}	1.3×10^{-4}	D	1
			[2438.6]	0	40995	4	4	m	0.0053	1.14×10^{-5}	C	1
			[2438.6]	0	40995	4	4	e	2.7×10^{-4}	5.5×10^{-5}	D	1
2		$^4S° - ^2P°$	[1609.0]	0	62150	4	2	m	0.53	1.64×10^{-4}	C	1
			[1609.0]	0	62150	4	2	e	8.6×10^{-6}	1.1×10^{-7}	D	1
			[1608.8]	0	62157	4	4	m	1.33	8.2×10^{-4}	C	1
			[1608.8]	0	62157	4	4	e	1.5×10^{-7}	3.8×10^{-9}	D	1
3		$^2D° - ^2D°$	$[22.2 \times 10^5]$	40950	40995	6	4	m	1.48×10^{-6}	2.40	C+	1
			$[22.2 \times 10^5]$	40950	40995	6	4	e	1.1×10^{-17}	0.0014	D	1

No.	Transition Array	Multiplet	λ(Å)	E_i(cm^{-1})	E_k(cm^{-1})	g_i	g_k	Type of Transition	A_{ki}(sec^{-1})	S(at.u.)	Accuracy	Source
4		$^2D°-{}^2P°$ (1 F)										
			4714.25	40950	62150	6	2	e	0.110	0.305	C	1
			4715.61	40950	62157	6	4	m	0.210	0.00327	C	1
			4715.61	40950	62157	6	4	e	0.191	1.06	C	1
			4724.15	40995	62157	4	4	m	0.358	0.0056	C	1
			4724.15	40995	62157	4	4	e	0.079	0.439	C	1
			4725.62	40995	62150	4	2	m	0.229	0.00179	C	1
			4725.62	40995	62150	4	2	e	0.160	0.446	C	1
5		$^2P°-{}^2P°$										
			[15.6 × 10^6]	62150	62157	2	4	m	2.36 × 10^{-9}	1.33	C+	1
			[15.6 × 10^6]	62150	62157	2	4	e	2.6 × 10^{-22}	5.7 × 10^{-4}	D	1

Ne V.

Ground State $1s^2 2s^2 2p^2\ {}^3P_0$

Ionization Potential   126.3 eV = 1018634 cm^{-1}

Allowed Transitions

List of tabulated lines:

Wavelength [Å]	No.	Wavelength [Å]	No.	Wavelength [Å]	No.
142.44	8	173.932	6	572.336	1
142.52	8	357.955	3	2224.12	14
142.58	8	358.472	3	2227.42	14
142.66	8	359.385	3	2232.41	14
142.72	8	365.594	5	2236.29	14
143.22	7	416.198	4	2245.48	14
143.27	7	480.406	2	2256.05	14
143.30	7	481.281	2	2257.9	14
143.34	7	481.361	2	2259.57	13
143.42	7	482.987	2	2263.39	13
143.45	7	568.418	1	2265.71	13
147.13	11	569.759	1	2274.54	14
148.78	10	569.830	1	2282.61	13
151.42	9	572.03	1	2306.31	13
156.61	12	572.106	1	2330.3	13

For the $2s^2 2p^2 - 2s2p^3$ transition array, values are available from the calculations of Bolotin et al. [1] which include the important effects of configuration interaction only in a limited way. Hence, fairly large uncertainties must be expected.

The values for several other transitions are taken from the self-consistent field calculations (with exchange) by Weiss [2]. These calculations neglect the effects of configuration interaction entirely. The average of the dipole length and the velocity approximations is adopted [2].

References

[1] Bolotin, A. B., Levinson, I. B., and Levin, L. I., Soviet Phys.—JETP **2**, 391–395 (1956).

[2] Weiss, A. W., private communication (1965).

No.	Transition Array	Multi-plet	$\lambda(\text{Å})$	$E_i(\text{cm}^{-1})$	$E_k(\text{cm}^{-1})$	g_i	g_k	$A_{ki}(10^8 \text{sec}^{-1})$	f_{ik}	$S(\text{at.u.})$	$\log gf$	Accu-racy	Source
1	$2s^2 2p^2 -$ $2s2p^3$	$^3P - ^3D°$ (1 uv)	571.04	756	175876	9	15	14	0.11	1.9	0.00	E	1
			572.336	1112	175834	5	7	14	0.094	0.89	−0.33	E	ls
			569.830	414	175905	3	5	10	0.084	0.47	−0.60	E	ls
			568.418	0	175927	1	3	7.7	0.11	0.21	−0.95	E	ls
			572.106	1112	175905	5	5	3.5	0.017	0.16	−1.07	E	ls
			569.759	414	175927	3	3	5.8	0.028	0.16	−1.07	E	ls
			[572.03]	1112	175927	5	3	0.40	0.0012	0.011	−2.23	E	ls
2		$^3P - ^3P°$ (2 uv)	482.15	756	208161	9	9	40	0.14	2.0	0.10	E	1
			482.987	1112	208157	5	5	30	0.10	0.83	−0.28	E	ls
			481.361	414	208157	3	3	10	0.036	0.17	−0.97	E	ls
			482.987	1112	208157	5	3	17	0.035	0.28	−0.75	E	ls
			481.281	414	208193	3	1	40	0.046	0.22	−0.86	E	ls'
			481.361	414	208157	3	5	10	0.059	0.28	−0.75	E	ls
			480.406	0	208157	1	3	13	0.14	0.22	−0.86	E	ls
3		$^3P - ^3S°$ (3 uv)	358.93	756	279365	9	3	220	0.14	1.5	0.10	E	1
			359.385	1112	279365	5	3	120	0.14	0.83	−0.15	E	ls
			358.472	414	279365	3	3	73	0.14	0.50	−0.37	E	ls
			357.955	0	279365	1	3	25	0.14	0.17	−0.84	E	ls
4		$^1D - ^1D°$ (4 uv)	416.198	30294	270564	5	5	110	0.28	1.9	0.14	E	1
5		$^1D - ^1P°$ (5 uv)	365.594	30294	303812	5	3	150	0.18	1.1	−0.04	E	1
6	$2p^2 -$ $2p(^2P°)3s$	$^1D - ^1P°$ (6 uv)	173.932	30294	605231	5	3	230	0.063	0.18	−0.50	E	2
7	$2p^2 -$ $2p(^2P°)3d$	$^3P - ^3D°$	143.32	756	698517	9	15	1200	0.61	2.6	0.74	D −	2
			[143.34]	1112	698735	5	7	1200	0.51	1.2	0.41	D −	ls
			[143.27]	414	698382	3	5	900	0.46	0.65	0.14	D −	ls
			[143.22]	0	698231	1	3	670	0.62	0.29	−0.21	D −	ls
			[143.42]	1112	698382	5	5	300	0.093	0.22	−0.33	D −	ls
			[143.30]	414	698231	3	3	500	0.16	0.22	−0.33	D −	ls
			[143.45]	1112	698231	5	3	32	0.0059	0.014	−1.53	D −	ls
8		$^3P - ^3P°$	142.61	756	701945	9	9	670	0.20	0.86	0.26	D −	2
			[142.72]	1112	701765	5	5	500	0.15	0.36	−0.12	D −	ls
			[142.52]	414	702074	3	3	170	0.051	0.072	−0.81	D −	ls
			[142.66]	1112	702074	5	3	280	0.051	0.12	−0.59	D −	ls
			[142.44]	414	702459	3	1	670	0.068	0.096	−0.69	D −	ls
			[142.58]	414	701765	3	5	170	0.085	0.12	−0.59	D −	ls
			[142.44]	0	702074	1	3	220	0.20	0.096	−0.69	D −	ls
9		$^1D - ^1D°$	[151.42]	30294	690691	5	5	400	0.14	0.34	−0.17	D −	2
10		$^1D - ^1P°$	[148.78]	30294	702412	5	3	37	0.0073	0.018	−1.43	D −	2
11		$^1D - ^1F°$	[147.13]	30294	709956	5	7	1300	0.58	1.4	0.46	D −	2
12		$^1S - ^1P°$	[156.61]	63900	702412	1	3	690	0.76	0.39	−0.12	D −	2

No.	Transition Array	Multiplet	$\lambda(\text{Å})$	$E_i(\text{cm}^{-1})$	$E_k(\text{cm}^{-1})$	g_i	g_k	$A_{ki}(10^8 \text{ sec}^{-1})$	f_{ik}	$S(\text{at.u.})$	$\log gf$	Accuracy	Source
13	$2p3s -$ $2p(^2P°)3p$	$^3P° - {}^3D$	2269.0	*597083*	*641142*	9	15	2.2	0.28	19	0.40	D	*ca*
			2265.71	597523	641646	5	7	2.2	0.24	8.9	0.07	D	*ls*
			2259.57	596626	640868	3	5	1.7	0.21	4.7	−0.20	D	*ls*
			2263.39	596254	640422	1	3	1.2	0.28	2.1	−0.55	D	*ls*
			2306.31	597523	640868	5	5	0.52	0.042	1.6	−0.68	D	*ls*
			2282.61	596626	640422	3	3	0.89	0.070	1.6	−0.68	D	*ls*
			[2330.3]	597523	640422	5	3	0.056	0.0027	0.11	−1.86	D	*ls*
14	$2s2p^23s -$ $2s2p^2(^4P)3p$	$^5P - {}^5D°$											
			2232.41	698504	743285	7	9	0.20	0.019	0.96	−0.88	D	*ca, ls*
			2227.42	697935	742816	5	7	0.13	0.014	0.50	−1.17	D	*ca, ls*
			2224.12	697507	742455	3	5	0.069	0.0085	0.19	−1.59	D	*ca, ls*
			2256.05	698504	742816	7	7	0.063	0.0048	0.25	−1.47	D	*ca, ls*
			2245.48	697935	742455	5	5	0.11	0.0084	0.31	−1.37	D	*ca, ls*
			2236.29	697507	742210	3	3	0.15	0.011	0.24	−1.49	D	*ca, ls*
			2274.54	698504	742455	7	5	0.012	6.8×10^{-4}	0.036	−2.32	D	*ca, ls*
			[2257.9]	697935	742210	5	3	0.047	0.0022	0.080	−1.97	D	*ca, ls*

Forbidden Transitions

The adopted values represent, as in the case of F IV, the work of Garstang [1] and Naqvi [2], who independently have done essentially the same calculations and have arrived at very similar results. For the selection of values, the same considerations as for F IV have been applied.

References

[1] Garstang, R. H., Monthly Notices Roy. Astron. Soc. **111**, 115–124 (1951).
[2] Naqvi, A. M., Thesis Harvard (1951).

Ne V. Forbidden Transitions

No.	Transition Array	Multiplet	$\lambda(\text{Å})$	$E_i(\text{cm}^{-1})$	$E_k(\text{cm}^{-1})$	g_i	g_k	Type of Transition	$A_{ki}(\text{sec}^{-1})$	$S(\text{at.u.})$	Accuracy	Source
1	$2p^2 - 2p^2$	$^3P - {}^3P$										
			$[24.15 \times 10^4]$	0	414	1	3	m	0.00129	2.00	B	1, 2
			$[8.990 \times 10^4]$	0	1112	1	5	e	5.2×10^{-9}	0.091	C	1
			$[14.32 \times 10^4]$	414	1112	3	5	m	0.00459	2.50	B	1, 2
			$[14.32 \times 10^4]$	414	1112	3	5	e	1.10×10^{-9}	0.197	C	1
2		$^3P - {}^1D$ (1 F)										
			[3300.0]	0	30294	1	5	e	1.9×10^{-5}	2.2×10^{-5}	D	1
			3345.9	414	30294	3	5	m	0.138	9.6×10^{-4}	C	1, 2
			3345.9	414	30294	3	5	e	6.2×10^{-5}	7.7×10^{-5}	D	1
			3425.8	1112	30294	5	5	m	0.382	0.00285	C	1, 2
			3425.8	1112	30294	5	5	e	3.9×10^{-4}	5.5×10^{-4}	D	1
3		$^3P - {}^1S$										
			[1575.2]	414	63900	3	1	m	4.20	6.1×10^{-4}	C	1
			[1592.7]	1112	63900	5	1	e	0.0068	4.1×10^{-5}	D	1
4		$^1D - {}^1S$ (2 F)										
			2972	30294	63900	5	1	e	2.60	0.359	C	1

Ne VI.

Ground State	$1s^2 2s^2 2p \ ^2P^\circ_{1/2}$

Ionization Potential $157.91 \ eV = 1274000 \ cm^{-1}$

Allowed Transitions

List of tabulated lines:

Wavelength [Å]	No.	Wavelength [Å]	No.	Wavelength [Å]	No.
122.49	9	440.404	5	571.00	6
122.69	9	440.46	5	637.90	7
138.39	8	440.60	5	638.19	7
138.64	8	451.843	4	641.26	7
399.82	3	452.745	4	641.55	7
401.14	3	454.072	4	2042.38	10
401.93	3	558.59	1	2055.93	10
403.26	3	562.71	1	2213.1	11
433.176	2	562.80	1	2229.1	11
435.649	2	570.77	6		

The transition probabilities are taken from the self-consistent field calculations (with exchange) by Weiss [1]. These calculations neglect the effects of configuration interaction entirely. The average of the dipole length and velocity approximations is adopted [1].

Reference

[1] Weiss, A. W., private communication (1965).

Ne VI.   Allowed Transitions

No.	Transition Array	Multi-plet	λ(Å)	E_i(cm^{-1})	E_k(cm^{-1})	g_i	g_k	A_{ki}(10^8 sec^{-1})	f_{ik}	S(at.u.)	log gf	Accu-racy	Source
1	$2s^2 2p -$ $2s2p^2$	$^2P^\circ - ^2D$	561.38	873	179004	6	10	17	0.14	1.5	−0.09	E	1
			[562.80]	1310	178992	4	6	17	0.12	0.90	−0.31	E	ls
			[558.59]	0	179021	2	4	15	0.14	0.50	−0.57	E	ls
			[562.71]	1310	179021	4	4	2.8	0.013	0.10	−1.27	E	ls
2		$^2P^\circ - ^2S$	434.82	873	230853	6	2	32	0.030	0.26	−0.74	E	1
			435.649	1310	230853	4	2	21	0.030	0.17	−0.93	E	ls
			433.176	0	230853	2	2	11	0.031	0.087	−1.21	E	ls
3		$^2P^\circ - ^2P$	401.66	873	249839	6	6	100	0.25	2.0	0.18	E	1
			[401.93]	1310	250112	4	4	86	0.21	1.1	−0.08	E	ls
			[401.14]	0	249292	2	2	69	0.17	0.44	−0.48	E	ls
			[403.26]	1310	249292	4	2	34	0.041	0.22	−0.78	E	ls
			[399.82]	0	250112	2	4	17	0.084	0.22	−0.78	E	ls
4	$2s2p^2 - 2p^3$	$^4P - ^4S^\circ$	453.26	[101204]	[321829]	12	4	82	0.084	1.5	0.00	E	1
			454.072	[101600]	[321829]	6	4	41	0.084	0.75	−0.30	E	ls
			452.745	[100954]	[321829]	4	4	27	0.084	0.50	−0.47	E	ls
			451.843	[100513]	[321829]	2	4	14	0.084	0.25	−0.77	E	ls

No.	Transition Array	Multi-plet	$\lambda(\text{Å})$	$E_i(\text{cm}^{-1})$	$E_k(\text{cm}^{-1})$	g_i	g_k	$A_{ki}(10^8 \text{ sec}^{-1})$	f_{ik}	$S(\text{at.u.})$	$\log gf$	Accu-racy	Source
5		^{2}D — ^{2}P°	440.47	179004	406032	10	6	25	0.044	0.64	−0.36	E	1
			440.404	178992	406056	6	4	23	0.044	0.38	−0.58	E	ls
			440.60	179021	405984	4	2	25	0.036	0.21	−0.84	E	ls
			[440.46]	179021	406056	4	4	25	0.0074	0.043	−1.53	E	ls
6		^{2}S — ^{2}P°	570.84	230853	406032	2	6	12	0.17	0.64	−0.47	E	1
			[570.77]	230853	406056	2	4	12	0.11	0.43	−0.64	E	ls
			[571.00]	230853	405984	2	2	12	0.056	0.21	−0.95	E	ls
7		^{2}P — ^{2}P°	640.23	249839	406032	6	6	19	0.12	1.5	−0.15	E	1
			[641.26]	250112	406056	4	4	16	0.098	0.83	−0.41	E	ls
			[638.19]	249292	405984	2	2	13	0.079	0.33	−0.80	E	ls
			[641.55]	250112	405984	4	2	6.5	0.020	0.17	−1.09	E	ls
			[637.90]	249292	406056	2	4	3.3	0.040	0.17	−1.09	E	ls
8	$2p - (^1\text{S})3s$	^{2}P° — ^{2}S	138.55	873	722610	6	2	300	0.029	0.078	−0.77	E	1
			[138.64]	1310	722610	4	2	200	0.028	0.052	−0.94	E	ls
			[138.39]	0	722610	2	2	100	0.029	0.026	−1.24	E	ls
9	$2p - (^1\text{S})3d$	^{2}P° — ^{2}D	122.62	873	816405	6	10	1400	0.54	1.3	0.51	D	1
			[122.69]	1310	816405	4	6	1400	0.48	0.78	0.29	D	ls
			[122.49]	0	816405	2	4	1200	0.53	0.43	0.03	D	ls
			[122.69]	1310	816405	4	4	240	0.054	0.087	−0.67	D	ls
10	$3s - (^1\text{S})3p$	^{2}S — ^{2}P°	2046.9	722610	771449	2	6	2.72	0.51	6.9	0.010	C	1
			2042.38	722610	771557	2	4	2.73	0.342	4.60	−0.165	C	ls
			2055.93	722610	771234	2	2	2.68	0.170	2.30	−0.469	C	ls
11	$3p - (^1\text{S})3d$	^{2}P° — ^{2}D	2223.7	771449	816405	6	10	1.82	0.225	9.9	0.131	C	1
			[2229.1]	771557	816405	4	6	1.80	0.201	5.9	−0.095	C	ls
			[2213.1]	771234	816405	2	4	1.54	0.226	3.30	−0.344	C	ls
			[2229.1]	771557	816405	4	4	0.302	0.0225	0.66	−1.046	C	ls

Forbidden Transitions

Naqvi's calculation [1] of the one possible transition in the ground state configuration $2p$ is the only available source. The line strength should be quite accurate, since it does not sensitively depend on the choice of the interaction parameters.

Reference

[1] Naqvi, A. M., Thesis Harvard (1951).

Ne VI. Forbidden Transitions

No.	Transition Array	Multiplet	$\lambda(\text{Å})$	$E_i(\text{cm}^{-1})$	$E_k(\text{cm}^{-1})$	g_i	g_k	Type of Transition	$A_{ki}(\text{sec}^{-1})$	$S(\text{at.u.})$	Accu-racy	Source
1	$2p - 2p$	^{2}P° — ^{2}P°	[76.32 × 10³]	0	1310	2	4	m	0.0202	1.33	B	1

Ne VII.

Ground State $\qquad$ $1s^2 2s^2\,{}^1S_0$

Ionization Potential $\qquad$ $207.21\ \text{eV} = 1671700\ \text{cm}^{-1}$

Allowed Transitions

The values are taken from the calculations of Veselov [1] who has used relatively simple wave functions and neglected the effects of configuration interaction entirely.   Hence, large uncertainties are to be expected.

Reference

[1] Veselov, M. G., Zhur. Eksptl. i Teoret. Fiz. **19,** 959–964 (1949).

Ne VII.   Allowed Transitions

No.	Transition Array	Multi-plet	$\lambda(\text{Å})$	$E_i(\text{cm}^{-1})$	$E_k(\text{cm}^{-1})$	g_i	g_k	$A_{ki}(10^8\ \text{sec}^{-1})$	f_{ik}	S(at.u.)	$\log gf$	Accuracy	Source
1	$2s^2 -$ $2s(^2S)2p$	$^1S - ^1P°$	465.221	0	214952	1	3	58	0.57	0.87	-0.25	E	1
2	$2s2p - 2p^2$	$^3P° - ^3P$	*561.59*	*[112208]*	*[290273]*	9	9	33	0.16	2.6	0.14	E	1
			561.728	[112700]	[290722]	5	5	25	0.12	1.1	-0.23	E	*ls*
			561.378	[111706]	[289839]	3	3	8.2	0.039	0.21	-0.94	E	*ls*
			564.529	[112700]	[289839]	5	3	14	0.040	0.37	-0.70	E	*ls*
			562.992	[111706]	[289328]	3	1	32	0.051	0.28	-0.81	E	*ls*
			558.61	[111706]	[290722]	3	5	8.6	0.067	0.37	-0.70	E	*ls*
			559.947	[111251]	[289839]	1	3	11	0.15	0.28	-0.81	E	*ls*
3	$2s3s -$ $2s(^2S)3p$	$^3S - ^3P°$	*1987.0*	*[978300]*	*[1028626]*	3	9	2.3	0.41	8.1	0.09	D	*ca*
			1981.97	[978300]	[1028755]	3	5	2.4	0.23	4.5	-0.16	D	*ls*
			1992.06	[978300]	[1028499]	3	3	2.3	0.14	2.7	-0.38	D	*ls*
			1997.35	[978300]	[1028367]	3	1	2.3	0.046	0.90	-0.86	D	*ls*

Forbidden Transitions

Naqvi's calculations [1] are the only available source.   The results for the $^3P° - ^3P°$ transitions are essentially independent of the choice of the interaction parameters.   For the $^3P° - ^1P°$ transitions, Naqvi uses empirical term intervals, i.e., the effects of configuration interaction should be partially included.

Reference

[1] Naqvi, A. M., Thesis Harvard (1951).

Ne VII. Forbidden Transitions

No.	Transition Array	Multi-plet	λ(Å)	E_i(cm⁻¹)	E_k(cm⁻¹)	g_i	g_k	Type of Transition	A_{ki}(sec⁻¹)	S(at.u.)	Accu-racy	Source
1	2s2p − 2s(²S)2p	³P° − ³P°										
			[21.97 × 10⁴]	111251	111706	1	3	m	0.00170	2.00	B	1
			[10.06 × 10⁴]	111706	112700	3	5	m	0.0132	2.50	B	1
2		³P° − ¹P°										
			[964.31]	111251	214952	1	3	m	0.91	9.1 × 10⁻⁵	C	1
			[968.56]	111706	214952	3	3	m	100	0.0101	C	1
			[977.98]	112700	214952	5	3	m	1.10	1.14 × 10⁻⁴	C	1

Ne VIII.

Ground State

$$1s^2 2s\ ^2S_{1/2}$$

Ionization Potential

$$239\ eV = 1928000\ cm^{-1}\ (?)$$

Allowed Transitions

The extensive self-consistent field calculations including exchange by Weiss [1] are used for this ion. Values have been calculated in both the dipole length and velocity approximations and agree quite well. The dipole length values are chosen. For the $2s - 2p$ transition an experimental result from the lifetime measurement of Berkner et al. [2] is available and agrees very well with Weiss' value.

References

[1] Weiss, A. W., Astrophys. J. **138,** 1262–1276 (1963).
[2] Berkner, K. H., Cooper, W. L., Kaplan, S. N., and Pyle, R. V., Phys. Letters **16,** 35 (1965).

Ne VIII. Allowed Transitions

No.	Transition Array	Multi-plet	λ(Å)	E_i(cm⁻¹)	E_k(cm⁻¹)	g_i	g_k	A_{ki}(10⁸ sec⁻¹)	f_{ik}	S(at.u.)	log gf	Accu-racy	Source
1	2s − 2p	²S − ²P°	773.69	0	129251	2	6	5.64	0.152	0.774	−0.517	B+	1, 2
			770.402	0	129801	2	4	5.72	0.102	0.516	−0.692	B+	ls
			780.324	0	128152	2	2	5.50	0.0502	0.258	−0.998	B+	ls
2	2s − 3p	²S − ²P°	[88.134]	0	[1134634]	2	6	853	0.298	0.173	−0.225	B	1
3	2p − 3s	²P° − ²S	[103.05]	129251	[1099681]	6	2	462	0.0245	0.0499	−0.833	B	1
4	2p − 3d	²P° − ²D	[98.308]	129251	[1146459]	6	10	2760	0.667	1.30	0.602	B	1
5	3s − 3p	²S − ²P°	[2860.1]	[1099681]	[1134634]	2	6	0.696	0.256	4.82	−0.291	B	1
6	3p − 3d	²P° − ²D	[8454.3]	[1134634]	[1146459]	6	10	0.0214	0.0382	6.38	−0.640	B	1

Ne IX.

Ground State $1s^2\,{}^1S_0$

Ionization Potential $1195\,\text{eV} = 9641000\,\text{cm}^{-1}$ (?)

Allowed Transitions

The results of extensive non-relativistic variational calculations by Weiss [1] are chosen. Values have been calculated in both the dipole length and dipole velocity approximations and agree to within 1%, except for the $3p\,{}^1P^\circ - 3d\,{}^1D$ transition where agreement is not as good. The average of the two approximations is adopted [1].

Reference

[1] Weiss, A. W., private communication (1964).

Ne IX. Allowed Transitions

No.	Transition Array	Multi-plet	$\lambda(\text{Å})$	$E_i(\text{cm}^{-1})$	$E_k(\text{cm}^{-1})$	g_i	g_k	$A_{ki}(10^8\text{sec}^{-1})$	f_{ik}	$S(\text{at.u.})$	$\log gf$	Accu-racy	Source
1	$1s^2 - 1s2p$	${}^1S - {}^1P^\circ$	[13.460]	0	[7429270]	1	3	8.87×10^4	0.723	0.0320	-0.141	A	1
2	$1s^2 - 1s3p$	${}^1S - {}^1P^\circ$	[11.558]	0	[8652380]	1	3	2.48×10^4	0.149	0.00567	-0.827	A	1
3	$1s2s - 1s2p$	${}^1S - {}^1P^\circ$	[1901.5]	[7376680]	[7429270]	1	3	0.329	0.0535	0.335	-1.272	A	1
4	$1s2s - 1s3p$	${}^1S - {}^1P^\circ$	[78.388]	[7376680]	[8652380]	1	3	1400	0.386	0.0996	-0.413	A	1
5	$1s2p - 1s3d$	${}^1P^\circ - {}^1D$	[82.010]	[7429270]	[8648630]	3	5	4180	0.703	0.569	0.324	A	1
6	$1s3d - 1s3p$	${}^1D - {}^1P^\circ$	[26660]?	[8648630]	[8652380]	5	3	9.99×10^{-4}	0.00639	2.80	-1.496	C+	1
7	$1s2s - 1s2p$	${}^3S - {}^3P^\circ$	[1297.5]	[7294740]	[7371810]	3	9	0.980	0.0742	0.951	-0.653	A	1
8	$1s2s - 1s3p$	${}^3S - {}^3P^\circ$	[74.527]	[7294740]	[8636540]	3	9	1460	0.365	0.269	0.039	A	1
9	$1s2p - 1s3d$	${}^3P^\circ - {}^3D$	[78.356]	[7371810]	[8648030]	9	15	4380	0.672	1.56	0.782	A	1
10	$1s3p - 1s3d$	${}^3P^\circ - {}^3D$	[8700.8]	[8636540]	[8648030]	9	15	0.0155	0.0294	7.58	-0.577	A	1

List of Recent Additional Material
(New material which would have been employed if received before cut-off date)

Spectrum	References	Spectrum	References
He I	D, H, K	N II	L
		N III	C, L
Li I	A, B	N IV	I
		N V	B, E
Be I	I		
Be II	B	O I	G, J
		O II	F
B I	C, L	O III	F
B II	L	O IV	C
B III	B	O V	I
		O VI	B, E
C I	L		
C II	C	F V	C
C III	I		
C IV	B, E	Ne I	D
		Ne II	F
N I	G, J, L	Ne VI	C

References and Comments

A. Anderson, E. M., and Zilitis, V. A., Optics and Spectroscopy (U.S.S.R.) **16**, 211–214 (1963).
   Li I.
   Semi-empirical calculations. Extensive tabulations, in fair agreement with our adopted values except for some of the high-lying transitions, especially those of the resonance series where these values are as much as 50% lower.

B. Flannery, M. R., and Stewart, A. L., Monthly Notices Roy. Astron. Soc. **126**, 387–392 (1963).
   Li I, Be II, B III, C IV, N V, O VI.
   Variational calculations. Good agreement with tabulated values, usually within 10–25%, except for cases where cancellation occurs. Some transitions are covered for which we have no values. Has been used for F VII.

C. Nikitin, A. A., and Yakubovskii, O. A., Soviet Phys. -Doklady **9**, 409–411 (1964).
   B I, C II, N III, O IV, F V, Ne VI.
   Quantum mechanical calculations for forbidden transitions. Values are presented for quadrupole transitions in sp² configurations. We have no values for these transitions.

D. Bennett, Jr., W. R., Kindlmann, P. J., and Mercer, G. N., Applied Optics Supplement 2 of Chemical Lasers pp. 34–57, (1965).
   He I, Ne I.
   Lifetime determinations. The results for Ne agree within 25% with the adopted values and with the experimental results of Klose. The He results have been incorporated from an earlier paper which was referenced in this tabulation.

E. Berkner, K., Cooper III, W. S., Kaplan, S. N., and Pyle, R. V., Physics Letters **16**, 35–36 (1965).
   C IV, N V, O VI.
   Lifetime determinations using the accelerator technique. Agrees with Weiss' extensive calculations within the stated experimental and theoretical error limits. Has been used for F VII and Ne VIII.

F. Froese, C., Phys. Rev. **137**, A1644–A1648 (1965).
   O II, O III, Ne II.
   Self-consistent field calculations. Excellent agreement with the adopted values of Kelly, Mastrup, and Wiese, and the Coulomb approximation. Tends to be a few percent high in all cases except one and should be used in preference to the Coulomb approximation.

G. Morse, F. A., and Kaufman, F., J. Chem. Phys. **42**, 1785–1790 (1965).
   N I, O I.
   Absorption of resonance radiation. The lower limit given for N I is considerably lower than the values from the arc experiment of Labuhn and the lifetime determination of Lawrence and Savage (See ref. L), but is closer to the value of Prag, Fairchild, and Clark (See ref. J). For O I the values are in excellent agreement with the tabulated values.

H. Pendleton, W. R., and Hughes, R. H., Phys. Rev. **138**, A683–A687 (1965).
   He I.
   Lifetime determination. Supports the theory quite well and usually agrees with other referenced lifetime experiments within the stated error limits.

I. Pfennig, H., Steele, R., and Trefftz, E., J. Quant. Spectrosc. Radiat. Transfer **5**, 335–357 (1965).
   Be I, C III, N IV, O V.
   Self-consistent field calculations. Good agreement with tabulated values of Weiss; fair agreement with Kelly and the Coulomb approximation, with better agreement for the visible lines where Kelly and the Coulomb approximation have been averaged. Large divergences may occur where cancellation is significant.

J. Prag, A. B., Fairchild, C. E., and Clark, K. C., Phys. Rev. **137**, A1358–A1363 (1965).
   N I, O I.
   Absorption of resonance radiation. For N I, disagrees by as much as a factor of 3–4 (low) with the adopted values (arc experiment by Labuhn) and with the lifetime experiment of Lawrence and Savage (See ref. L). Agrees well for O I but this is to be expected because of the choice of "best" values.

K. Green, L. C., Kolchin, E. K., and Johnson, N. C., Submitted for publication in the Transactions of the International Astronomical Union Symposium, #26 (1965).
   He I.
   Extensive variational calculations. Excellent agreement, within the assigned error limits, except for $1^1S - 7, 8^1P$. where the disagreement is 10 − 15% low. These new values should be used for $1^1S - 7, 8^1P$.

L. Lawrence, G. M., and Savage, B. D., (To be published in Phys. Rev.)
   B I, II, C I, N I, II, III.
   Lifetime experiment using the phase shift method. Supports the adopted results of Weiss and Bolotin and the arc experiments of Boldt and Labuhn. The lifetimes tend to be somewhat longer than the adopted values.

National Standard Reference Data Series–
National Bureau of Standards

National Standard Reference Data System, Plan of Operation NSRDS–NBS 1 – 15¢*

Thermal Properties Of Aqueous Uni-univalent Electrolytes NSRDS–NBS 2 – 45¢*

Selected Tables of Atomic Spectra, Atomic Energy Levels and Multiplet Tables –
  Si II, Si III, Si IV
    NSRDS – NBS 3 Section 1 – 35¢*

Atomic Transition Probabilities, Hydrogen Through Neon NSRDS – NBS 4 Volume I –
  $2.50*

*Send orders with remittance to: Superintendent of Documents, U.S. Government Printing Office, Washington, D.C., 20402. Remittances from foreign countries should include an additional one-fourth of the purchase price for postage.

THE NATIONAL BUREAU OF STANDARDS

The National Bureau of Standards is a principal focal point in the Federal Government for assuring maximum application of the physical and engineering sciences to the advancement of technology in industry and commerce. Its responsibilities include development and maintenance of the national standards of measurement, and the provisions of means for making measurements consistent with those standards; determination of physical constants and properties of materials; development of methods for testing materials, mechanisms, and structures, and making such tests as may be necessary, particularly for government agencies; cooperation in the establishment of standard practices for incorporation in codes and specifications; advisory service to government agencies on scientific and technical problems; invention and development of devices to serve special needs of the Government; assistance to industry, business, and consumers in the development and acceptance of commercial standards and simplified trade practice recommendations; administration of programs in cooperation with United States business groups and standards organizations for the development of international standards of practice; and maintenance of a clearinghouse for the collection and dissemination of scientific, technical, and engineering information. The scope of the Bureau's activities is suggested in the following listing of its three Institutes and their organizational units.

Institute for Basic Standards. Applied Mathematics. Electricity. Metrology. Mechanics. Heat. Atomic Physics. Physical Chemistry. Laboratory Astrophysics.* Radiation Physics. Radio Standards Laboratory:* Radio Standards Physics; Radio Standards Engineering. Office of Standard Reference Data.

Institute for Materials Research. Analytical Chemistry. Polymers. Metallurgy. Inorganic Materials. Reactor Radiations. Cryogenics.* Materials Evaluation Laboratory. Office of Standard Reference Materials.

Institute for Applied Technology. Building Research. Information Technology. Performance Test Development. Electronic Instrumentation. Textile and Apparel Technology Center. Technical Analysis. Office of Weights and Measures. Office of Engineering Standards. Office of Invention and Innovation. Office of Technical Resources. Clearinghouse for Federal Scientific and Technical Information.**

---

*Located at Boulder, Colorado, 80301.
**Located at 5285 Port Royal Road, Springfield, Virginia, 22171.

Announcement of New Publications on Standard Reference Data

Superintendent of Documents,
Government Printing Office,
Washington, D.C.   20402

Dear Sir:

Please add my name to the announcement list of new publications to be issued in the series: National Standard Reference Data Series—National Bureau of Standards.

Name _____

Company _____

Address _____

City _____ State _____ Zip Code_____

(Notification Key N337)

(cut here)

U.S. GOVERNMENT PRINTING OFFICE : 1966 OL—766-655